SOLID GEOMETRY

WITH CHAPTERS ON
SPACE-LATTICES, SPHERE-PACKS
AND CRYSTALS

BY

L. LINES, M.A., B.Sc.

DOVER PUBLICATIONS, INC., NEW YORK

Published in the United Kingdom by Constable
and Company, Limited, 10 Orange Street, London,
W.C.2.

This Dover edition, first published in 1965, is an
unabridged and corrected republication of the work
first published by Macmillan and Company, Limited, in 1935.

This edition is published by special arrangement
with Macmillan and Company, Limited.

Library of Congress Catalog Card Number: 65-15514

Manufactured in the United States of America

Dover Publications, Inc.
180 Varick Street
New York 14, N.Y.

CONTENTS

PREFACE

THE following work is intended primarily for the use of pupils preparing for one of the Higher School Certificate examinations.

The Theorems are arranged with a view to simplicity and conciseness not only in their own proofs, but also in the proofs of examples depending on them. In this connection it should be noticed that the generality of the basic theorem on Normals (4T1) requires the previous establishment of the concept of mutually perpendicular *skew* straight lines, which, in turn, requires an independent proof of the fact that *straight lines that are parallel to the same straight line are parallel to one another* (3T2).

The theorems are grouped in chapters, each of which concludes with *Worked Examples* and *Examples for the Student*, these last being arranged in three classes, A, B, C, in order of difficulty. The *Answers and Hints* are meant for the student's own use in checking his methods and results, and in affording just sufficient aid in cases of difficulty to enable him to renew his efforts with success. Except in the later chapters, the *Hints* generally consist of mere references to Theorems or Examples, in the order in which their results may be employed, or their proofs imitated.

Reference Symbols are a marked feature of the book : thus 4T1 stands for the *First Theorem of Chapter IV* (i.e. on *Normals*), or one of its corollaries ; 5W2 for the *Second Worked Example of Chapter V* (i.e. on *Polyhedral Angles*) ; and so on.

Analogy is employed from the outset in the *discovery* of new facts and relationships (e.g. pp. 7, 26, 63, 76, etc.) ; and *series* and *groups* of facts are deduced and exhibited with the help of *tabulation* (e.g. pp. 137, 153, 165, 195, etc.).

Great stress is laid on simplicity and clarity of diagrams, and the student is advised to dispense with the use of instruments except in the case of practical constructions where exact measurements are required. The ideal is, never to use ruler, compasses, or protractor without endeavouring to make every measurement correct to the nearest hundredth of an inch or fifth of a degree. When accuracy is not necessary, instruments only hamper the imagination. The student should, of course, never read a theorem without drawing the figure for himself, preferably from a different point of view from that of the book.

The discussion of Semi-Regular Solids (Chapter XII) serves (*a*) as an introduction to the *Principle of Duality*, (*b*) as an example of the deduction of the *existence* as well as the properties of a set of figures from a single definition, and (*c*) as a preparation for parts of the chapter on *Crystals*, where the same Reference Symbols are conveniently adapted to Cubic Forms.

The geometrical study of the orderly arrangement of points and spheres in space (Chapters XIII-XV) is a necessary accompaniment of the experimental investigation of the arrangement of atoms in crystals, some account of which should be read alongside these chapters.

Among works consulted special mention must be made of the following :

X-Rays and Crystal Structure, W. H. and W. L. Bragg ;
Crystallography and Practical Crystal Measurement, A. E. H. Tutton ;
Mathematical Crystallography, H. Hilton ;
Anschauliche Geometrie, D. Hilbert and S. Cohn Vossen ;

and articles in the *Encyclopædia Britannica* (XIVth Edition), on

" Crystals ", L. J. Spencer ;
" Solids ", G. A. Pfeifer ; and
" X-Rays and Crystal Structure ", J. D. Bernal.

Grateful acknowledgments are due to the following authorities for permission to reprint questions from Higher Certificate Papers :

The Syndics of the University of Cambridge (Camb.) ;
The Central Welsh Board (C.W.B.) ;
The Northern Universities Joint Board (Joint Bd.) ;
The Senate of the University of London (Lond.) ;
The Oxford Delegates for Local Examinations (Oxf.) ; and
The Oxford and Cambridge Joint Board (Oxf. & Camb.).

I also wish to record my obligation to Messrs. Macmillan & Co. for their unfailing courtesy, advice and help at every stage of the production of the book, and to Messrs. MacLehose for the excellence of their printing and arrangement.

I shall be grateful for any corrections, additional examples, or other suggestions for the improvement of the book.

L. LINES.

October, 1934.

DETAILED SUMMARY

CHAPTER I.   INTRODUCTION

CHAPTER II.   INTERSECTIONS

CHAPTER III.   PARALLELS

CHAPTER VI.   POLYHEDRAL ANGLES

CHAPTER XIII. SPACE LATTICES

CHAPTER XIV. SPHERE-PACKS

CHAPTER I

INTRODUCTION

In Plane Geometry our thoughts of straight lines, which have neither breadth nor thickness, are guided by the *actions* of drawing, and moving the eye along, fairly thick pencil strokes on *a flat sheet of paper*. Even when we use imagination instead of pencil and paper, we still take for granted some kind of firm background for our diagrams.

In Solid Geometry, however, it is more useful to think of straight lines as stiff wires, or tightly-stretched strings. *Planes* are simply regions where the laws of Plane Geometry hold sway.

This does not prevent us, in the earlier stages of our study, from fixing our ideas by the aid of simple solid models, improvised with knitting needles, cork, and cardboard, or, preferably, with pens, rulers, and books, or, still better, with gas-pendants, picture-rails, and walls. The larger the model the more instructive it can be, especially if the student is free to *walk about inside it*. It should be borne in mind that our sense of the solidity of things depends primarily not on their *appearance*, but on our ability to *handle* them, and to *move about* in relation to them.

The following rules enable us to represent solid figures on paper. Although the underlying theory cannot be fully explained without the help of certain theorems that will be proved in later chapters, we shall run no risk of arguing in a circle, for, in the proof of every theorem, we shall refer, not to the diagram, but to the solid figure itself.

RULE 1.   **Every pair of equal parallel straight lines in a solid figure will be represented by a pair of equal parallel straight lines in the diagram.** (Cf. 1W1.)

RULE 2.   When it is required to represent right angles, or angles of any specified magnitude, three equal, mutually perpendicular straight lines in the solid figure will be chosen as *axes*, and represented by equal straight lines, OX, OY, OZ, inclined to one another at angles of 120° (**Isogonal Projection**), or OY, OZ may be horizontal and vertical, and OX drawn in any other direction and reduced in any ratio (**Oblique Projection**).   (See 1W2.)

RULE 3.   Sometimes, in order to give an appearance of solidity, we shall suppose that some faces are *opaque*, obliterating all that lies behind them, others partially so, causing all lines behind them to be dotted.   Partially *transparent* faces, on the other hand, merely reduce the apparent thickness of lines seen through them, while wholly transparent faces have no effect whatever.   (See Worked Example 1W1.)

DEF. : A **surface** is a boundary separating one portion of space from a neighbouring portion.

DEF. : A **line** is a boundary separating one portion of a surface from a neighbouring portion.

DEF. : A **point** is a boundary separating one portion of a line from a neighbouring portion.

In general, a line intersects another line, or a surface, in one or more *points*, and two surfaces intersect one another in one or more *lines*.

A moving point may *trace* a line ; a moving point or line may *carve out* a surface ; and a moving point, line or surface may *sweep out* a portion of space.

A point has no dimension ; a line has *one*, a surface *two*, and space itself *three dimensions*. Magnitudes of one, two, and three dimensions respectively are called length, area, and volume.

DEF. : A **plane** is a surface such that the infinite straight line through every pair of its points lies wholly in it.

When planing a piece of wood, a joiner uses this definition to test its flatness. His method is to lay a straight-edge across the surface in a number of positions between his eye and a window ; any glint of light between them reveals imperfect contact, and proves that the surface is not truly plane.

DEF. : Points, lines and surfaces, their parts, and parts of space, are classed together as **figures** ; and any group of figures may itself be called a **figure**.

DEF. : If a single portion of space *not pierced by holes* is bounded only by plane polygons, it is called a **polyhedral solid**, and its surface is called a **polyhedron**.

DEF. : If two faces of a polyhedron are congruent polygons, and all the remaining faces are parallelograms, the polyhedron is called a **prism**.

DEF. : A prism whose faces are *all* parallelograms is called a **parallelepiped**. If every face is a rectangle, it is called a **cuboid**, and if every face is a square, it is called a **cube.**

DEF. : If one face of a polyhedron is a polygon, and all the remaining faces are triangles with a common vertex, the polyhedron is called a **pyramid**.

DEF. : A triangular pyramid is called a **tetrahedron.**

DEF. : A polyhedron consisting of eight triangular faces, with four at each vertex, is called an **octahedron.** (Fig. 1.)

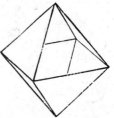

FIG. 1.—OCTAHEDRON.

DEF. : Two planes, a straight line and a plane, or two straight lines in the same plane, are said to be **parallel** if they have no point in common.

DEF. : A straight line which remains parallel to a fixed straight line while intersecting a fixed line (curved, straight, or consisting of segments of curves and straight lines), carves out a **cylindrical surface.** (Fig. 2.)

DEF.: A straight line which passes through a fixed point while intersecting a fixed line carves out a **conical surface,** and the fixed point is called its vertex. (Fig. 3.)

DEF.: The portion of space enclosed by a cylindrical surface and two parallel planes is called a **cylinder.**

DEF.: The portion of space enclosed by a conical surface and a plane is called a **cone.**

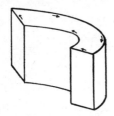

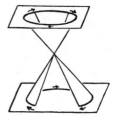

FIG. 2.—CYLINDRICAL SURFACE.   FIG. 3.—CONICAL SURFACE.

DEF.: The part of a cylinder, cone, prism, or pyramid that is intercepted between the base and any other plane is called a **truncated cylinder, cone, prism, or pyramid.** (Fig. 4.)

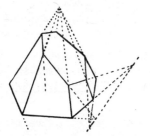

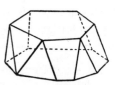

FIG. 4.—TRUNCATED PYRAMID.   FIG. 5.—FRUSTUM OF A CONE.   FIG. 6.—PRISMOID.

DEF.: The part of a cone or pyramid intercepted between its base and a *parallel* plane is called a **frustum.** (Fig. 5.)

DEF.: A polyhedron all of whose vertices lie in one or other of two parallel planes is called a **prismoid.** (Fig. 6.)

DEF. : A **spherical surface** is the locus of a point whose distance from a fixed point, called the centre, is constant. The part of space inside a spherical surface (and sometimes the surface itself) is called a **sphere**.

WORKED EXAMPLES

1W1. Show graphically how a cube can be cut up into six equal square pyramids. (Fig. 7.)

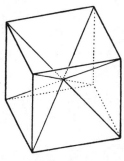

FIG. 7.

For this purpose an accurate representation is unnecessary, and a symmetrical one unsuitable.

We simply use Rule 1, representing the cube by two equal parallelograms and the parallel joins of corresponding vertices.

It follows from symmetry that the four diagonals bisect one another and form the oblique edges of square pyramids standing on the faces of the cube.

A clearer diagram can be obtained by supposing the faces of the cube to be nearly transparent, and the triangular faces of the pyramids to be nearly opaque. In this case we first draw faintly the twelve edges and the four diagonals of the cube, and then indicate " degrees of visibility " in accordance with Rule 3.

NOTE : " Pictorial Effect " should be employed only when it

really serves to clarify a problem. It must never be used as a substitute for logical thinking and exact statement.

1W2. In a diagram employing Rule 2, given any straight line cutting the axes OX, OY in A, B respectively, and any point P in the plane XOY, construct a straight line from P at right angles to AB. (Fig. 8 and Fig. 8a.)

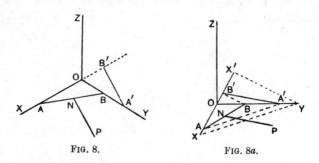

FIG. 8. FIG. 8a.

From OY and XO produced, cut off OA′, OB′ equal to OA, OB respectively. In Fig. 8 a, where OX is drawn on a reduced scale, make OX′ = OX and draw AA′ ∥ XY, and BB′ ∥ YX′.

Then AOB, A′OB′ represent congruent right-angled triangles, with corresponding sides at right angles to one another.

From P draw PN ∥ A′B′.

Then PN represents the perpendicular to AB. (Q.E.F.)

1W3. Show that a tetrahedron can be inscribed in any parallelepiped with one edge of the former lying on each face of the latter. (Fig. 9.)

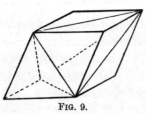

FIG. 9.

The tetrahedron has six edges, arranged three at each vertex, while the parallelepiped has six faces, also arranged three at each vertex.

Hence, by symmetry, the edges of the inscribed tetrahedron are diagonals of the faces of the parallelepiped, as shown in the figure. (Q.E.D.)

1W4. **Starting from F_0, a figure of zero dimension, viz. a point, form a series of figures, F_1, F_2, F_3, of 1, 2, 3 dimensions respectively, such that each is formed from the preceding by " expanding " all its points into equal parallel straight lines. (Fig. 10.)**

Starting with a point A for F_0, we get a straight line AB for F_1; expanding again, we get a parallelogram ABCD for F_2; and this, on expansion, gives a parallelepiped ABCD,EFGH for F_3.

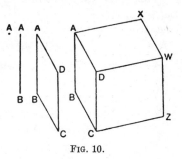

FIG. 10.

NOTE : Such figures are said to be **analogous**, and each is said to be an **analogue** of the others. Thus, in two dimensions, the analogue of the parallelepiped is the parallelogram. In three dimensions, however, there is more than one analogue of the parallelogram, for the latter can be formed from the straight line by more than one law of formation, just as, in Algebra, an A.P. and a G.P. may have two terms in common.

EXAMPLES 1A

1A1. Find, by means of a rough sketch, what polyhedron has its vertices at the middle points of the edges of a tetrahedron.

1A2. Show graphically that the joins of the middle points of opposite edges of any tetrahedron bisect one another.

1A3. State the two - dimensional analogue of the following theorem in three dimensions :

" The volume of a pyramid is equal to one-third of that of a prism on the same base and with the same height."

1A4. Form a series of figures of 1, 2, and 3 dimensions, the law of formation being that all points on the boundaries of the figures are to be at the same distance from a fixed point.

1A5. Tabulate the numbers of vertices, edges, and faces belonging to the parallelepiped, tetrahedron, and octahedron.

EXAMPLES 1B

1B1. Draw the plane-faced solid whose vertices are the centres of the faces of a given parallelepiped ABCD,XYZW.

1B2. Draw an irregular octahedron, U,ABCD,V, where U, V are a pair of opposite vertices, and show graphically that the centres of its faces are vertices of a parallelepiped.

1B3. Draw a triangular prism and cut it up into three tetrahedra.

1B4. Using Rule 2, represent a regular octahedron with all its vertices on the axes.

1B5. Construct a cube with the centres of its faces on the axes.

1B6–9. Discover one or more three-dimensional analogues of the following two-dimensional theorems :

(1B6) " If two straight lines are parallel to the same straight line they are parallel to one another."

(1B7) " The square on the diagonal of a rectangle is equal to the sum of the squares on two adjacent sides."

(1B8) " The locus of a point which moves so that its distances from the ends of a straight line are equal is the straight line which bisects it at right angles."

(1B9) " If two circles intersect, their line of centres bisects their common chord at right angles."

EXAMPLES 1C

1C1. In the plane XOY construct any triangle with one vertex on OX and its orthocentre at O.

1C2, 3. Form series of figures, each starting with a point, using the following laws of formation :

(1C2) " All points of one figure are joined to the same point outside it to form the next figure of the series."

(1C3) " All points of each figure are joined to both extremities of a straight line whose middle point is the centre of the figure."

1C4. What theorem of Plane Geometry is analogous to the following three-dimensional theorem :

" Of three plane angles at a corner of a triangular pyramid, any two are together greater than the third."

1C5. Discover, and state without proof, a theorem of Solid Geometry analogous to the following two-dimensional theorem :

" One and only one circle will pass through any three points that do not lie in the same straight line."

1C6. By considering the usual method of folding a filter-paper, show that the inner surface of a common laboratory filter is a surface of revolution carved out by a straight line inclined to the axis at an angle of 30°.

CHAPTER II

INTERSECTIONS

Axiom 1. **Through any two points in space there is one and only one infinite straight line.**

If a straight line passes through two points A and B, we may therefore refer to it simply as " AB ". Similarly, if a point lies on two straight lines a, b, we may call it the point " ab ".

Axiom 2. **Through any three points which are not in the same straight line there is one and only one plane.**

From the definition of a plane it follows that two points A, B fix one str. line in a plane. We can think of the points as hinges, and of the plane as a door rotating about the line of the hinges until it comes to rest in contact with the third point C.

If a plane passes through three points A, B, C, we may therefore refer to it simply as " pl. ABC ". If the str. line AB is called " m ", the plane ABC can be called " mC "; and if the str. line BC is called " n ", the plane ABC can be called " mn ".

Axiom 3. **If two planes have a common point they have a common straight line.**

This fact is liable to be overlooked when the planes are represented in a diagram by parallelograms or triangles.

If we represent the planes by the Greek letters α and β, we can call their line of intersection $\alpha\beta$. Similarly, the str. line m cuts the plane α in the point αm ; and $\beta\gamma$, the line of intersection of the planes β, γ, cuts the plane α in the point $\alpha\beta\gamma$; $\therefore \alpha\beta\gamma$ is the point of intersection of the planes α, β, γ.

10

DEF. : Points in the same straight line are said to be **collinear.**

DEF. : Figures of less than three dimensions are said to be
         concurrent, if they have *one* common point,
         coaxal, if they have *two* common points, and
         coplanar, if they lie in the same plane.

DEF. : Sets of lines that are not coplanar are said to be **skew.**

Any two upright lamp-posts are coplanar ; a piece of canvas,
for example, if they are sufficiently close together, could be
stretched flat between them in a vertical plane ; but each of
them is skew to the tram-lines down the centre of the road.
(The student may amuse himself by considering whether the
above statement is *strictly* true of *every* pair of upright lamp-
posts, e.g. one in Capetown and the other in New York.)

WORKED EXAMPLES

2W1. OAA′, OBB′, OCC′, ODD′ are four straight lines through the same
point O, and no three of them are coplanar. If AB meets CD in E, and
A′B′ meets C′D′ in E′, prove that the points O, E, E′ are collinear.

(Fig. 11.)

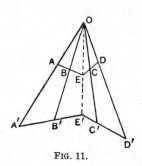

FIG. 11.

O, E, and E′ are in both planes OAB and OCD ; and these have
a common point O ;

    ∴ they have a common straight line ;   (Ax. 3)

    ∴ O, E, E′ lie in this straight line.   (Q.E.D.)

DEF. : A straight line joining a vertex of a triangle to the middle point of the opposite side is called a **median** of the triangle.

DEF. : The point of intersection of the medians of a triangle is called its **centroid**.   (Cf. Ch. IX.)

DEF. : The straight line joining a vertex of a tetrahedron to the centroid of the opposite face is called a **median** of the tetrahedron.

2W2. Prove that the medians of a tetrahedron are concurrent and divide each other in the ratio 3 : 1.   (Fig. 12.)

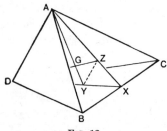

FIG. 12.

Let X *be the middle point of the edge* BC *of any tetrahedron* ABCD, *and let* Z, Y *divide* XA, XD *respectively in the ratio* 1 : 2.

Then AY and DZ are medians of the tetrahedron, and lie in the plane AXD.   ∴ they intersect at some point G.

YZ is parallel to DA, making two pairs of similar triangles ;

$$\therefore \ \ \text{YG : GA} = \text{YZ : AD} = \text{YX : DX} = 1 : 3 \ ;$$

∴ the median AY is *quadrisected* (i.e. divided in the ratio 3 : 1) by one of the other medians ; it follows that every median is quadrisected by each of the others ; ∴ they must have a common point of quadrisection.

i.e. the medians are concurrent, and divide one another in the ratio 3 : 1.   (Q.E.D.)

2W3. OA, OB, OC are three coplanar straight lines, and OD is any straight line not in their plane. A straight line cuts planes AOD, BOD in the points P, Q respectively. Represent these in a diagram, and show how to find the point R, where PQ cuts plane COD. (Fig. 13.)

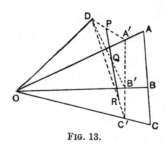

FIG. 13.

PQ cuts plane OCD at some point on the line of intersection of planes DPQ and OCD.

But plane DPQ cuts plane OABC in the points A′, B′, C′, where DP, DQ, DR cut OA, OB, OC respectively.

Hence the method : Draw DPA′, DQB′, then A′B′C′, and finally DC′, cutting PQ in the required point R.

2W4. If three planes intersect, two by two, show that their lines of intersection are either concurrent or parallel.

Let the three planes be α, β, γ. The straight lines $\gamma\alpha$ and $\alpha\beta$ lie in the same plane α ; $\therefore$ they either intersect or are parallel.

If they intersect, their common point lies on all three planes ; i.e. it is $\alpha\beta\gamma$;

$\therefore$ it lies on $\beta\gamma$;

$\therefore$ $\beta\gamma$, $\gamma\alpha$, $\alpha\beta$ are concurrent.

(Q.E.D. (i).)

If $\gamma\alpha$ and $\alpha\beta$ are parallel, there is no point $\alpha\beta\gamma$;

$\therefore$ neither $\gamma\alpha$ nor $\alpha\beta$ can cut $\beta\gamma$.

But $\alpha\beta$ and $\beta\gamma$ lie in plane β ;

$\therefore$ they are parallel.

Similarly $\gamma\alpha$ and $\beta\gamma$ are parallel. (Q.E.D. (ii).)

2W5. Prove that, if the joins of corresponding vertices of two triangles are concurrent, the intersections of their corresponding sides are collinear. (Fig. 14.)

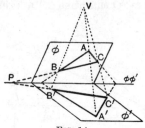

FIG. 14.

Let ϕ and ϕ' be the planes of two triangles ABC, A′B′C′, *and let* AA′, BB′, CC′ *intersect in the point* V.

Then V, B, C, B′, C′ are coplanar and their plane cuts $\phi\phi'$ in some point P ;

$$\therefore \text{ BC cuts B′C′ at P in } \phi\phi'.$$

Similarly the other pairs of corresponding sides intersect at points on $\phi\phi'$, the line of intersection of the planes of the triangles.   (Q.E.D.)

NOTE : The case of coplanar triangles may be regarded as the limiting case, where the angle between the two planes is infinitely small, or it can be proved independently by Menelaus' Theorem.

DEF. : If the joins of corresponding vertices of two plane polygons are concurrent, they are said to be in perspective.

2W6. Prove that through any point on one of three skew straight lines one and only one straight line can be drawn to cut the other two, or to cut one and be parallel to the other.

Let m, n, p *be the given skew straight lines, and* P *any point on* p.

Then the planes Pm, Pn have the common point P ;

$\therefore$ they have a common straight line PQ.   (Ax. 3)

As PQ is coplanar with *m*, they must either be parallel or intersect; and similarly with *n*.   (Q.E.D.)

DEF.: The system of straight lines that cut three given skew straight lines, or cut two while being parallel to the third, is called a **Regulus**.

2W7. Given points P, Q, R on the sides AB, BC, CD of a skew quadrilateral, find S, the point of intersection of AD with the plane PQR.

(Fig. 15.)

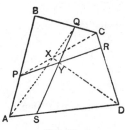

FIG. 15.

In plane ABC, AQ cuts PC in some point X.
In plane XCD, XD cuts PR in some point Y.
In plane XAD, QY cuts AD in some point S.
Then S is the point on AD coplanar with P, Q, and R.

(Q.E.D.)

EXAMPLES 2A

2A1. Discuss whether any of the following figures are impossible. Give reasons in each case, and mention familiar examples of the others.

(1) Three parallel straight lines that do not lie in a plane.

(2) Three concurrent straight lines that are not coplanar.

(3) Two skew straight lines cut by two intersecting straight lines.

(4) Three planes having only two lines of intersection.

(5) Two intersecting planes cutting another plane in parallel straight lines.

(6) Three skew straight lines cutting each of two others.

2A2. In Algebra, we often express the argument

$$\text{"} a=b, \quad \text{and} \quad b=c\,;$$
$$\therefore \; a=c \text{"}$$

in the form

$$\text{"} a=b=c.\text{"}$$

In a similar way, using the sign $\parallel$ for " is parallel to ", and small letters for straight lines, and Greek letters for planes, we can write

" If $\qquad\qquad \alpha \parallel \beta \parallel \gamma, \quad$ then $\quad \alpha \parallel \gamma$ " ;

for the following statement :

" If two planes are parallel to the same plane they are parallel to one another."

Where possible, complete the following statements in this way, and express them in words :

        (1) If $a \parallel b \parallel c$, then … .

        (2) If $\alpha \parallel \beta \parallel c$, then … .

        (3) If $a \parallel b \parallel \gamma$, then … .

        (4) If $\alpha \parallel b \parallel \gamma$, then … .

        (5) If $a \parallel \beta \parallel c$, then … .

2A3. If the edges DA, DB, DC ; BC, CA, AB of a tetrahedron are respectively 3, 7, 9 ; 4, 10, 8 cm. long, find graphically the length of the shortest string that can be stretched from B to D over the edge AC. (Notice that the length of one of the edges does not affect the problem ; imagine it to be *lengthened* (not *produced*) until the whole figure can be drawn in a plane.)

EXAMPLES 2B

2B1. Find the locus of a point P which is free to move in a straight line m which itself passes through a fixed point O and a fixed straight line n.

2B2. Find the locus of a straight line p which intersects two fixed straight lines m and n, (1) if m and n intersect one another, and (2) if m and n are skew.

2B3. If AB and CD are skew straight lines, prove that AD and BC are skew.

2B4. If A and B are fixed points and m and n are fixed straight lines, find the locus of a point P such that the straight lines PA, PB pass through m and n respectively.

2B5. Prove that, if three straight lines intersect, two by two, they are either coplanar or concurrent.

2B6. Two long, unequal nails project vertically from the upper surface of a table, and a flat card leans across their heads, and slips into several successive positions, its lower edge leaving marks in the dust on the table. Prove that these marks, if produced, will be concurrent straight lines.

2B7. A leaf of a book is folded twice, forming a triangular funnel, with the free edge in contact with the undisturbed part of the leaf. If the creases cut the top edge of the leaf 1 inch and 3 inches respectively from the free corner, and the second crease cuts the bottom 2 inches from the free corner, find where the first crease cuts the bottom edge.

2B8. Show that, if three or more coaxal planes cut another plane, the lines of intersection are either concurrent or parallel.

2B9. If P, Q, R, S are points on the sides AB, BC, CD, DA of a skew quadrilateral ABCD, and PS and QR intersect one another, prove that PQ, RS, and AC are concurrent.

2B10. The side AB of a skew quadrilateral ABCD is 4 inches long, and is cut at the point P by a plane which divides BC, CD, DA in the ratios $2:3$, $3:4$, $4:5$ respectively. Find graphically the length of AP.

EXAMPLES 2C

2C1. If ABCD is the base of a pyramid with its triangular faces equilateral, prove that ABCD is a square.

2C2. If ABCD is any tetrahedron, and the bisectors of the three angles at D cut the edges BC, CA, AB in the points X, Y, Z respectively, prove that AX, BY, CZ are concurrent.

2C3. Given a diagram of two straight lines the representation of whose point of intersection would require the sheet of paper to be extended, show how to construct a concurrent straight line through a given point.

2C4. Given, in representation, one of two triangles in perspective, one vertex of the other, the direction of the median through it, and the line of intersection of their planes, construct the second triangle.

2C5. If two triangles lie in different planes, and corresponding sides intersect, prove that, in general, the joins of corresponding vertices are concurrent. Discuss the exceptional case.

CHAPTER III

PARALLELS

DEF. : Two planes, a straight line and a plane, or two straight lines, are said to be **exclusive,** or to **exclude** one another, if they have no point in common.

It is sometimes useful to consider a straight line, which *lies in* a plane, as being *parallel* to it ; if we can prove, for example, that a straight line is *parallel* to a plane and passes through one point in it, then the straight line must *lie in* the plane.

AXIOM 4. (**Playfair's Axiom.**) **Through any point in space there is one and only one straight line parallel to a given straight line.**

NOTATION : The sign ‖ stands for " is (or *are*) parallel to ".

Theorem 3T1

If a straight line is parallel to one straight line in a plane, it is parallel to the plane; *and, conversely,* **if a straight line in one plane is parallel to another plane, it is parallel to their line of intersection.** (Fig. 16.)

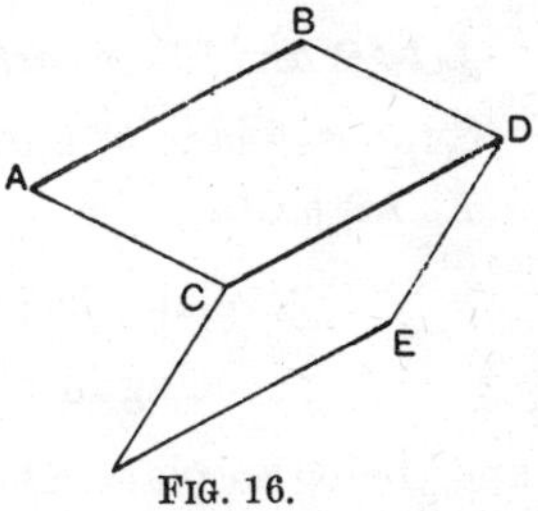

Let AB *be any straight line parallel to any straight line* CD *in the plane* CDE ; *to prove that* AB ‖ CDE.

As AB and CD are parallel, they are coplanar.

FIG. 16.

Plane ABCD meets plane CDE in the straight line CD, and in no other point, unless they coincide. (Ax. 3)

19

But AB does not meet CD, as they are parallel.

∴ AB does not meet plane CDE, unless it lies wholly in it ;

∴ AB ‖ CDE.　　　(Q.E.D.)

CONVERSE : *Let* AB *in plane* ABCD *be parallel to plane* CDE ; to prove *that* AB ‖ CD.

AB excludes plane CDE ;

∴ AB excludes CD.

But they are coplanar ;

∴ they are parallel.　　　(Q.E.D.)

Theorem 3T2

If two straight lines are each parallel to a third, they are parallel to one another.　(Fig. 17.)

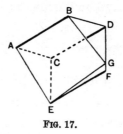

FIG. 17.

Let AB *and* EF *be each parallel to* CD ; to prove *that* AB ‖ EF.

Suppose plane ABE to cut plane CDEF in the straight line EG.

As AB ‖ CD,

∴ plane EAB ‖ CD, and plane ECD ‖ AB ;　　(3T1)

∴ being in plane ECD, EG ‖ CD,　　(3T1)

and, being in plane EAB, EG ‖ AB ;　　(3T1)

∴ EG coincides with EF ; and ‖ AB ;　　(Ax. 4)

∴ EF ‖ AB.　　　(Q.E.D.)

Theorem 3T3

Through any point there is one and only one plane parallel to two given non-parallel straight lines. (Fig. 18.)

Let m and n be any two non-parallel straight lines (either co-planar or skew), *and let* O *be any point ;* to prove *that there is one and only one plane through* O *parallel to m and n.*

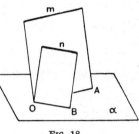

FIG. 18.

Let planes O*m*, O*n* meet any plane α through O in the straight lines OA, OB.

If α ∥ *m* and *n*,

then OA in pl. O*m* is parallel to *m*. (3T1)

Similarly OB ∥ *n*.

Through O there is one and only one straight line parallel to each of the straight lines *m* and *n*. (Ax. 4)

These straight lines, OA, OB, lie in *any* plane α, which is parallel to *m* and *n*.

∴ there is one and only one such plane.

(Q.E.D.)

COROLLARIES :

(1) IF TWO PLANES ARE PARALLEL TO THE SAME PAIR OF NON-PARALLEL STRAIGHT LINES, THEY ARE PARALLEL TO ONE ANOTHER.

(2) THERE IS ONE AND ONLY ONE PAIR OF PARALLEL PLANES ON EACH OF WHICH LIES ONE OF A GIVEN PAIR OF SKEW STRAIGHT LINES.

(3) IF TWO ANGLES HAVE THEIR CORRESPONDING ARMS PARALLEL, THEY LIE IN PARALLEL PLANES.

(4) PLANES THAT ARE PARALLEL TO THE SAME PLANE ARE PARALLEL TO ONE ANOTHER.

Proof of each of the above corollaries :

" . . . For otherwise there would be two planes through the same point parallel to each of two non-parallel straight lines."

Note on (3) : Observe first that the arms of one angle are parallel to the plane of the other by 3T1.

Theorem 3T4

If a plane cuts two parallel planes, the lines of intersection are parallel. (Fig. 19.)

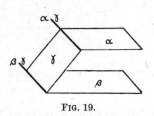

FIG. 19.

Let the parallel planes α, β cut any plane γ ; to prove that

$$\alpha\gamma \parallel \beta\gamma.$$

As α excludes β, every line in α excludes every line in β ;

∴ αγ excludes βγ.

But they are coplanar ;

∴ αγ ∥ βγ.   (Q.E.D.)

COROLLARY : TWO SETS OF PARALLEL PLANES INTERSECT IN PARALLEL STRAIGHT LINES.

Theorem 3T5

If any two straight lines are cut by a number of parallel planes, their intercepts are proportional. (Fig. 20.)

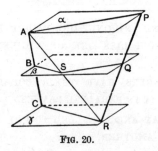

FIG. 20.

Let the parallel planes α, β, γ *cut any two straight lines in the sets of points* A, B, C *and* P, Q, R *respectively;* to prove *that*

$$AB : BC = PQ : QR.$$

Let AR cut β in S.

Then the plane ACR cuts the parallel planes β, γ in BS, CR respectively;

$$\therefore \ BS \parallel CR. \tag{3T4}$$

Also the plane APR cuts the parallel planes α, β in AP, SQ respectively;

$$\therefore \ AP \parallel SQ ; \tag{3T4}$$

$$\therefore \ AB : BC = AS : SR = PQ : QR. \qquad (\text{Q.E.D.})$$

DEF. : If, through a given point, straight lines are drawn respectively parallel to any two given straight lines in space, the four angles so formed are said to be **determined** at the given point by the given straight lines.

Theorem 3T6

Any two straight lines determine equal angles at all points of space. (Fig. 21.)

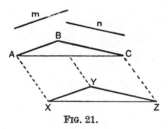

FIG. 21.

Let $\hat{ABC}$, $\hat{XYZ}$ *be the angles determined at* B *and* Y *respectively by any two straight lines* m, n *; and let their corresponding arms be equal and drawn in the same sense;* to prove *that* $\hat{ABC} = \hat{XYZ}$.

As AB and XY are $\parallel$ m ;

$$\therefore \ AB \parallel XY. \tag{3T2}$$

Similarly BC ∥ YZ.

But   AB = XY,   and   BC = YZ ;

∴ AX = and ∥ BY,   and   BY = and ∥ CZ ;

∴ AX = and ∥ CZ ;   (3T2)

∴ AC = and ∥ XZ ;

∴ the triangles ABC, XYZ have three sides of one equal respectively to three sides of the other ;

$$\therefore\ \hat{ABC} = \hat{XYZ}. \qquad \text{(Q.E.D.)}$$

COROLLARY : IF TWO ANGLES HAVE CORRESPONDING ARMS DRAWN PARALLEL AND IN THE SAME SENSE, THEY ARE EQUAL.

DEF. : The angle determined at any point by two skew straight lines is called **the angle between them.**

WORKED EXAMPLES

3W1. Prove that, if a straight line is parallel to two planes, it is parallel to their line of intersection. (Fig. 22.)

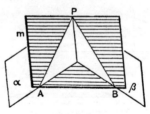

FIG. 22.

Let m be the given straight line, and P *any point on the line of intersection of the given planes* α *and* β *; to prove that* m ∥ αβ.

Let plane P*m* cut α in PA, and β in PB.
As *m* in P*m* is ∥ α,

$$\therefore\ m \parallel \text{PA}. \qquad (3T1)$$

As m in Pm is $\parallel \beta$,

$$\therefore \quad m \parallel \text{PB} ; \qquad\qquad\qquad\qquad (3\text{T}1)$$
$$\therefore \quad \text{PA and PB coincide} ; \qquad\quad (\text{Ax. } 4)$$
$$\therefore \quad \text{they coincide with } \alpha\beta ;$$
$$\therefore \quad m \parallel \alpha\beta. \qquad\qquad\qquad (\text{Q.E.D.})$$

3W2. Prove that the joins of middle points of opposite edges of a tetrahedron bisect one another. (Fig. 23.)

Let P, Q, R, S *be the middle points of the edges* AB, BC, CD, DA *respectively ;* to prove *that* PR *and* QS *bisect one another.*

As PQ bisects two sides of the triangle ABC,

$$\therefore \quad \text{PQ} \parallel \text{AC, and} = \tfrac{1}{2}\text{AC}.$$
Similarly RS $\parallel$ AC, and $= \tfrac{1}{2}$AC ;
$$\therefore \quad \text{PQ} = \text{and} \parallel \text{RS} ; \qquad\qquad (3\text{T}2)$$
$$\therefore \quad \text{PQRS is a parallelogram} ;$$
$$\therefore \quad \text{PR and QS bisect one another.}$$

Similarly other pairs of joins of middle points of opposite edges bisect one another.   (Q.E.D.)

3W3. *If no three of the concurrent straight lines* OA, OB, OC, OD *are coplanar, find points on them which are vertices of a parallelogram. How many solutions are there, if the vertex P, on* OA, *is given ?*   (Fig. 24.)

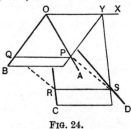

FIG. 24.

The planes OAB, OCD intersect in a straight line OX. (Ax. 3)
Draw PY, PQ $\parallel$ BO, XO, cutting OX, OB in Y, Q respectively.

Draw YS, SR ∥ OC, XO, cutting OD, OC in S, R respectively.

Then PQ = and ∥ YO = and ∥ SR, being opposite sides of parallelograms ;

∴ PQRS is a parallelogram.   (Q.E.D. (i).)

The four given straight lines determine three different pairs of planes : OAB, OCD ; OBC, OAD ; OCA, OBD ;

∴ there are three different solutions.

(Q.E.F. (ii).)

3W4. *Given, in a diagram, any two triangles* ABC, XYZ *in parallel planes, and a point* P *on* AX *produced, construct a straight line through* P *to cut* BY *and* CZ. (Fig. 25.)

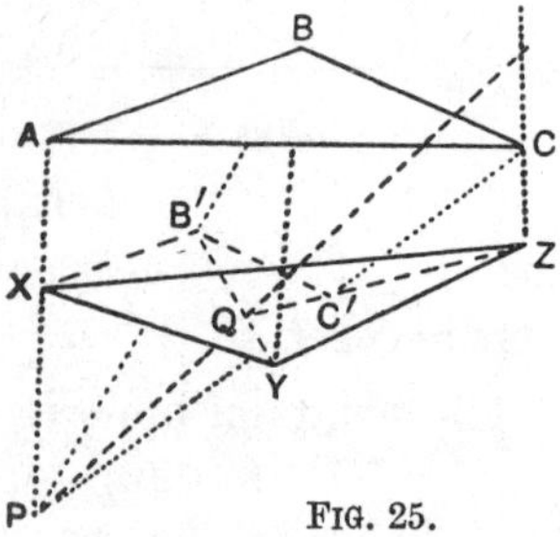

FIG. 25.

Draw XB′, B′C′ ∥ AB, BC, cutting PB, PC in B′, C′ respectively. These are the lines of intersection of planes ABP, BCP with plane XYZ.

Let B′Y cut C′Z in some point Q.

Then Q lies in planes PBY, PCZ ;

∴ PQ cuts BY and CZ.   (Q.E.F.)

3W5. NOTE : Intervals measured in opposite directions along the same straight line are regarded as having opposite signs.

Thus   AB = − BA.

It follows that if A, B, C are points in order on a straight line,

AB : BC is positive,

and   AC : CB is negative.

Prove the following three-dimensional extension of the Theorem of Menelaus :

If the sides AB, BC, CD, DA *of any skew quadrilateral are cut by any plane in the points* P, Q, R, S *respectively, then*

$$\frac{AP}{PB} \frac{BQ}{QC} \frac{CR}{RD} \frac{DS}{SA} = 1,$$

and, conversely, *points which divide the sides in such a way that the above relation is true, are coplanar.* (Fig. 26.)

On one side of the plane there may be

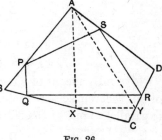

FIG. 26.

(*a*) four vertices, or none ;
(*b*) three vertices, or one ;
(*c*) two adjacent vertices, or
(*d*) two opposite vertices.

In Case (*a*), all the edges are cut externally, making all four ratios negative ; in Cases (*b*) and (*c*), two edges are cut externally, and two internally, making two ratios negative, and two positive ; while in Case (*d*), all are cut internally, making all four ratios positive.

Thus in every case the product of the four ratios is positive.

Let the plane through A *parallel to* PQRS *cut* BC, CD *in* X, Y *respectively.*

Then AX, XY, YA are parallel to PQ, QR, RS respectively ; (3T4)

$$\therefore \ \frac{AP}{PB}=\frac{XQ}{QB}, \ \frac{XQ}{QC}=\frac{YR}{RC}, \ \frac{DS}{SA}=\frac{DR}{RY}.$$

$$\therefore \ \frac{AP}{PB}\frac{BQ}{QC}\frac{CR}{RD}\frac{DS}{SA}=\frac{XQ}{QB}\frac{BQ}{QC}\frac{CR}{RD}\frac{DR}{RY}$$

$$=\left(-\frac{XQ}{QC}\right)\cdot\left(-\frac{CR}{RY}\right)$$

$$=\frac{YR}{RC}\cdot\frac{CR}{RY}$$

$$=1. \qquad \text{(Q.E.D.)}$$

CONVERSE : *If* P, Q, R, S *are points on the sides* AB, BC, CD, DA *of a skew quadrilateral, and*

$$\frac{AP}{PB}\frac{BQ}{QC}\frac{CR}{RD}\frac{DS}{SA}=1,$$

then P, Q, R, S *are coplanar.*

Suppose that plane PQR cuts DA in T.

Then $\dfrac{AP}{PB}\dfrac{BQ}{QC}\dfrac{CR}{RD}\dfrac{DT}{TA}=1$;

$$\therefore \frac{DT}{TA}=\frac{DS}{SA};$$

∴ T and S coincide ;

∴ P, Q, R, S are coplanar.   (Q.E.D.)

NOTE : By means of a convention, we can extend the scope of this theorem so as to include the case where the cutting plane is parallel to one of the sides of the skew quadrilateral.

The ratio

$$\frac{DS}{SA}=\frac{DA+AS}{SA}$$

$$=\frac{DA}{SA}+\frac{AS}{SA}$$

$$=\frac{DA}{SA}-1.$$

∴ the ratio $\dfrac{DS}{SA}$ becomes indistinguishable from -1, when S moves to an infinite distance from A, making the ratio $\dfrac{DA}{SA}$ zero ; i.e. when the plane PQR becomes parallel to DA.

3W6. If a straight line cuts (or is parallel to) three generators of a regulus, it cuts (or is parallel to) every generator. (Fig. 27.)

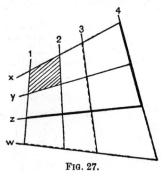

FIG. 27.

Let x, y, z be three skew straight lines determining a regulus, and w a straight line cutting three generators, 1, 2, 3 ; to prove that w cuts any other generator, 4, or is parallel to it.

If $(x, y, 1, 2)$ be any one of the skew quadrilaterals formed by any two lines from each of the sets x, y, z ; 1, 2, 3 ; consider the intersections of its sides with the pairs of lines $(z, 3)$, $(z, 4)$, $(w, 3)$ in turn ; and let each point of intersection be named by means of a letter and a suffix.

Then
$$\frac{x_1 z_1}{z_1 y_1} \frac{y_1 y_3}{y_3 y_2} \frac{y_2 z_2}{z_2 x_2} \frac{x_2 x_3}{x_3 x_1} = 1, \qquad (3\text{W}5)$$

$$\frac{x_1 z_1}{z_1 y_1} \frac{y_1 y_4}{y_4 y_2} \frac{y_2 z_2}{z_2 x_2} \frac{x_2 x_4}{x_4 x_1} = 1, \qquad (3\text{W}5)$$

$$\frac{x_1 w_1}{w_1 y_1} \frac{y_1 y_3}{y_3 y_2} \frac{y_2 w_2}{w_2 x_2} \frac{x_2 x_3}{x_3 x_1} = 1. \qquad (3\text{W}5)$$

Multiplying the last two ratios together, and dividing by the first, we get

$$\frac{x_1 w_1}{w_1 y_1} \frac{y_1 y_4}{y_4 y_2} \frac{y_2 w_2}{w_2 x_2} \frac{x_2 x_4}{x_4 x_1} = 1 \; ;$$

∴ w and 4 are coplanar ;   (3W5)

∴ they either intersect, or are parallel.

(Q.E.D.)

NOTE : It follows from 2W6 and 3W6 that through any point on a regulus one and only one straight line can be drawn to cut every generator but one, to which it is parallel.

Hence the generators of any regulus determine a second regulus ; and those of the second determine the first.

Two such reguli are said to be conjugate to one another, and the *surface* determined by them is called a hyperboloid of one sheet.

EXAMPLES 3A

3A1. State and prove 3T1, using exclusively the notation of 3T4 ; namely, a single Greek letter for a plane, and the letters of the two planes for their line of intersection.

3A2. Prove 3T2, using the ordinary notation, namely, one capital letter for a point, two for a straight line, and three for a plane.

3A3. State and prove a converse of 3T5.

3A4. If two planes are parallel to one another, prove that each is parallel to every straight line in the other.

3A5. Interchange the words " line " and " plane " in the previous question.

3A6. If two skew straight lines are parallel to a plane, any straight line that cuts them both also cuts the plane.

3A7. The side AB of a skew quadrilateral is 4 inches long, and is cut at the point P by a plane which divides BC, CD, DA, in the ratios $x : 1$, $y : 1$, $z : 1$ respectively. Calculate the length of AP.

3A8. If a plane is parallel to any two sides of a skew quadrilateral, show that it divides the other two sides proportionally.

3A9. Defining a parallelepiped as " the part of space enclosed by three pairs of parallel planes ", prove that its diagonals bisect one another.

EXAMPLES 3B

3B1. If a straight line and a plane are both parallel to another straight line, show that they are parallel to one another.

3B2. If a straight line is parallel to two of a set of coaxal planes, it is parallel to them all.

3B3. If a straight line and a plane are both parallel to another plane, they are parallel to one another.

3B4. Three planes have a straight line in common ; show that if a fourth plane is parallel to one of them, it cuts the other two in parallel straight lines.

3B5. From three collinear points A, B, C, two sets of parallel straight lines, AP, BQ, CR, and AX, BY, CZ are drawn, cutting any plane in the sets of points, P, Q, R ; and X, Y, Z respectively. Prove that PX, QY, RZ are parallel.

3B6. If a and b are straight lines in the planes α and β respectively, and $a \parallel \beta$ and $b \parallel \alpha$, prove that $a \parallel b$.

3B7. Prove that the middle points of the edges of a regular tetrahedron are vertices of a regular octahedron.

3B8. Prove that the centroids of the faces of a cube are vertices of a regular octahedron.

3B9. Prove that planes drawn through the edges of any tetrahedron so as to bisect the opposite edges are concurrent.

3B10. If M and N are opposite vertices of any parallelepiped, prove that the middle points of the edges that do not reach M or N form a plane hexagon with concurrent diagonals.

3B11. A number of electric lamps hang by separate cables from a flat ceiling, and only one is lighted. Prove that the shadows cast on the ceiling by the other cables are parts of concurrent straight lines.

3B12. If ABCD,XYZW is any parallelepiped, and P any point in space, prove that the planes PAX, PBY, PCZ, PDW are coaxal.

3B13. The bases of three equal upright poles AA′, BB′, CC′ are in a straight line ABC, and AB : BC = 1 : 2. On a sunny day shadows of the tops of the poles fall on an inclined roof at P, Q, R. If the distances of P and Q from the ridge of the roof are 5 ft. and 8 ft. respectively, find the distance of R from the ridge.

3B14. Show that the centroids of the faces of any octahedron are vertices of a parallelepiped.

3B15. Omit.

3B16. If P, Q are given points on two opposite edges of a tetrahedron, show that through every point on PQ there is one and only one plane section of the tetrahedron whose diagonals intersect on PQ.

3B17. Show that there are three directions in which parallel straight lines can be drawn through the four vertices of any tetrahedron so that they may cut every plane in the vertices of a parallelogram.

3B18. Show that, parallel to each of any three skew straight lines, there is one straight line that intersects the other two.

3B19. If two parallel straight lines lie one on each of two intersecting planes, show that they are both parallel to the line of intersection of the planes.

3B20. P, Q, R, S are fixed points, one on each of four rods which are loosely hinged together at their extremities to form a variable skew quadrilateral. Show that, if P, Q, R, S are coplanar in one position of the rods, they will be coplanar in every position.

EXAMPLES 3C

3C1. Find the locus of the centre of a variable parallelogram whose vertices move on four skew straight lines.

3C2. Prove that a section of a tetrahedron made by a plane parallel to two opposite edges is a parallelogram whose diagonals intersect in the line joining the middle points of opposite edges.

3C3. Prove that, if the base of a pyramid is a parallelogram, then every section which is a parallelogram is parallel to the base.

3C4. If ABCD is one face of a parallelepiped, and the edges through A, B, C, D are cut by any plane in the points P, Q, R, S respectively, prove that AP + CR = BQ + DS.

3C5. Prove that the medians of any tetrahedron intersect at the middle point of every straight line joining the middle points of opposite edges.

3C6. Show that there is one and only one parallelepiped which has three edges lying in three given skew straight lines.

3C7. If the joins of points on two pairs of opposite edges of a tetrahedron bisect one another, show that they divide those edges proportionally.

3C8. If ABCD,XYZW is any parallelepiped, then through any point on AY a straight line can be drawn to intersect BZ, CW, and DX.

3C9. ABCD and XYZW are any two parallelograms with corresponding sides parallel, and a variable straight line through AY, BZ, CW cuts the plane ADWX in the point P. Find the locus of P.

3C10. Show how to construct a parallelepiped so that three given skew straight lines may be diagonals of three of its faces. How many solutions are there ?

3C11. Given the representations of ABCD, XYZW, two parallelograms with corresponding sides parallel, and any point P on AY, construct a straight line through P to cut BZ, CW, and DX ; and find its points of intersection with planes ABCD and XYZW.

3C12. Two circles are drawn in parallel planes, and OA_1, QB_1 ; OA_2, QB_2 ; OA_3, QB_3 ; etc., are pairs of parallel radii such that the angles A_1OA_2, A_2OA_3, etc. are equal. Prove that A_1B_2 cuts each of the lines B_1A_2, B_2A_3, B_3A_4, etc.

3C13. Show that, if a regulus is determined by three skew straight lines which are all parallel to the same plane, then its generators are all parallel to another fixed plane.

CHAPTER IV

NORMALS

DEF. : If the angle between two straight lines (whether skew or coplanar) is a right angle, they are said to be " **at right angles** ", or " **perpendicular** to one another ".

DEF. : If a straight line is perpendicular to *every* straight line in a plane, it is said to be **normal** to the plane, or to be perpendicular, or at right angles to it.

NOTATION : The sign $\perp$ stands for " is (or *are*) perpendicular to ".

Theorem 4T1

If a given straight line is perpendicular to a pair of non-parallel straight lines in or parallel to a plane, it is normal to the plane itself. (Fig. 28.)

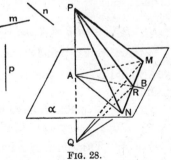

Let $p \perp m$ *and* n, *and let* m *and* $n \parallel \alpha$; to prove *that* $p \perp \alpha$.

Let AB be any straight line in α.

Draw AP $\parallel p$, and let planes Am, An cut α in AM, AN respectively.

Then

AM $\parallel m$, and AN $\parallel n$. (3T1)

FIG. 28.

Produce PA to Q, making AQ = AP, and let MN cut AB in R.

As MA, NA bisect PQ at right angles, (3T6)

∴ PMQ, PNQ are isosceles triangles ;

∴ triangles MPN, MQN are congruent ;

33

∴ PR = QR ;

∴ triangles PAR, QAR are congruent ;

∴ AR ⊥ PA ;

∴ AB ⊥ p ;   (3T6)

∴ p ⊥ every straight line in a ;

∴ p ⊥ $α$.   (Q.E.D.)

COR. 1. IF A STRAIGHT LINE IS NORMAL TO ONE OF A SET OF PARALLEL PLANES, IT IS NORMAL TO THEM ALL.   (3T3)

COR. 2. IF A PLANE IS NORMAL TO ONE OF A SET OF PARALLEL STRAIGHT LINES, IT IS NORMAL TO THEM ALL.   (3T6)

Theorem 4T2

Planes that are normal to the same straight line are parallel to one another. (Fig. 29.)

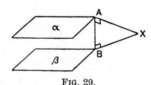

FIG. 29.

Let AB ⊥ $α$ *and* $β$ *at* A *and* B *respectively.*

If there were a point X common to planes $α$ and $β$, $X\hat{A}B$ and $X\hat{B}A$ would be right angles ; but this is impossible, as XAB is a triangle.

∴ $α$ and $β$ have no common point ;

∴ they are parallel.   (Q.E.D.)

COR. 1. THROUGH ANY POINT IN SPACE THERE IS ONE AND ONLY ONE PLANE NORMAL TO A GIVEN STRAIGHT LINE.

COR. 2. IF A SET OF CONNECTED STRAIGHT LINES ARE ALL PERPENDICULAR TO A GIVEN STRAIGHT LINE, THEY ARE CO-PLANAR ; for each pair determines a plane normal to the given straight line.

E.g. : if the straight lines AB, BC, CD, CE, CF are all perpendicular to the straight line p, they are coplanar.

Theorem 4T3

Straight lines that are normal to the same plane are parallel to one another. (Fig. 30.)

Let AB *and* CD $\perp$ *plane* BDE ; to prove *that* AB $\parallel$ CD.

In plane BDE, draw BF $\perp$ BD.

Then AB, BD, DC are all perpendicular to BF;

FIG. 30.

    $\therefore$ they are coplanar.   (4T2)

But AB, CD are both $\perp$ BD ;

        $\therefore$ they are parallel.   (Q.E.D.)

COR. 1. THROUGH ANY POINT IN SPACE THERE IS ONE AND ONLY ONE STRAIGHT LINE NORMAL TO A GIVEN PLANE.

COR. 2. IF A SET OF CONNECTED STRAIGHT LINES ARE ALL PERPENDICULAR TO A GIVEN PLANE, THEY ARE COLLINEAR.

Theorem 4T4

There is one and only one common perpendicular intersecting two skew straight lines, and its intercept is the shortest distance between them. (Fig. 31.)

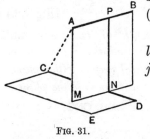

FIG. 31.

Let AB, CD *be any two skew straight lines, and let* AC *be any straight line joining them.*

    (i) Let DE $\parallel$ AB.

Then AB $\parallel$ plane CDE.   (3T1)

Let AM $\perp$ plane CDE.   (4T3)

Let plane ABM cut CD in N.

As AB in plane ABM is parallel to plane CDE,

    $\therefore$ AB $\parallel$ MN.   (3T1)

Complete the parallelogram AMNP.

Then PN ∥ AM, and AM ⊥ plane CDE ;

$$\therefore \text{ PN} \perp \text{pl. CDE ;} \tag{4T1}$$
$$\therefore \text{ PN} \perp \text{CD and DE ;}$$
$$\therefore \text{ PN} \perp \text{CD and AB.} \tag{3T6}$$

(Q.E.D. (i).)

(ii) If P'N' were another common normal,

$$\text{P'N'} \perp \text{pl. CDE ;} \tag{3T6}$$
$$\therefore \text{ P'N'} \parallel \text{PN ;} \tag{4T3}$$

which is impossible, as AB, CD are not coplanar ;

$$\therefore \text{ the common normal is unique.}$$

(Q.E.D. (ii).)

(iii) As AM ⊥ pl. CDE,

$$\therefore \text{ AM} \perp \text{CM ;}$$
$$\therefore \text{ AM} < \text{AC ;}$$
$$\therefore \text{ PN} < \text{AC.}$$

Similarly PN < any other line joining AB and CD.

∴ PN is the shortest distance between AB and CD.

(Q.E.D. (iii).)

WORKED EXAMPLES

4W1. Show that **every plane section of a sphere is a circle.**

(Fig. 32.)

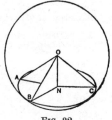

FIG. 32.

If O *be the centre of the sphere, and* A, B, C *any three points on the line of section of the spherical surface with a plane, let* ON *be the normal from* O *to the plane.*

In triangles ONA, ONB, ONC,

    ON is common,

    OA = OB = OC (radii of sphere),

ONA, ONB, ONC are right angles ;

∴ the triangles are congruent ;

∴ NA = NB = NC ;

∴ the line of section is a circle with centre at the foot of the perpendicular from the centre of the sphere to the plane of section. (Q.E.D.)

4W2. Show that **one and only one sphere will pass through any four points not in the same plane.** (Fig. 33.)

(i) *Let* A, B, C, D *be the given points,* R *the middle point of* BD, *and* P, Q *the centres of circles* BCD, ABD.

As A, B, C, D are not co-planar, PRQ is not a straight line.

In plane PRQ, draw PS, QS ⊥ PR, QR respectively, and let S be their point of intersection.

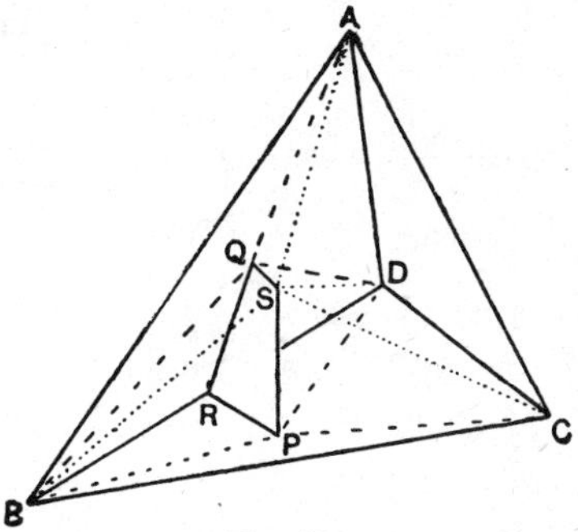

FIG. 33.

As   BD ⊥ RP, RQ,

∴ BD ⊥ SP, SQ ;   (4T1)

∴ SP ⊥ BD, RP,   and   SQ ⊥ BD, RQ ;

∴ SP ⊥ pl. BCD, and SQ ⊥ pl. ABD.   (4T1)

Triangles AQS, BQS, DQS are congruent, as AQ = BQ = DQ, and angles at Q are right angles. Similarly triangles BPS, CPS, DPS are congruent ;

∴ AS = BS = CS = DS ;

∴ S is the centre of a sphere through A, B, C, D.

(Q.E.D. (i).)

(ii) *Suppose* S′ *is the centre of another sphere through* A, B, C, D ; *and draw* S′P′, S′Q′ ⊥ *planes* BCD, ABD *respectively.*

Then triangles AQ′S′, BQ′S′, DQ′S′ will be congruent, as AS′ = BS′ = DS′, and the angles at Q′ are right angles.

∴ Q′ must coincide with Q ; and similarly P′ will coincide with P ;   ∴ S′ must coincide with S ;

∴ there is a unique spherical surface through the four given points A, B, C, D.   (Q.E.D. (ii).)

4W3. If the middle points of the edges of a tetrahedron lie on a sphere, show that opposite edges are at right angles to one another. (Fig. 34.)

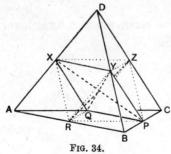

FIG. 34.

Let P, Q, R ; X, Y, Z *be the middle points of the edges* BC, CA, AB ; DA, DB, DC *of a tetrahedron, and let* P, Q, R ; X, Y, Z *lie on a sphere;* to prove *that* AB $\perp$ CD, *etc.*

XY, joining the middle points of DA, DB, is $\parallel$ AB and $= \frac{1}{2}$AB. Similarly, QP $\parallel$ AB and $= \frac{1}{2}$AB ;

$\therefore$ XY $=$ and $\parallel$ QP ;

$\therefore$ XYPQ is a parallelogram.

It is inscribed in a plane section of a sphere ; i.e. in a circle ;

$\therefore$ it is a rectangle ;

$\therefore$ XY $\perp$ YP ;

$\therefore$ AB $\perp$ CD.   (3T6)

Similarly, BC $\perp$ AD, and CA $\perp$ BD.   (Q.E.D.)

4W4. If two pairs of opposite edges of a tetrahedron are at right angles, show that the remaining pair of opposite edges are at right angles.

(Fig. 34.)

Let AB $\perp$ CD and BC $\perp$ AD ; to prove that CA $\perp$ BD.

As AB $\perp$ CD, XYPQ is a rectangle.   (3T6)

Similarly, QRYZ is a rectangle, as BC $\perp$ AD ;

$\therefore$ the diagonals PX, QY, RZ are equal, and bisect one another ;

$\therefore$ PRXZ is a rectangle ;

$\therefore$ AC $\perp$ BD.   (3T6)

(Q.E.D.)

4W5. If two pairs of opposite edges of a tetrahedron are at right angles to one another, the third pair are at right angles ; and the altitudes are concurrent, and pass through the ortho-centres of the opposite faces. (Fig. 35.)

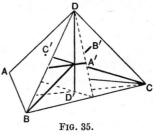

FIG. 35.

Let AA′, BB′, CC′, DD′ *be the altitudes of a tetrahedron* ABCD ; *let* AD ⊥ BC *and* CD ⊥ AB ; *to prove that* BD ⊥ AC, *that* A′, B′, C′, D′ *are the orthocentres of the faces, and that* AA′, BB′, CC′, DD′ *are concurrent.*

AD ⊥ BC, AA′ ⊥ DBC, and DD′ ⊥ ABC ;

∴ AD, AA′, DD′ are connected straight lines ⊥ BC ;

∴ they lie in a plane ⊥ BC ;   (4T2)

∴ AD′ ⊥ BC.

Similarly, as CD ⊥ AB,

∴ CD′ ⊥ AB ;

∴ D′ is the orthocentre of triangle ABC ; and similarly A′, B′, C′ are orthocentres of the other faces ;   (Q.E.D. (i).)

∴ AC ⊥ BD′ and DD′ ;

∴ AC ⊥ BD.   (4T1)

(Q.E.D. (ii).)

Again, from the fact that AD ⊥ BC, it has been shown that DD′ is coplanar with AA′ ;

∴ DD′ meets AA′.

But *every* two opposite edges are at right angles ; ∴ every altitude intersects every other altitude.

∴, if three of the altitudes were not concurrent, they would determine a plane, and the other would lie in it. This is impossible, as A, B, C, D are not coplanar ;

∴ the altitudes are concurrent. (Q.E.D. (iii).)

Def. : If the altitudes of a tetrahedron are concurrent, their point of intersection is called the **orthocentre** of the tetrahedron, which is said to be **orthocentric**.

EXAMPLES 4A

4A1. If two planes meet in a straight line, and, from any number of given points in the line, pairs of straight lines are drawn at right angles to it, one in each plane, show that the angles so formed are equal.

4A2. ABCDEF is a skew hexagon, and every pair of adjacent and alternate sides are equal and perpendicular to one another. Show that opposite vertices are at equal distances apart.

4A3. If a, b, c are sides of a triangle, and $a \perp x \perp b \perp y \perp c$, state and prove the relation that exists between x and y.

4A4. If a set of skew straight lines are parallel to the same plane, prove that the shortest lines joining them in pairs are all parallel to one another.

4A5. If a plane is normal to one of two perpendicular straight lines, prove that it is parallel to the other.

4A6. Why cannot the word " *non-parallel* " be omitted from the statement of 4T1 ?

4A7. What conclusion can be drawn if $\alpha\beta \perp \alpha\gamma$ and $\beta\gamma$?

4A8. If a, b are two parallel straight lines, and c, d two intersecting straight lines, and if $a \perp c$, and $b \perp d$, prove that $a \perp$ pl. cd.

4A9. AC is a diagonal of a parallelogram ABCD, and P a point outside its plane. If PA, PC are perpendicular to AB, CD respectively, prove that $AC \perp AB$.

4A10. Find the locus of tangents to a sphere at a given point on it.

4A11. Prove that the extremities of any straight line are equidistant from any plane that bisects it.

4A12. Prove that the diagonals of a skew rhombus, (a skew quadrilateral with four equal sides), are at right angles to one another.

EXAMPLES 4B

4B1. From a point outside a plane normals are drawn to the plane and to a given straight line in it. Prove that the given straight line is at right angles to the join of the feet of the normals.

4B2. From a point A in a plane α, AB is drawn $\perp \alpha$, and AC $\perp$ another plane β; AB and AC meet β in B and C respectively. Prove that BC $\perp \alpha\beta$, the line of intersection of the planes.

4B3. Prove that, if three concurrent edges of a rectangular parallelepiped are equally inclined to the diagonal through their point of intersection, the parallelepiped is a cube.

4B4. If two circles, not in the same plane, intersect in two points, or touch one another (i.e. touch the same straight line at the same point), prove that they lie on a sphere.

4B5. If two planes are respectively perpendicular to two straight lines in a third plane, prove that the latter is perpendicular to their line of intersection.

4B6. Prove that the locus of points equidistant from two given points is the plane which bisects at right angles the straight line joining them.

4B7. Show that the locus of points equidistant from three given points is the normal to their plane at the centre of the circle through them.

4B8. Prove that the three perpendiculars drawn from a given point to two planes and their line of intersection are coplanar.

4B9. If two rectangles, coplanar or otherwise, have a common diagonal, prove that their free corners are vertices of a third rectangle.

4B10. If A, B, C, ... are the feet of the perpendiculars from the vertex V of a pyramid upon the sides a, b, c, ... of its irregular plane base, prove that the straight lines x, y, z, ... drawn through A, B, C, ... at right angles respectively to a, b, c, ... in the plane of the base, are concurrent.

4B11. If two opposite edges of a tetrahedron are at right angles, show that every section parallel to them is a rectangle.

4B12. Find a point in a given plane such that the sum of its distances from two given points on the same side of the plane is a minimum.

4B13. Find a point in a given plane such that the difference of its distances from two given points on opposite sides of the plane is a maximum.

4B14. ABCD,XYZW is a parallelepiped. BP, PQ, QR are normal respectively to the planes DXZ, CYW, and BCZY. Prove that the plane PQR passes through B.

4B15. Given any triangle ABC and any three points P, Q, R in space, show that there is one and only one triangle XYZ with YZ through P and perpendicular to BC, ZX through Q and perpendicular to CA, and XY through R and perpendicular to AB. Point out one degenerate case.

4B16. Prove that, if all the angles of a quadrilateral are right angles, it must lie in a plane.

4B17. Prove that, if three angles of a skew quadrilateral are right angles, the remaining angle is acute, and the sides containing it are together greater than the other two.

4B18. Show that the line of intersection of two spheres is a circle.

4B19. If three spheres intersect, two by two, prove that their planes of section have one straight line in common.

4B20. Show that, if four spheres intersect, two by two, they have six planes of section, and that they are concurrent.

4B21. Find the length of a diagonal of a regular octahedron, taking an edge as unit of length.

4B22. If each of four equal spheres touches three of the others, find the distance of the centre of one from the plane of the centres of the others, the unit of length being the radius of one of the spheres.

4B23. If a variable straight line through a fixed point O cuts a fixed sphere in the points P, Q, show that the area of the rectangle OP . OQ is constant.

DEF. : **A cone** whose vertex is equidistant from every point on the edge of its base is said to be a **right cone**.

4B24. Prove that the base of a right cone is a circle whose centre is the foot of the normal from the vertex to the plane of the base.

4B25. Find the height of a regular tetrahedron, with each edge of length $2a$.

4B26. If three mutually perpendicular generators can be drawn on a right cone, find the ratio of its height to the radius of the base.

4B27. If the generators $a, b, c, \ldots$ of a cone cut two parallel planes in the points A, B, C, ... and A′, B′, C′, ... respectively, prove that the polygons ABC ... , A′B′C′ ... , are similar ; and hence show that parallel sections of a cone are similar curves.

4B28. Show that, if two opposite edges of a tetrahedron are at right angles, there is a square section parallel to them, dividing their common perpendicular in the ratio of their lengths.

4B29. If two triangles that are not in the same plane have a common base at right angles to the straight line joining their vertices, prove that the latter are coplanar with the orthocentres.

4B30. If one pair of opposite edges of a tetrahedron are equal, prove that the joins of the middle points of the other two pairs are at right angles.

4B31. If one pair of opposite edges of a tetrahedron are at right angles, show that the joins of the middle points of the other two pairs are equal.

4B32. PQRS is a tetrahedron, and angles PQR, PQS, PRS are right angles. Prove, either by means of Pythagoras' Theorem, or by the methods of this chapter, that there is one other right angle.

4B33. Show that no edge of an octahedron can be skew to more than five, or less than four of the remaining edges ; and, of these, it cannot be at right angles to more than three or two respectively.

4B34. QR is the common perpendicular of two straight lines PQ, RS, which are equal in length to QR, and inclined to one another at an angle of 60°. Find the ratio of PS : PQ.

4B35. Construct a normal to a given plane from a given external point.

EXAMPLES 4C

4C1. If a tetrahedron has three right angles, no two of which are adjacent to the same edge, prove that the fourth face is obtuse-angled.

4C2. If three skew straight lines are cut by a common perpendicular, prove that all the straight lines that intersect them are cut by a common perpendicular.

4C3. If AA', BB', CC' are concurrent diagonals of an octahedron, and ABC, ABC', ACB', AC'B', A'B'C', A'B'C are all right angles, prove that BCA' and BC'A' are right angles.

4C4. On the same equilateral triangular base, two tetrahedra are constructed, one regular, and the other having three right angles at the vertex. Prove that the height of the former is double that of the latter.

4C5. Two unequal circular holes are cut in a card. Show that the card can be folded so that a given sphere, with radius larger than that of either of the holes, may be gripped firmly between them.

4C6. Find the locus in space of a point which moves so that its distances from two given points are in a constant ratio.

4C7. Find the locus of a point which moves in space so that the sum of the squares of its distances from two given points is constant.

DEF. : If a is the distance of a point P from the centre of a sphere with radius r, then $a^2 - r^2$ is called the **power** of P with respect to the sphere.

4C8. Show that the locus of points which have equal powers with respect to two given spheres is a plane at right angles to their line of centres.

4C9. If a variable straight line cuts two given spheres in the pairs of points P, Q ; R, S respectively, and if PQ = RS, find the locus of the middle point of QR. What are the limiting positions of the line ?

4C10. If the radii of the spheres in 4C9 are a and b respectively, a being the greater, prove that the area of the locus is $\pi a b$.

4C11. Show that, in general, there is one and only one point which has equal powers with respect to four given spheres ; and discuss the exceptional cases.

DEF. : If Q is a variable point on a given surface, and O a fixed point in space, and on OQ, or OQ produced, a point P is taken, such that

$$OP \cdot OQ = a^2,$$

where a is constant, then the locus of P is called the **inverse** of the given surface with respect to a sphere with centre O and radius a. O and a are called respectively the **pole** and **radius** of **inversion**.

We are also said to have **inverted** the given surface with respect to that sphere ; and the locus of P is the result of that process of inversion.

4C12. Find the inverse of a sphere. What special form does it take if the pole of inversion lies on the sphere ?

4C13. Find the inverse of a plane.

4C14. Find the inverse of a circle with respect to any pole, not necessarily in its own plane.

4C15. Parallel to the circular base of a given cone with vertex V is a variable plane φ cutting a fixed plane α in a straight line q. If the diameter PR of the circular section φ cuts q at right angles in Q, and VP, VR cut the plane α in A and B respectively, prove that the ratio

$$PQ . QR : AQ . QB$$

is constant, and hence show that the section of the cone by the plane α can be constructed as the orthogonal projection of a circle.

4C16. Show that the ratio of the length of the edge of a regular tetrahedron to that of an inscribed cube having four edges lying in four different faces is given by

$$2 + \sqrt{2} : 1.$$

4C17. If a straight line is equally inclined to three sides of a triangle, show that it is normal to its plane.

4C18. If two opposite angles of a skew quadrilateral are equal, show that the centre of the sphere through its vertices is equidistant from the planes of those angles.

4C19. If a quadrilateral (skew or otherwise) has two pairs of equal opposite angles, show that *either* there are two pairs of equal sides, *or* the rectangle contained by the diagonals is equal to the difference between the rectangles contained by pairs of opposite sides.

4C20. State the two theorems of plane geometry which are particular cases of 4C19.

CHAPTER V

ORTHOGONAL PROJECTION AND DIHEDRAL ANGLES

Def. : The foot of the perpendicular from a given point to a given plane or straight line is called the **orthogonal projection of that point** on the given plane or straight line.

If the given point trace out a given figure, its orthogonal projection traces out the **orthogonal projection of that figure**.

Theorem 5T1

The orthogonal projection of a straight line on a plane is either a point, or a straight line.   (Fig. 36.)

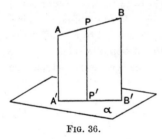

Fig. 36.

If the straight line is normal to the plane, its orthogonal projection is clearly their point of intersection.

If not, *let* P *be any point on a straight line* AB, *and let* A', P', B' *be the projections of* A, P, B *respectively on any plane* α *; to prove that* A'P'B' *is a straight line.*

AA', BB', PP' are perpendicular to α ;

∴ they are parallel to one another ;   (4T3)

∴ PP' and BB' lie in the plane ABA' ;

∴ P' lies on the line of intersection of the planes α and ABA', and this is a straight line ;   (Axiom 3)

∴ the projection of the straight line AB is the straight line A'B'.   (Q.E.D.)

46

Cor. : A straight line and its projection on a plane are coplanar.

We shall require the following theorems of Euclid : (I. 24, I. 25).

L E M M A.

If two triangles have two sides of one equal respectively to two sides of the other, but the included angles unequal, then the greater of these angles is opposite to the greater base, and conversely. (Fig. 37.)

In the triangles ABC, PQR, *let* AB = PQ, AC = PR, *but* $B\hat{A}C < Q\hat{P}R$; to prove *that* BC < QR.

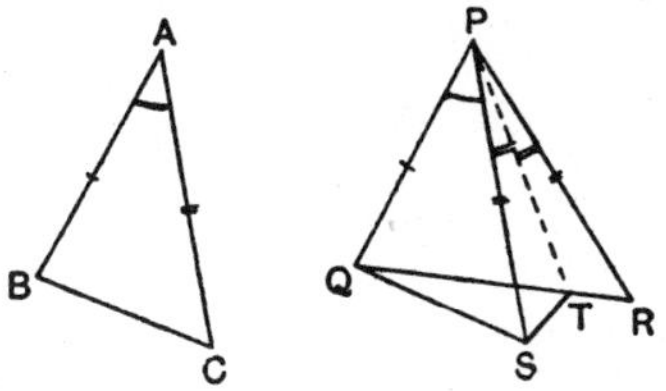

Between PQ and PR draw PS

Fig. 37.

making $Q\hat{P}S = B\hat{A}C$, and PS = AC. Let the bisector of $R\hat{P}S$ cut QR in T. Join SQ, ST.

By construction, triangles BAC, QPS are congruent ;

$$\therefore \ BC = QS.$$

Also triangles RPT, SPT are congruent ;

$$\therefore \ TR = TS.$$

Two sides of a triangle are together greater than the third side ;

$$\therefore \ QT + ST > QS ;$$
$$\therefore \ QT + TR > BC ;$$
$$\therefore \qquad QR > BC. \qquad \text{(Q.E.D.)}$$

Conversely, if the bases are unequal, it follows that the shorter base cannot be opposite to the greater angle ; while the angles cannot be equal without the triangles being congruent ;

$\therefore$ the angle opposite to the greater base must be the greater.

(Q.E.D.)

Theorem 5T2

The angle between a straight line and its projection on a plane is the least angle between that straight line and any straight line in the plane. (Fig. 38.)

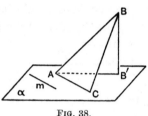

Fɪɢ. 38.

Let AB′ *be the projection of any straight line* AB *on any plane* α, *and let* AC *be* =AB′ *and* ∥ m, *any other straight line in* α.

The angle between AB and m is equal to BAC.　　　(3T6)

If m ∥ AB′, C coincides with B′, and the inclinations of AB to m and AB′ are equal.

Otherwise, as BB′⊥α, we have

$$BB′⊥CB′ ;$$

$$∴ \quad BB′<BC ;$$

$$∴ \quad B\hat{A}B′<B\hat{A}C ; \qquad \text{(Lemma)}$$

∴ the inclination of AB to AB′ is less than its inclination to m.

(Q.E.D.)

DEF. : The angle between a straight line and its projection on a plane is called the **angle between the straight line and the plane.**

DEF. : A **line of slope** of one plane to another is a straight line in the first plane drawn at right angles to the line of intersection of the two planes.

Theorem 5T3

Parallel straight lines have parallel projections on parallel planes. (Fig. 39.)

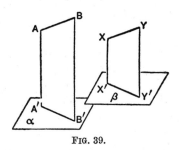

Fig. 39.

Let AB, XY *be parallel straight lines, and* A′B′, X′Y′ *their projections on the parallel planes* α, β ; *to prove that* A′B′ ∥ X′Y′.

AA′ and XX′ are normal to parallel planes ;

$$\therefore \text{ AA}' \parallel \text{XX}' ; \qquad\qquad (4\text{T1}, 3)$$

But $\qquad\qquad$ AB ∥ XY ;

$$\therefore \text{ plane ABA}' \parallel \text{plane XYX}' ; \qquad\qquad (3\text{T3})$$

∴ these planes cut planes α and β in parallel straight lines ; $\qquad\qquad$ (3T4)

$$\therefore \text{ A}'\text{B}' \parallel \text{X}'\text{Y}'. \qquad\qquad (\text{Q.E.D.})$$

Corollaries :

(1) Parallel straight lines are equally inclined to parallel planes.

(2) Lines of slope of one plane to another are equally inclined to the second plane.

Def. : The mutual inclination of two planes is called **their dihedral angle,** and is measured by the inclination of one to the lines of slope of the other.

Theorem 5T4

If a plane and a straight line are at right angles to the same plane, they are parallel to one another; *and, conversely,* if a straight line is parallel to one plane and normal to another, the planes are at right angles to one another. (Fig. 40.)

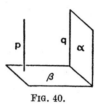

Fig. 40.

Let $\alpha \perp \beta \perp p$; to prove that $\alpha \parallel p$.
If q be a line of slope of α to β, then

$$q \perp \beta ; \qquad \text{(Def.)}$$

But $\qquad p \perp \beta ;$

$$\therefore \ p \parallel q ; \qquad \text{(4T3)}$$

$$\therefore \ p \parallel \alpha. \qquad \text{(3T1)}$$

(Q.E.D.)

CONVERSE : *Let $\beta \perp p \parallel \alpha$; to prove that $\alpha \perp \beta$.*
If any plane through p cut α in q, then

$$p \parallel q. \qquad \text{(3T1)}$$

But $\qquad p \perp \beta ;$

$$\therefore \ q \perp \beta ; \qquad \text{(4T1)}$$

$$\therefore \ q \perp \alpha\beta ;$$

$$\therefore \ q \text{ is a line of slope of } \alpha \text{ to } \beta ;$$

$$\therefore \ \alpha \perp \beta. \qquad \text{(Q.E.D.)}$$

COROLLARIES :

(1) IF A STRAIGHT LINE IN ONE PLANE IS NORMAL TO ANOTHER PLANE, THE TWO PLANES ARE AT RIGHT ANGLES TO ONE ANOTHER.

(2) AT EVERY POINT IN THE LINE OF INTERSECTION OF TWO
PERPENDICULAR PLANES THE NORMAL TO EACH LIES IN THE
OTHER.   Hence,

(3) IF ONE PLANE IS AT RIGHT ANGLES TO TWO OTHERS, IT IS
AT RIGHT ANGLES TO THEIR LINE OF INTERSECTION ;   for, at the
common point of the three planes, the normal to the first lies in
each of the others.

Theorem 5T5

**Any dihedral angle is supplementary to the angle be-
tween normals drawn to its faces from any internal point.**
(Fig. 41.)

Let P *be any point inside the dihedral
angle* $\alpha\beta$, *and let* PM, PN *be normals to
planes* α *and* β *respectively ;* to prove
that angle MPN *is the supplement of the
dihedral angle* $\alpha\beta$.

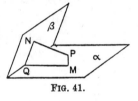

FIG. 41.

Let plane PMN cut the straight line
$\alpha\beta$ in the point Q.

Then $\alpha\beta \perp$ PM and PN ;

$\therefore \ \alpha\beta \perp$ plane PMN ;   (4T1)

$\therefore \ \alpha\beta \perp$ QM and QN ;

$\therefore$ M$\overset{\wedge}{\text{Q}}$N is the measure of the dihedral angle $\alpha\beta$.

In the plane quadrilateral PMQN, the angles M and N are
right angles ;

$\therefore$ the angles P and Q are supplementary ;

$\therefore$ the angle MPN is the supplement of the dihedral angle $\alpha\beta$.

(Q.E.D.)

COROLLARY : STRAIGHT LINES THAT ARE NORMAL TO PER-
PENDICULAR PLANES ARE PERPENDICULAR TO ONE ANOTHER,
and, conversely, PLANES THAT ARE NORMAL TO PERPENDICULAR
STRAIGHT LINES ARE PERPENDICULAR TO ONE ANOTHER.

Theorem 5T6

The length of the projection of a straight line is equal to that of the original line multiplied by the cosine of the angle it makes with the plane or line of projection.   (Fig. 42.)

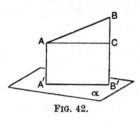

FIG. 42.

CASE 1.   PROJECTION ON A PLANE.

Let A′B′ *be the projection of* AB *on plane α.*

Then AB and A′B′ are coplanar.

(5T1)

Draw AC ∥ A′B′, and let it meet BB′ in C.

Then ACB′A′ is a rectangle ;

∴   A′B′ = AC

        = AB . cos BAC

        = AB . cos (angle between AB and A′B′)   (3T6)

        = AB . cos (angle between AB and α).

(Q.E.D. (i).)

CASE 2.   PROJECTION ON A STRAIGHT LINE. (Fig. 43.)

Let A′B′ *be the projection of* AB *on the straight line* XY.

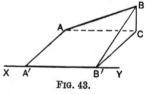

FIG. 43.

Draw   AC = and ∥ A′B′ ;

then   CB′ = and ∥ AA′.

But   AA′ and BB′ are ⊥XY ;

       ∴   CB′ and BB′ are ⊥XY ;   (3T6)

       ∴   BC ⊥ XY ;   (4T1)

       ∴   BC ⊥ AC ;   (3T6)

       ∴   AC = AB . cos BAC

                  = AB . cos (angle between AB and XY);

∴   A′B′ = AB . cos (angle between AB and XY).

(Q.E.D. (ii).)

Theorem 5T7

The area of a plane figure is reduced, by projection, in the ratio of the cosine of the dihedral angle between the plane of the figure and the plane of projection.   (Fig. 44.)

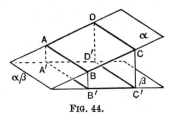

FIG. 44.

CASE 1.   (Fig. 44.)

Let ABCD *be any rectangle in the plane* α, *with* AB *and* CD $\parallel \alpha\beta$, *the line of intersection of* α *with any other plane* β ; *and let* A'B'C'D' *be the projection of* ABCD *on* β ; *to prove that*

$$A'B'C'D' = ABCD \cdot \cos \alpha\beta.$$

As $\qquad$ AB $\parallel \alpha\beta$, AB $\parallel \beta$; $\qquad\qquad\qquad$ (3T1)

$\qquad \therefore$ A'B' = AB. $\qquad\qquad\qquad\qquad\qquad$ (5T6)

As $\qquad$ BC $\perp$ AB, $\therefore$ BC $\perp \alpha\beta$; $\qquad\qquad\qquad$ (3T6)

$\qquad \therefore$ BC is a line of slope of a to β ;

$\qquad \therefore$ B'C' = BC $\cdot \cos \alpha\beta$. $\qquad\qquad\qquad\quad$ (5T6)

As $\qquad$ BB' $\perp \beta$, $\therefore$ BB' $\perp \alpha\beta$.

But $\qquad$ BC $\perp \alpha\beta$;

$\qquad \therefore$ plane BCB' $\perp \alpha\beta$; $\qquad\qquad\qquad\quad$ (4T1)

$\qquad \therefore$ B'C' $\perp \alpha\beta$;

$\qquad \therefore$ B'C' $\perp$ A'B'. $\qquad\qquad\qquad\qquad\quad$ (3T6)

It follows that A'B'C'D' is a rectangle ;

$\qquad \therefore$ A'B'C'D' = A'B' $\cdot$ B'C'

$\qquad\qquad\qquad = $ AB $\cdot$ BC $\cdot \cos \alpha\beta$

$\qquad\qquad\qquad = $ ABCD $\cdot \cos \alpha\beta$. $\qquad$ (Q.E.D. (i).)

Case 2. (Fig. 45.)

If we are given any figure F *in plane* α, *we can construct two rectangular polygons,* X *and* Y, *with parallel sides, one*

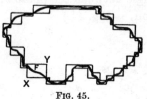

FIG. 45.

inside F, *and the other surrounding* F. Let F′, X′. Y′ be the projections on β.

The areas of F and F′ are intermediate between those of X and Y, and X′ and Y′ respectively.

By removing small rectangles from X and adding small rectangles to Y, we can make the difference between X and Y, and consequently the difference between X′ and Y′, as small as we please, while still keeping Y inside F, and F inside X.

If we make the sides of the figures X and Y parallel and perpendicular to αβ, they and their projections can be cut up exactly into rectangles like those of Case 1.

Then $X' = X . \cos αβ,$

and $Y' = Y . \cos αβ ;$

∴, to any required degree of accuracy, it may be proved that

$$F' = F . \cos αβ. \qquad \text{(Q.E.D. (ii).)}$$

Def. : Any three concurrent straight lines X′OX, Y′OY, Z′OZ, not lying in a plane, may be called a set of **axes**. If they are mutually at right angles, they are called **rectangular axes** ; otherwise they are said to be **oblique**.

X, Y, Z are said to be on the **positive,** and X′, Y′, Z′ on the **negative** sides of the **axial planes** YOZ, ZOX, XOY respectively.

The distances of a given point P from the axial planes, measured parallel to the axes, are called the **coordinates** (x, y, z) of P, and each is said to be positive or negative according as P is on the positive or negative side of the corresponding plane.

Def. : The cosines of the inclinations of a straight line to three axes are called its **direction cosines** with respect to those axes.

Theorem 5T8

Given any set of axes, if (x, y, z) are the coordinates of any point P in a given plane α, and (u, v, w) the direction cosines of the normal OQ from the origin to α, then

$$OQ = ux + vy + wz. \quad \text{(Fig. 46.)}$$

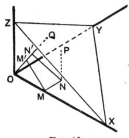

FIG. 46.

Draw PN ∥ ZO, meeting the plane XOY in N ; and draw NM ∥ YO, meeting OX in M.

Then OM $= x$, MN $= y$, and NP $= z$.

As OQ $\perp \alpha$, $\therefore$ Q is the orthogonal projection of P on OQ ; let M′, N′ be the orthogonal projections of M, N on OQ.

Then OM′ $= x$. cos QOX, M′N′ $= y$. cos QOY, and

$$N'Q = z \text{ . cos QOZ} ; \qquad \qquad (5T6)$$
$$\therefore \quad OM' = ux, \ M'N' = vy, \ N'Q = wz ;$$
$$\therefore \quad OQ = OM' + M'N' + N'Q$$
$$= ux + vy + wz. \qquad \text{(Q.E.D.)}$$

COROLLARY : IF (u, v, w) ARE THE DIRECTION COSINES OF THE NORMAL TO ANY PLANE THROUGH THE ORIGIN, AND p IS THE DISTANCE OF ANY POINT (x, y, z) FROM THE PLANE, THEN

$$p = ux + vy + wz.$$

WORKED EXAMPLES

DEF. : The line of intersection of the **plane of the figure** and the **plane of projection** is called the **axis of projection**.

5W1. Construct a triangle given its projection, the axis of projection, and the magnitude of one angle. (Fig. 47.)

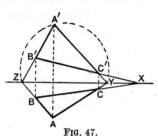

Let ABC *be the projection of the triangle, and let the axis of projection cut* BC, CA, AB *in* X, Y, Z *respectively, and let the magnitude of the original angle* A *be given.*

On ZY construct a segment of a circle containing angles equal to the true size of A.

Fig. 47.

Through A, B, C draw AA′, BB′, CC′ ⊥ XY, cutting the arc in A′, and ZA′, YA′ in B′, C′ respectively.

Then A′B′C′ is the original triangle; for angle A′ has the given magnitude, lengths parallel to the axis of projection are unaltered, and lengths at right angles to the axis are all changed in the same ratio.

NOTE : If either of the angles AYZ, AZY is obtuse, there will be two solutions, both of which may be admissible. (A solution obtained by the above method must be disregarded if A′ is nearer to XY than A ; for lengths at right angles to the axis of projection must necessarily be *reduced* by orthogonal projection.) Given angle B, we should construct a segment on ZX containing angles equal to the supplement of B.

5W2. Construct a triangle given its projection, ABC, the axis of projection, XYZ, and AD, the projection of the bisector of the angle A′. (Fig. 48.)

Draw DP ∥ BA, cutting AC in P, and complete the parallelogram APDQ.

This is the projection of a parallelogram, A′P′D′Q′ ;

(5T3)

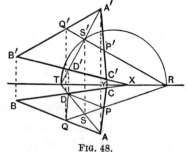

Fig. 48.

A'D' is the bisector of P'$\hat{A'}$Q' ;

∴ A'P'D'Q' is a rhombus ;

∴ its diagonals are at right angles.

Let PQ cut AD, XY in S, R respectively, and let AD meet XY in T.
Construct the right-angled triangle RS'T as in 5W1, and so
proceed.

5W3. If a, b, c, d are four straight lines in space, and ad represents any
plane parallel to a and d, and so on ;
and if $ad \perp bc$, and $bd \perp ca$, prove that
$cd \perp ab$. (Fig. 49.)

From any point O draw OA,
OB, OC, OD ∥ a, b, c, d respectively, and consider the tetrahedron whose vertices A', B', C',
D' are the centres of the spheres
OBCD, OACD, OABD and OABC
respectively.

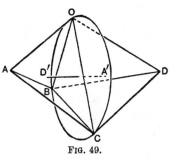

FIG. 49.

The circumcentre of the triangle OBC is the foot of each of
the normals from A' and D'.   (4W1)

∴ A'D' $\perp$ plane OBC ;

∴ A'D' $\perp$ OB and OC ;

∴ A'D' $\perp b$ and c ;   (3T6)

∴ A'D' $\perp$ plane bc ;   (4T1)

Similarly,   B'C' $\perp$ plane ad.

But $bc \perp ad$;

∴ A'D' $\perp$ B'C'.   (5T5)

Also $ca \perp bd$;

∴ B'D' $\perp$ C'A'.

If two pairs of opposite edges of a tetrahedron are at right
angles, the remaining pair are at right angles.   (4W4)

∴ C'D' $\perp$ A'B' ;

∴ $ab \perp cd$.   (5T5)

(Q.E.D.)

5W4. If OA, OB, OC are three mutually perpendicular lines, and OP is perpendicular to the plane ABC, prove that

$$\frac{1}{OP^2} = \frac{1}{OA^2} + \frac{1}{OB^2} + \frac{1}{OC^2}. \quad \text{(Fig. 50.)}$$

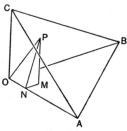

FIG. 50.

Draw   PM $\perp$ plane OAB, and MN $\perp$ OA.

Then   ON $\perp$ PM and MN ;

     $\therefore$ ON $\perp$ plane PMN ;   (4T1)

     $\therefore$ ON $\perp$ PN ;

     $\therefore$ ON is the projection of OP on OA.

As PM and CO are $\perp$ plane OAB,

     $\therefore$ they are parallel ;   (4T3)

     $\therefore$ the projection of OP on OC

                = its projection on PM

                = PM.

Similarly, the projection of OP on OB

                = MN.

By the Theorem of Pythagoras,

$$OP^2 = ON^2 + NP^2$$
$$= ON^2 + NM^2 + MP^2 ;$$
$$\therefore 1 = \frac{ON^2}{OP^2} + \frac{NM^2}{OP^2} + \frac{MP^2}{OP^2}.$$

But $\frac{ON}{OP} = \cos POA = \frac{OP}{OA}.$

By this, and similar identities,

$$1 = \frac{OP^2}{OA^2} + \frac{OP^2}{OB^2} + \frac{OP^2}{OC^2} \; ;$$

$$\therefore \quad \frac{1}{OP^2} = \frac{1}{OA^2} + \frac{1}{OB^2} + \frac{1}{OC^2}.$$

(Q.E.D.)

EXAMPLES 5A

5A1. If three planes are perpendicular to the same plane, prove that their mutual lines of intersection, if any, are parallel.

5A2. Show that three mutually perpendicular planes determine three mutually perpendicular straight lines.

5A3. State and prove the converse of 5A2.

5A4. The locus of a point whose distances from two fixed planes are equal is the pair of planes which bisect the dihedral angles between the given planes.

5A5. When a plane figure is projected on to another plane, straight lines that are equally inclined to the axis of projection are reduced in the same ratio.

5A6. Show that, if a circle is projected orthogonally on to a plane, the projection of its centre is the middle point of the projection of every diameter.

DEF. : The orthogonal projection of a circle is called an **ellipse**, and the projections of the centre and diameters of the circle are termed the **centre** and **diameters** of the ellipse. The circle is called the **auxiliary circle** of the ellipse.

The diameters of an ellipse parallel and perpendicular respectively to the axis of projection are called its **major** and **minor axes**.

5A7. Prove that the major and minor axes of an ellipse are respectively its longest and shortest diameters.

5A8. Prove that the area of an ellipse is given by the expression πab, where a, b are its semi-major and minor axes.

5A9. Find the locus of a point P such that a given triangle ABC may have equal projections on the planes PBC, PCA, PAB.

5A10. If ABC is any given triangle, find the locus of a point P such that the projections of the triangles PBC, PCA, PAB upon the plane ABC may be equal.

5A11. Prove that, with rectangular axes, the sum of the squares of the direction cosines of any straight line is equal to unity.

5A12. Show that the middle points of parallel chords of an ellipse lie on a diameter.

5A13. Show that the square on any straight line is equal to the sum of the squares on its projections on any three mutually perpendicular straight lines.

5A14. Show that the square on any straight line is equal to half the sum of the squares on its projections on any three mutually perpendicular planes.

5A15. If three sides of a triangle are equal respectively to three sides of its projection, prove that their planes must be parallel.

5A16. Show, by referring to an exception, that the word " sides " in 5A15 cannot be replaced by the word " angles ".

5A17. Show that a straight line inclined at an angle φ to the axis of projection is reduced in the ratio

$$\sqrt{(\cos^2\varphi + \sin^2\varphi \cos^2\theta)} : 1,$$

where θ is the angle between the planes.

EXAMPLES 5B

5B1. Calculate the dihedral angles of a regular tetrahedron.

5B2. Calculate the dihedral angles of a regular octahedron.

5B3. If a point moves so that the sum of its distances from two fixed planes is constant, show that its locus is a plane equally inclined to the given planes. (*Note* : Each plane is supposed to have a " front " and a " back " ; and the distances of points in front and behind are regarded as respectively positive and negative.)

5B4. Show that, if regular tetrahedra are constructed on two opposite faces of a regular octahedron, the resulting figure is a parallelepiped.

Hence deduce a relation between the dihedral angles of a regular octahedron and those of a regular tetrahedron.

5B5. Prove that straight lines in one plane which are equally inclined to another plane are also equally inclined to the line of intersection of the planes.

5B6. Show that a diagonal of a cube is equally inclined to all its edges, and calculate the angle of inclination.

5B7. Find a plane on which the projection of a given cube is a regular hexagon and its diagonals.

5B8. All the faces of a certain pyramid are inclined at the same angle α to a certain axis through the vertex, and the base is inclined at the angle β to the same axis. Prove that the ratio of the area of the base to that of the sum of the remaining faces is equal to

$$\sin \alpha : \sin \beta.$$

5B9. Prove that the sum of the projections of any straight line in space on the sides of any triangle ABC is zero, if the directions AB, BC, CA are all given the same sign.

5B10. Given the sides of a triangle and the distances of its vertices from a plane, construct its projection on that plane.

5B11. Show that any prism may be adequately defined as a solid figure with plane faces, two of which are parallel to one plane, and the rest perpendicular to another.

5B12. Construct the projection of a given triangle, given the axis of projection and the dihedral angle between the plane of the triangle and that of its projection.

5B13. Find a straight line on which the projections of all the twelve edges of a cube are equal.

5B14. Find a plane on which the projections of the six faces of a cube are equal. Show that there are four such planes through every point in space.

5B15. If each of a system of concurrent planes is at right angles to one of a system of coplanar straight lines, show that the planes are coaxal.

5B16. If each of a system of connected straight lines is perpendicular to one of a system of coaxal planes, show that the straight lines are coplanar.

5B17. Find the locus of a point P such that the sum of its coordinates with respect to a given set of axes is constant.

5B18. Construct a triangle, given its projection, the axis of projection, and the true length of one side.

EXAMPLES 5C

5C1. Three planes are mutually at right angles. Construct a plane whose section with them is congruent to a given triangle.

5C2. Show that, if the straight lines OA, OB, OC are mutually at right angles, the square of the area of the triangle ABC is equal to the sum of the squares of the areas of triangles OBC, OCA, OAB.

5C3. If OX, OY, OZ are any three straight lines not in the same plane, and, from any point P in a given plane φ, straight lines PK, PM, PN are drawn parallel to them and meet planes YOZ, ZOX, XOY in the points K, M, N respectively, and if the inclinations of φ to OX, OY, OZ are α, β, γ, prove that the expression

$$PK \sin \alpha + PM \sin \beta + PN \sin \gamma$$

is constant.

5C4. If a straight line of constant length has its extremities on two mutually perpendicular skew straight lines, show that the locus of its middle point is a circle.

5C5. If a triangle and its projection are equiangular, prove that they must be congruent, and in parallel planes, provided that each angle is equal to its own projection. (Cf. 5A16.)

5C6, 7. Construct a triangle, given its projection, the axis of projection, and

(5C6), the projection of one altitude ;

(5C7), the points of contact of the inscribed circle with two of the sides.

5C8. Construct a rectangle, given its projection and the axis of projection.

5C9. Construct a rhombus, given its projection and the axis of projection.

5C10. Prove that the sum of the distances of the vertices of a tetrahedron from any given point is greater than one-third of the sum of the edges.

5C11. Prove that, if a tetrahedron is divided into four others, the total area of the common faces is more than half that of the external faces.

CHAPTER VI

POLYHEDRAL ANGLES

DEF. : The angles subtended by the sides of a plane polygon at any point outside its plane are said to be the **face angles** of a **polyhedral angle** ; their arms are its **edges,** and the angles between their planes are its **dihedral angles.**

A polyhedral angle with 3 faces is called **trihedral,** with 4, **tetrahedral,** and so on. Polyhedral angles are also called **solid angles.**

DEF. : A polyhedral angle is said to be **concave** if any face angle is cut by the plane of another.

Polyhedral angles that are not concave are said to be **convex.**

Vertically opposite solid angles are not, in general, superposable, but have the same relation to one another as a pair of gloves, or a right-hand and a left-hand screw. They are said to be **enantiomorphous** (Gr. *enantios*, opposite), and to have **reflex congruence.**

A solid angle with n equal face angles and n equal dihedral angles is called a **regular n-hedral angle.**

There are many analogies between the sides and angles of plane polygons and the face angles and dihedral angles of a solid angle. Some of these analogies will be found in the theorems and examples of this chapter, and will often point the way to their solution.

The following theorem enables us to deduce properties of the dihedral angles of one solid angle from those of the face angles of another, and conversely.

Theorem 6T1

If the edges of one polyhedral angle are at right angles to the faces of another, the edges of the second are at right angles to the faces of the first, and the face angles of each are supplementary to the dihedral angles of the other. (Fig. 51.)

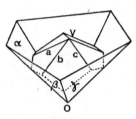

FIG. 51.

Let V, O *be vertices of the given polyhedral angles.*

Let a, b, c, ... be consecutive edges of the first, and let α, β, γ, ... *be the faces of the second at right angles to a, b, c, ... respectively ;* to prove that *the edges* $\alpha\beta$, ... *are at right angles to the faces ab, ... ; and that the face angles ab, ... are supplementary to the dihedral angles* $\alpha\beta$, ... , *and,* $\therefore$, *similarly, that the face angles* α, ... *are supplementary to the dihedral angles a, ...*

As $\qquad a \perp \alpha, \therefore a \perp \alpha\beta ;$

and as $\qquad b \perp \beta, \therefore b \perp \alpha\beta ;$

$\qquad \therefore \alpha\beta \perp \text{plane } ab.$ (4T1)

(Q.E.D. (i).)

Again, the dihedral angle $\alpha\beta$ is supplementary to ab, the angle between the normals to planes α and β. (5T5)

(Q.E.D. (ii).)

Similarly, the dihedral angle a is supplementary to α, the angle between the normals to its faces. (Q.E.D. (iii).)

DEF. : If the edges of one polyhedral angle are normal to the faces of another, they are said to be **conjugate polyhedral angles.**

Theorem 6T2

Any two face angles of a trihedral angle are together greater than the third. (Fig. 52.)

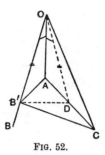

FIG. 52.

Let A$\hat{O}$C *be any face angle of any trihedral angle* O,ABC ; to prove *that*

$$A\hat{O}B + B\hat{O}C > A\hat{O}C.$$

If A$\hat{O}$B $\geqq$ A$\hat{O}$C, the proposition requires no proof ; if not, from A$\hat{O}$C cut off A$\hat{O}$D = A$\hat{O}$B, and let OD cut AC in the point D.

From OB cut off OB' = OD ; join B'A, B'D, B'C.

By construction, triangles AOD, AOB' are congruent.

$$\therefore\ AB' = AD.$$

But $\qquad AB' + B'C > AC$;

$$\therefore\ AD + B'C > AD + DC$$;

$$B'C > \qquad DC.$$

Then, in the triangles COD, COB', we have CO, OD respectively equal to CO, OB', but B'C > DC ;

$$\therefore \qquad B'\hat{O}C > D\hat{O}C$$; (Lemma, *after* 5T1)

$$\therefore\ A\hat{O}B' + B'\hat{O}C > A\hat{O}D + D\hat{O}C$$;

$$\therefore\ A\hat{O}B + B\hat{O}C > A\hat{O}C. \qquad (\text{Q.E.D.})$$

Theorem 6T3

The sum of the face angles of any convex polyhedral angle is less than four right angles. (Fig. 53.)

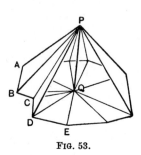

Fig. 53.

Let P,ABC ... *be any n-hedral angle cut by any plane* ABC, *and let* Q *be any point inside the polygon* ABC ... .

Considering the face angles of the trihedral angles at A, B, C, ... , we get

$$\hat{ABP} + \hat{PBC} > \hat{ABC},$$

$$\hat{BCP} + \hat{PCD} > \hat{BCD}, ...$$

and similar inequalities.   (6T2)

In Fig. 53, in which the polyhedral angle is concave *along* PC, *the angle* BCD *is* exterior *to the polygon;* but, if P,ABC ... is *convex*, each of the angles ABC, BCD, ... is an *interior* angle, and forms two angles of the triangles QAB, QBC, ...

Hence $\hat{ABP} + \hat{PBC} > \hat{ABQ} + \hat{QBC},$

and similar inequalities.

The sum of the angles of the n " sloping " triangles PAB, PBC, ... is equal to the sum of the angles of the n " horizontal " triangles QAB, QBC, ... ;

∴ at A, B, C, ... , the sum of the " sloping " angles is greater than the sum of the " horizontal " angles ;

∴ the sum of the remaining angles of the " sloping " triangles must be less than the sum of the remaining angles of the " horizontal " triangles ;

i.e., the sum of the angles at P is less than the sum of those at Q ;

i.e., less than four right angles.   (Q.E.D.)

Theorem 6T4

In any trihedral angle, the sines of the dihedral angles are proportional to the sines of the opposite face angles. (Fig. 54.)

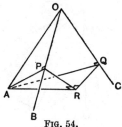

FIG. 54.

Let A, B, C *be the dihedral angles of any trihedral angle* O,ABC ; to prove *that*

$$\frac{\sin BOC}{\sin A} = \frac{\sin COA}{\sin B} = \frac{\sin AOB}{\sin C}.$$

Let AP, AQ, AR be perpendicular to the straight lines OB, OC and the plane BOC respectively.

Then $\qquad\qquad$ OB $\perp$ AP and AR ;

$\qquad\qquad\therefore$ OB $\perp$ PR. $\qquad\qquad\qquad$ (4T1)

Similarly, $\qquad\qquad$ OC $\perp$ QR ;

$\therefore$ the angles APR, AQR are the measures of the dihedral angles B, C ;

$$\therefore \frac{\sin B}{\sin C} = \frac{\sin APR}{\sin AQR} = \frac{AR/AP}{AR/AQ} = \frac{AQ}{AP} ;$$

and $\qquad \dfrac{\sin AOC}{\sin AOB} = \dfrac{AQ/OA}{AP/OA} = \dfrac{AQ}{AP} ;$

$$\therefore \frac{\sin B}{\sin C} = \frac{\sin AOC}{\sin AOB} ;$$

$$\therefore \frac{\sin COA}{\sin B} = \frac{\sin AOB}{\sin C} ,$$

and, similarly, each

$$= \frac{\sin BOC}{\sin A}. \qquad\qquad \text{(Q.E.D.)}$$

WORKED EXAMPLES

6W1. Show that the removal of a corner from a plane rectilinear figure reduces the sum of the angles subtended by its sides at any point outside its plane.   (Fig. 55.)

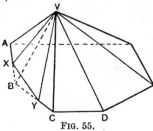

FIG. 55.

Let the corner B *of the figure* ABCDEF... *be cut off by the straight line* XY ; *and let* V *be the external point.*

$$X\hat{V}Y \quad < \quad X\hat{V}B + Y\hat{V}B ; \qquad (6T2)$$
$$\therefore \ A\hat{V}X + X\hat{V}Y + Y\hat{V}C < A\hat{V}X + X\hat{V}B + Y\hat{V}B + Y\hat{V}C,$$

i.e., $< \quad A\hat{V}B \quad + \quad B\hat{V}C.$

The angles subtended by the other sides are not affected ;

∴ the sum of the angles subtended at V by all the sides of the new figure is less than the sum of the angles subtended at V by all the sides of the old figure.   (Q.E.D.)

6W2. Show that, if one convex figure lies entirely inside another, the sum of the angles subtended at any point outside their plane by the sides of the inner figure is less than the sum of the angles subtended at the same point by the sides of the outer.

To show this, we first state and prove 6W1, and then proceed as follows :

The inner figure can be cut from the outer by the repeated removal of corners ; it follows from the above that each time the sum of the angles subtended by its sides at the given point will be reduced.   The proposition is therefore proved.

(Q.E.D.)

6W3. If F is any plane rectilinear figure, O any point outside its plane, and Q any point inside the pyramid OF, show that the face angles of the solid angle FQ are together less than those of the solid angle FO. (Fig. 56.)

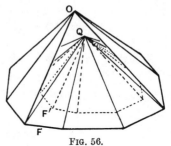

FIG. 56.

From Q draw straight lines parallel to the edges of the solid angle OF. Clearly, they must meet the plane of F at points inside F. Let F′ be the figure of which these points are vertices.

Corresponding face angles of the solid angles OF, QF′, are equal, as their corresponding arms are parallel. (3T6)

The face angles of QF′ are together less than those of QF.

(6W2)

∴ the face angles of OF are together less than those of QF.

(Q.E.D.)

6W4. Calculate the dihedral angles of a trihedral angle whose face angles are 90°, 60°, 60°.

Let O,ABC *be the trihedral angle, with* $\widehat{BOC} = 90°$, *and*

$$\widehat{AOB} = \widehat{COA} = 60°.$$

To find dihedral angle OA, *make* AB, AC $\perp$ OA. (Fig. 57.)

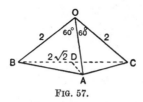

FIG. 57.

AOB, AOC are halves of equal equilateral triangles ;

∴ AB = AC = $\sqrt{3}$. OA, and OB = OC = 2 . OA ;

∴ BOC is half of a square ;

∴ BC = $\sqrt{2}$. OB = $2\sqrt{2}$. OA.

Let D be the middle point of BC.

Then $\quad \sin \text{BAD} = \dfrac{\text{BD}}{\text{AB}} = \dfrac{\sqrt{2}}{\sqrt{3}}$;

$\therefore \cos \text{BAD} = \sqrt{(1 - \sin^2 \text{BAD})} = \dfrac{1}{\sqrt{3}}$.

Dihedral angle $\quad$ OA = twice $\overset{\wedge}{\text{BAD}}$. $\hspace{2cm}$ (i)

To find dihedral angle OB, make AB, AC perpendicular to OB, OC respectively, and draw AD $\perp$ plane OBC. (Fig. 58.)

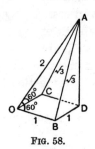

FIG. 58.

AOB and AOC are halves of equilateral triangles ;

$$\therefore \quad \text{AB} = \text{AC} = \dfrac{\sqrt{3}}{2}\, \text{OA} = \sqrt{3} \cdot \text{OB} = \sqrt{3} \cdot \text{OC}.$$

Also AD and AB $\perp$ OB ;

$\therefore \hspace{1.5cm} \text{BD} \perp \text{OB}.$ $\hspace{2cm}$ (4T1)

Similarly, $\quad$ CD $\perp$ OC ;

$\therefore \hspace{1.5cm} \overset{\wedge}{\text{ABD}} = \text{dihedral angle OB,}$

and COBD is a square ;

$\therefore \hspace{1.5cm} \text{BD} = \text{OB} ;$

$\therefore \quad \cos \text{ABD} = \dfrac{\text{BD}}{\text{AB}} = \dfrac{\text{OB}}{\sqrt{3} \cdot \text{OB}} = \dfrac{1}{\sqrt{3}}.$

$\therefore$ dihedral angle OB = half of dihedral angle OA, and its cosine $= \dfrac{1}{\sqrt{3}}$.
$\hspace{3cm}$ (ii)

EXAMPLES 6A

6A1. Show that, if a trihedral angle has two right face angles, it has two right dihedral angles, and conversely.

6A2. Show that, in any trihedral angle, any dihedral angle increased by two right angles is greater than the sum of the other two dihedral angles.

6A3. Show that solid angles that are conjugate to congruent angles are congruent to one another.

6A4. Show that the greatest angle between a given straight line and lines in a given plane lies in a plane at right angles to the latter.

6A5. If four straight lines radiate from a point, show that the six plane angles so formed are together less than eight right angles.

6A6. Of two unequal circular sections of a sphere, show that the greater is in a plane nearer to the centre.

6A7. State and prove a two-dimensional analogue of the first part of 6C16. Is there a two-dimensional analogue of the second part ?

6A8. State and prove a two-dimensional analogue of 6C17.

EXAMPLES 6B

6B1. If two face angles of a trihedral angle are equal, and the third is equal to the dihedral angle opposite to it, then the former are right angles.

6B2. If four straight lines radiate from a point making six equal angles, show that the cosine of each is equal to $-\frac{1}{3}$.

6B3. Prove that the plane bisectors of the dihedral angles of any trihedral angle are coaxal.

6B4. Show that, if three planes bisect the face angles of any trihedral angle and are at right angles to their planes, they are coaxal.

6B5. If the face angles of a trihedral angle are respectively 45°, 45°, 60°, prove that one of its dihedral angles is a right angle.

6B6. If each of the face angles of a trihedral angle is 60°, show that the sine of each semi-dihedral angle is $\dfrac{1}{\sqrt{3}}$.

6B7. Show how to construct a straight line equally inclined to the edges of a given trihedral angle.

6B8. Calculate the inclinations of a straight line to the edges of a trihedral angle whose face angles are each 60°, if these inclinations are equal to one another.

6B9. If a pyramid has equal oblique edges, and the base has equal sides, show that the angles of the base are equal.

6B10. If the three face angles of one trihedral angle are equal respectively to those of another, show that the trihedral angles are congruent. (Take sections at right angles to a pair of corresponding edges and at equal distances from the vertices.)

6B11. If the three dihedral angles of one trihedral angle are equal respectively to those of another, show that the trihedral angles are congruent. (Use 6T1.)

6B12. If two face angles of a trihedral angle are equal, show that the dihedral angles opposite to them are equal.

6B13. State and prove the converse of 6B12.

6B14. If a tetrahedral angle has two pairs of equal opposite face angles, prove that it has two pairs of equal opposite dihedral angles.

6B15. State and prove the converse of 6B14.

6B16. Prove that two trihedral angles are congruent if two face angles and the dihedral angle between them in one are respectively equal to the corresponding parts of the other.

6B17. If two face angles of one trihedral angle are equal respectively to two face angles of another, and the dihedral angles opposite to the first of each pair are equal, show that the dihedral angles opposite to the second of each pair are either equal or supplementary.

6B18, 19. Interchange the words "face" and "dihedral" in 6B16, 17.

6B20. Show that, if a tetrahedral angle has two pairs of equal adjacent face angles, its diagonal planes are at right angles to each other.

6B21. Show that, if a tetrahedral angle has two pairs of equal opposite face angles, its diagonal planes bisect its diagonal angles.

6B22. Show that the n dihedral angles of any convex polyhedral angle, together with four right angles, are greater than $2n$ right angles.

6B23. If two face angles of one trihedral angle are supplementary to two face angles of another, and the included dihedral angles are equal, find the relation between the remaining face angles.

6B24. If two face angles and the included dihedral angle of one trihedral angle are respectively supplementary to two dihedral angles and the included face angle of another trihedral angle, find the relation between the remaining face angle of the first and the remaining dihedral angle of the second.

6B25. If $\alpha\beta\gamma$, $\alpha'\beta'\gamma'$ are two trihedral angles and $\alpha = \alpha'$ and $\beta + \beta' = \alpha\beta + \alpha'\beta' = 180°$, find the relation between the face angles γ and γ'.

6B26. Show that, *in general*, two trihedral angles are congruent if two face angles of one, and the dihedral angles opposite to them, are equal respectively to the corresponding parts of the other. Show that there is one, and only one, exceptional case.

EXAMPLES 6C

6C1. Show that, if a pyramid has equal oblique edges and the angles of its base are equal, then alternate sides of the base are equal, and hence that the base must be regular if it has an odd number of sides.

6C2. Two unequal polygons, each with n equal sides, are placed in two parallel planes so that the sides of one are bases of equal isosceles triangles with their vertices at the vertices of the other; prove that both polygons must be regular.

6C3. Show that, if three planes pass through the edges of any trihedral angle and are at right angles to the opposite faces, they are coaxal.

6C4. Show that the sum of the angles subtended by the edges of any tetrahedron at any point inside it is greater than half the sum of the face angles.

6C5. Each of the four face angles of a given quadrihedral angle is equal to 60°. Show that, if one of the diagonal angles is acute, the other must be obtuse.

6C6. A solid figure is bounded by twelve congruent rhombuses, and two opposite tetrahedral angles are regular. Sketch the figure, and prove that the largest square section has twice the area of the next largest.

6C7. In the solid figure of 6C6, prove that the diagonals of each rhombus are in the ratio $\sqrt{2} : 1$.

6C8. If the ratio of a sloping edge of a regular square pyramid to an edge of the base is as $\sqrt{3} : 2$, show that alternate triangular faces are at right angles to one another.

6C9. Show that the **rhombic dodecahedron** (the solid described in 6C6) has 24 dihedral angles, each of 120°.

6C10. If every face of a solid figure has n equal angles, and m edges meet at every vertex, show that

$$m + n > \tfrac{1}{2}mn.$$

6C11. If the sum of the face angles of a solid angle is equal to the sum of its dihedral angles, show that it must be trihedral.

6C12. If one straight line subtends equal obtuse angles at the extremities of another, show that it subtends a greater angle at any internal point of the second line.

6C13. Show that the sum of the angles between the edges of any trihedral angle and any straight line drawn inside it from its vertex is less than the sum of the face angles, but greater than half their sum.

6C14. Show that space can be filled by fitting together eight regular trihedral angles, and six regular tetrahedral angles, each face angle being of 60°.

6C15. Show why the word " obtuse " cannot be omitted from 6C12.

6C16. WVA and WVB are two equal angles. Show that there is, in general, one and only one straight line VP such that each of the dihedral angles W(AV)P, W(BV)P, is equal to half of the dihedral angle A(PV)B, inside which W lies.

Show also that, with one particular value of the angle WVA, there is an infinite number of possible positions of the straight line VP.

6C17. If $\alpha\beta\gamma$, $\alpha'\beta'\gamma'$ are two trihedral angles in which

$$\alpha = \alpha', \ \beta = \beta', \quad \text{and} \quad \beta\gamma + \beta'\gamma' = 180°,$$

find the relation between the dihedral angles $\gamma\alpha$ and $\gamma'\alpha'$.

6C18. If $\alpha\beta\gamma$, $\alpha'\beta'\gamma'$ are two trihedral angles in which $\alpha + \alpha' = 180°$, and $\beta\gamma = \beta'\gamma'$, and $\gamma\alpha = \gamma'\alpha'$, find the relation between the face angles β and β'.

CHAPTER VII

VOLUMES OF POLYHEDRAL SOLIDS

Theorem 7T1

The areas of parallel sections of a pyramid are proportional to the squares of their distances from the vertex. (Fig. 59.)

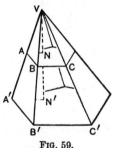

FIG. 59.

Let N, N′ *be the projections of the vertex* V *on any two parallel plane sections* ABCD... , A′B′C′D′... .

By similar triangles,

$$\frac{VN'}{VN} = \frac{A'V}{AV} = \frac{A'B'}{AB} \; ;$$

$$\therefore \frac{\text{Area A}'B'C'D'...}{\text{Area ABCD}...} = \frac{A'B'^2}{AB^2} = \frac{VN'^2}{VN^2}.$$

(Q.E.D.)

COROLLARY: THE SAME IS TRUE OF A CONE. (See Note before 8T1.)

DEF.: A **right prism** is one whose ends are orthogonal projections of one another.

DEF. : The **area** of a plane rectilinear figure is expressed as the number (integral or otherwise) of unit squares which can be formed from it by any process of subdivision and reconstruction.

DEF. : The **volume** of any polyhedral solid is expressed as the number (integral or otherwise) of unit cubes which can be formed from it by any process of subdivision and reconstruction.

NOTE : Subdivision may be *external* as well as *internal* ; i.e., if a figure is treated as part of a larger whole, it may be regarded as the algebraic sum of positive and negative parts.

In Plane Geometry we have the following propositions :

(1) *Every plane rectilinear figure can be subdivided into triangles.*

(2) *Any two congruent triangles can be put together to form a parallelogram.*

(3) *Two parallelograms on the same base and between the same parallels can be subdivided into the same set of parts.*

(4) Hence *every plane rectilinear figure can be dissected and reconstructed so as to form a rectangle.*

If the three-dimensional analogues of (1), (2), and (3) were all true, the analogue of (4) would follow. Actually there is no three-dimensional theorem analogous to (4) because there is none analogous to (2), although, corresponding to (1) and (3) we have the propositions :

(1) *Every plane-faced solid figure can be subdivided into tetrahedra.*

(3) *Any two parallelepipeds on the same base and between the same parallel planes can be subdivided into the same set of parts.*

It is therefore impossible to discuss the volumes of plane-faced solids in general without recourse to analytical methods.

These are employed in 7T3 to establish the fact that

Pyramids with equal bases and equal heights have equal

volumes ; which is the three-dimensional analogue of the proposition :

Triangles with equal bases and equal heights have equal areas.

We are then able, in 7T4, to prove that

The volume of any pyramid is equal to one-third of that of any prism on the same base and with the same height ; which is the analogue of the proposition :

The area of any triangle is equal to one-half of that of any parallelogram on the same base and with the same height.

We are then in a position to find the volume of any plane-faced solid.

Theorem 7T2

If two right prisms have equal heights and bases of equal area, they have equal volumes.   (Fig. 60.)

By definition, the bases can be cut up, and their parts rearranged to form the same number of unit squares.

If the dissection is made by planes at right angles to the bases, the prisms them-

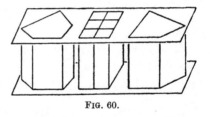

Fɪɢ. 60.

selves will be cut up at the same time, and their parts may be similarly rearranged to form the same number of right prisms on unit square bases.

These are equal in height ;

∴ they are congruent ;

∴ the original prisms are equal in volume.

(Q.E.D.)

Cᴏʀ. 1. Iғ ᴀɴʏ ʀɪɢʜᴛ ᴘʀɪsᴍ ɪs ᴏғ ʜᴇɪɢʜᴛ h, ᴀɴᴅ ʜᴀs ᴀ ʙᴀsᴇ ᴏғ ᴀʀᴇᴀ A, ɪᴛs ᴠᴏʟᴜᴍᴇ ɪs Ah.

Cᴏʀ. 2. Tʜᴇ sᴀᴍᴇ ɪs ᴛʀᴜᴇ ᴏғ ʀɪɢʜᴛ ᴄʏʟɪɴᴅᴇʀs.   (See Note before 8T1.)

Theorem 7T3

Pyramids with equal bases and equal heights have equal volumes. (Fig. 61.)

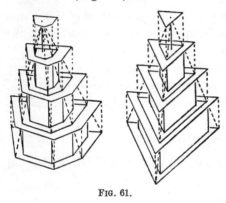

FIG. 61.

Let the altitude of each pyramid be divided into n equal parts by means of planes parallel to the base, and then construct $(n-1)$ right prisms, one on the under side of each section (*vertical edges black in diagram*), and n right prisms, one on the upper side of each section and one on the base (*vertical edges dotted*), and let each of these prisms lie between a neighbouring pair of parallel planes.

Evidently each given pyramid is greater than the first, and less than the second set of prisms formed on its sections ; and the second set is equal to the first with the addition of the lowest prism.

The areas of parallel sections of a pyramid are proportional to the squares of their distances from the vertex. (7T1)

∴ as the bases of the two given pyramids are equal in area, corresponding sections are also equal in area ;

∴ corresponding prisms are equal in volume ; (7T2)

∴ the volumes of the given pyramids cannot differ by more than that of the lowest prism, and this can be made as small as we please by taking all the planes of section sufficiently close together ;

∴ the given pyramids must be equal in volume.

(Q.E.D.)

COR. : THE SAME IS TRUE OF CONES. (See Note before 8T1.)

Theorem 7T4

The volume of any pyramid is equal to one-third of that of any prism with the same base and height. (Fig. 62.)

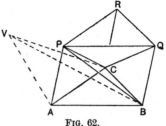

Let ABCV *be any tetrahedron and* ABC,PQR *any prism on the same base* ABC *and with the same height ;* to prove *that*

ABCV = $\frac{1}{3}$ ABC,PQR.

FIG. 62.

Join BP, PC, CQ.

Then the tetrahedron ABCV

= tet. ABCP with same base ABC and same height ;   (7T3)

= tet. BCPQ with equal bases ABP, BPQ, and same height ;

(7T3)

= tet. CPQR with equal bases BCQ, CQR, and same height ;

(7T3)

∴ tet. ABCV = $\frac{1}{3}$ prism ABC,PQR ;

∴ the theorem is proved for the case of a *triangular* pyramid.

Every pyramid can be cut up into triangular pyramids with the same vertex and the same height ;

∴ the theorem is true for all pyramids.

(Q.E.D.)

Corollaries :

(1) Prisms which have equal heights and bases of equal area have equal volumes.

(2) The volume of any prism is equal to Ah, where h is the height, and A the area of the base.

(3) The volume of any pyramid is equal to $\frac{1}{3}$Ah.

(4) This theorem and corollaries are true of cones and cylinders. (See Note before 8T1.)

Theorem 7T5

The volume of a prism of length k and cross-section S is equal to Sk. (Fig. 63.)

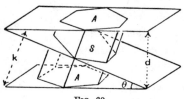

FIG. 63.

Let d *be the perpendicular distance between the ends, and* A *the area of each ; and let* θ *be the angle between the planes of* A *and* S.

As k and d are measured in directions at right angles to planes S and A respectively,

∴ θ is equal to the angle between the directions of k and d. (5T5)

d is the projection of k, and S the projection of A ;

$$\therefore \ d = k \cdot \cos \theta, \qquad (5T6)$$

and $$S = A \cdot \cos \theta. \qquad (5T7)$$

The volume of the prism

$$= Ad \qquad (7T4)$$

$$= \frac{S}{\cos \theta} k \cos \theta$$

$$= Sk. \qquad (\text{Q.E.D.})$$

COR. : THE SAME IS TRUE OF CYLINDERS. (See Note before 8T1.)

Theorem 7T6

The edges of any tetrahedron are diagonals of the faces of a parallelepiped whose volume is three times that of the tetrahedron. (Fig. 64.)

Let ACFH *be any tetrahedron. Through the middle point of* AC, *draw a straight line* BD = *and* ∥ FH *and bisected by* AC.

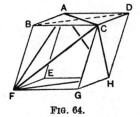

FIG. 64.

Then ABCD is a parallelogram.

Also   BF = and ∥ DH.

Draw   AE and CG = and ∥ BF.

Then EFGH is a parallelogram ;

∴ ABCD,EFGH is a parallelepiped, and the edges of the given tetrahedron ACFH are diagonals of its faces.

Tet. ABCF = $\frac{1}{3}$ prism ABC,EFG with same base ABC and same
           height   (7T4)

          = $\frac{1}{6}$ parallelepiped ABCD,EFGH.

Similarly, each of the tetrahedra ACDH, FGHC, HEFA is equal to $\frac{1}{6}$ of the parallelepiped ;

∴ together they make up $\frac{2}{3}$ of the parallelepiped ;

∴ when they are removed, the remaining tetrahedron ACFH must be $\frac{1}{3}$ of the parallelepiped.   (Q.E.D.)

COROLLARY : IF a, b ARE LENGTHS OF TWO OPPOSITE EDGES OF A TETRAHEDRON, h THE DISTANCE BETWEEN THEM, AND θ THE ANGLE BETWEEN THEM, THEN THE VOLUME = $\frac{1}{6}abh \sin \theta$.

The area of each of the four triangles into which AC and BD divide the parallelogram ABCD

$$= \frac{1}{2} \frac{AC}{2} \frac{BD}{2} \sin \theta \; ;$$

∴ ABCD = $\frac{1}{2}$AC . BD sin θ ;

∴ the volume of the parallelepiped = $\frac{1}{2}hab \sin \theta$;

∴ the volume of the tetrahedron, one-third as great,

$$= \frac{1}{6}hab \sin \theta. \qquad \text{(Q.E.D.)}$$

Theorem 7T7

The volume of a prismoid is equal to

$$\frac{h}{6}(A + 4B + C),$$

where h is the distance between the parallel faces, A and C are their areas, and B the area of the parallel section midway between them. (Fig. 65.)

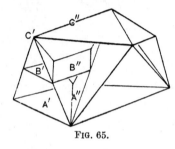

FIG. 65.

(This is a particular application of Simpson's Rule, which is discussed in books on Integral Calculus.)

Each end can be cut up into triangles, and, by joining their vertices, we can divide the solid into tetrahedra, each of which will have either one of its faces in one of the ends and the opposite vertex in the other, or a pair of opposite edges one in each end.

Let A′ stand for the base of a tetrahedron in end A, B′ for its middle section, and C′ for its vertex.

Then
$$B' = \tfrac{1}{4}A', \quad \text{and} \quad C' = O ; \tag{7T1}$$

$$\therefore \ \frac{h}{6}(A' + 4B' + C')$$

$$= \frac{h}{6}(A' + A' + O)$$

$$= \frac{h}{3} A'$$

= volume of the tetrahedron. (7T4)

Again, let B″ stand for the middle section of a tetrahedron which has a pair of opposite edges A″, C″ in the planes A, C respectively.

Then $\qquad$ A$'' =$ O, $\quad$ C$'' =$ O $\ (in\ area)$,

and B$''$ is a parallelogram with sides parallel and equal to halves of the edges A$''$ and C$''$;

$\therefore$ if $a,\ c$ are the *lengths* of A$''$, C$''$, and θ the angle between them,

$$B'' = \frac{a}{2}\frac{c}{2}\sin\theta\ ;$$

$$\therefore\ \frac{h}{6}(A'' + 4B'' + C'')$$

$$= \frac{h}{6}\left(O + 4 \cdot \frac{a}{2}\frac{c}{2}\sin\theta + O\right)$$

$$= \frac{h}{6}\,ac\sin\theta$$

$$= \text{volume of the tetrahedron.} \qquad (7T6)$$

$\therefore$ the Theorem applies to every tetrahedron into which the given solid has been divided ;

$\therefore$ the volume of the solid

$$= \sum\frac{h}{6}(A' + 4B' + C')$$

$$= \frac{h}{6}(\Sigma A' + 4\Sigma B' + \Sigma C')$$

$$= \frac{h}{6}(A + 4B + C). \qquad (\text{q.e.d.})$$

Theorem 7T8

The volumes of similar polyhedral solids are proportional to the cubes of corresponding lengths.

Let ABC..., A$'$B$'$C$'$... *be corresponding faces of any two similar solids, and let* VN, V$'$N$'$ *be normals drawn to them from corresponding internal points* V, V$'$.

Then V,ABC..., V',A'B'C'... are similar pyramids ;

$$\therefore \quad \frac{\text{vol. of V,ABC...}}{\text{vol. of V',A'B'C'...}} = \frac{\frac{1}{3}\text{VN . ABC...}}{\frac{1}{3}\text{V'N'. A'B'C'...}} \quad\quad (7\text{T}4)$$

$$= \frac{\text{VN}}{\text{V'N'}} \cdot \frac{\text{VN}^2}{\text{V'N'}^2} \quad\quad (7\text{T}1)$$

$$= \frac{\text{VN}^3}{\text{V'N'}^3}.$$

The same applies to pyramids with vertices at V, V', and bases on any other pair of corresponding faces.

Hence the proposition.

COROLLARY : THE THEOREM APPLIES TO EVERY PAIR OF SIMILAR SOLIDS, WHETHER THEIR FACES ARE PLANE OR NOT. (See Note before 8T1.)

NOTE : It is easy to prove the analogous two-dimensional theorem : THE AREAS OF THE SURFACES OF SIMILAR SOLIDS ARE PROPORTIONAL TO THE SQUARES OF CORRESPONDING LENGTHS.

WORKED EXAMPLES

7W1. Show that a plane which bisects two opposite edges of a tetrahedron bisects its volume. (Fig. 66.)

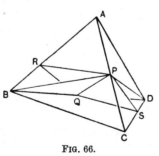

FIG. 66.

Let P, Q *be the middle points of* AC, BD *respectively, and let any plane through* PQ *cut* AB, CD *in* R, S *respectively; to prove that* AD,RPSQ *includes half of the volume of the tetrahedron* ABCD.

Through P there is a plane parallel to AB and CD.   (3T3)

As this plane bisects AC, it must also bisect BD and RS.   (3T5)

∴ PQ is the line of intersection of this plane with plane PRQS ;   ∴ PQ bisects RS.

It is easy to show that the ends of a straight line are at equal distances from any plane that bisects it ;

$\therefore$ R and S are equidistant from plane BPD through PQ, and A and C are equidistant from the same plane.

As PQ is a median of triangle BPD, it bisects its area ;

$\therefore$ tet. RBQP = tet. SPQD with equal base and height.   (7T3)

Also tet. ABDP = tet. CBDP with same base and equal height ;   (7T3)

$$\therefore \text{ AD,RPSQ} = \text{ABDP} - \text{BPQR} + \text{DPQS}$$
$$= \text{ABDP}$$
$$= \tfrac{1}{2}\text{ABCD}. \qquad \text{(Q.E.D.)}$$

7W2. If a triangular prism is cut off by a plane not parallel to the ends, show that the volume of the remainder

$$= \text{S} \cdot \frac{a+b+c}{3},$$

where S is the area of the right section, and a, b, c are the lengths of the parallel edges.   (Fig. 67.)

Let h *be the perpendicular height of the edge* a *above the plane* bc, *and let* d *be the perpendicular distance between* b *and* c.

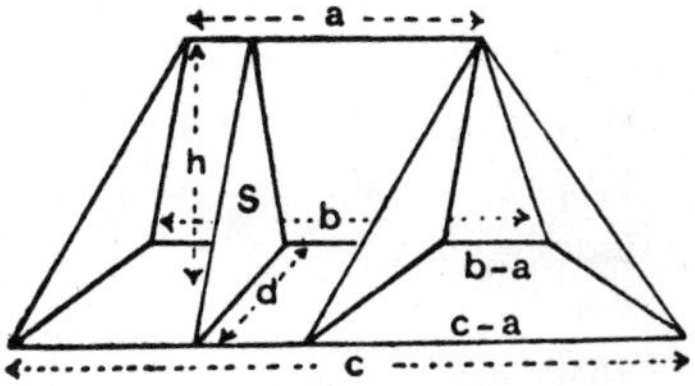

FIG. 67.

If a be the shortest of a, b, c, take a plane through one end of a parallel to the other end of the figure, cutting the figure into a triangular prism and a pyramid whose base is a trapezium.

$$\text{Volume of prism} = \text{S}a. \qquad (7\text{T5})$$

Volume of pyramid

$$= \frac{(b-a)+(c-a)}{2} \cdot d \cdot \frac{h}{3} \qquad (7\text{T4})$$

$$= \frac{b+c-2a}{3} \cdot d \cdot \frac{h}{2}, \text{ (transposing denominators),}$$

$$= \frac{b+c-2a}{3} \cdot \text{S}$$

$\therefore$ the total volume of the given solid

$$= \mathsf{S} \cdot \left(a + \frac{b + c - 2a}{3} \right)$$

$$= \mathsf{S} \cdot \frac{a + b + c}{3}.$$

(Q.E.D.)

EXAMPLES 7A

7A1. The four corners are cut from any tetrahedron by planes through the middle points of the edges. What solid is left ? Show that it contains half the volume of the tetrahedron.

7A2. Find the volume of a cube inscribed in a sphere of unit radius.

7A3. One edge of a tetrahedron is trisected in the points P and Q, and the opposite edge in the points R and S. Show that the tetrahedron PQRS contains rather more than 11 per cent. of the volume of the original tetrahedron.

7A4. If a pyramid is bisected by a plane parallel to its base, show that the plane of section is approximately four times as far from the vertex as from the plane of the base.

7A5. Show that any parallelepiped can be cut up into six pyramids equal to one another in volume and having parallelograms for their bases.

7A6. Show that the diagonal planes of any parallelepiped divide it into twenty-four tetrahedra of equal volumes.

7A7. Show that the centroids of the faces of any tetrahedron are vertices of a second tetrahedron which contains one twenty-seventh of the volume of the first.

7A8. The vertex of any pyramid is cut off by a variable plane parallel to a given plane outside the pyramid. Prove that the volume cut off varies as the cube of the distance of the vertex from the cutting plane.

7A9. By means of a proof analogous to that of the corresponding two-dimensional theorem, show that two parallelepipeds on the same base and between the same parallel planes are equal in volume.

7A10. Replace the word " six " in 7A5 by the word " three."

7A11. Show that more than 27 per cent. saving could have been effected in the cost of the materials for any of the Egyptian pyramids, by making every edge 10 per cent. shorter.

7A12. The volume of a cone is increased 10 per cent. by increasing its height. If this is done twelve times, what is the total percentage increase in height ?

EXAMPLES 7B

7B1. Find the volume of a regular octahedron each edge of which is 2 inches long.

7B2. Find the volume of a regular tetrahedron each edge of which is 2 inches long.

7B3. Find the volume of a regular tetrahedron inscribed in a sphere of radius r.

7B4. The vertices of an octahedron are centroids of the faces of a cube. Show that the former occupies rather less than 17 per cent. of the volume of the latter.

7B5. If the vertices of a cube are the centroids of the faces of a regular octahedron, show that the former occupies rather more than 22 per cent. of the volume of the latter.

7B6. If a cube is inscribed in a regular octahedron, so that each vertex of the former is on an edge of the latter, show that the cube occupies nearly 43 per cent. of the volume of the octahedron.

7B7. The ridge of a hipped roof is of length a, and is parallel to the plane of the eaves, which form a parallelogram with sides of length b and c inclined to one another at the angle θ. Prove that the volume enclosed by the roof and the plane of the eaves is given by the expression

$$\frac{ch}{6}(a+2b)\sin\theta,$$

where h is the height of the ridge above the eaves, and b is the longer side of the parallelogram.

7B8. If A′B′C′ is the projection of any triangle ABC on any plane, prove that the tetrahedra ABCA′ and A′B′C′A are equal in volume. Hence show that, if V is the vertex of any pyramid, D its base, O any point in D, and D′ the projection of D on any plane at right angles to VO, then the volume is equal to $\dfrac{D'.OV}{3}$.

7B9. Show that, if perpendiculars are drawn to the faces of a regular tetrahedron from any point inside it, their sum is constant.

7B10. The corners are cut from a regular octahedron by planes through the middle points of its edges. Find the volume of the resulting solid if each of its edges is of length a.

7B11. An earthwork consists of a zig-zag bank with its cross-section a trapezium with equal base angles. If the height is h and the areas of the flat top and of the ground covered are respectively A, B, find the volume of the earthwork.

7B12. Two unit squares are placed with their sides inclined to one another at 45° in two parallel planes at unit distance apart, and their alternate vertices are joined forming eight triangles. Find the volume enclosed.

7B13. Inside a regular tetrahedron of height h is a point whose distances from three of the faces are respectively $\dfrac{h}{2}, \dfrac{h}{4}, \dfrac{h}{6}$. Find its distance from the fourth face.

7B14. Two rectangles with sides a, b ; c, d ; are arranged in parallel planes at a distance h apart, with the edges a, b parallel respectively to the edges c, d. Find the volume enclosed by the rectangles and four trapeziums.

7B15. The area of each of the triangular faces of a square pyramid is equal to half of A, the area of the base. Find the volume of the pyramid.

7B16. Show that a cube can be divided into four congruent solids each consisting of two unequal tetrahedra on opposite sides of the same equilateral base.

7B17. A cube has the same volume as a tetrahedron ; find the ratio of the areas of their surfaces.

7B18. The surface of a cube has the same area as that of a tetrahedron ; find the ratio of their volumes.

EXAMPLES 7C

7C1. If a dihedral angle and its edge in one tetrahedron are equal respectively to a dihedral angle and its edge in another, and the pairs of faces about those edges are respectively equal in area, show that the tetrahedra are equal in volume.

7C2. A right prism stands on a regular hexagon base of side $2m$. If a plane cuts three successive edges at distances a, b, c from the base, show that the volume cut off

$$= 6\sqrt{3} \cdot m^2(a - b + c).$$

7C3. It is required to level a site whose plan is a rectangle measuring 132 feet by 64 feet. A line cutting the long sides 36 feet from opposite corners is found to be horizontal. Find the volume of soil that must be removed from the high to the low part of the ground if the greatest difference in level is 6 feet.

7C4. A solid figure has eight faces, four of which are regular hexagons, and the rest equilateral triangles, with two of the former and one of the latter at each vertex. Taking an edge as the unit of length, show that its volume $= \dfrac{23\sqrt{2}}{12}$.

7C5. Each of two opposite regular quadrihedral angles of a solid figure is formed by the acute angles of four rhombuses, and the four remaining faces are squares. Show that its volume is equal to $2\sqrt{2}$ times that of a cube with edges of the same length.

7C6. Four parallel edges of a cube are shaved off, making a regular octagonal prism, and then the remaining edges are shaved off in the same way. Show that the resulting figure has six square and twelve hexagonal faces, and that its volume is $4(14 - 9\sqrt{2})a^3$, where $2a$ is the length of an edge of the cube.

7C7. Two squares are arranged with the sides of one parallel to the diagonals of the other, and their vertices are joined alternately. Show that the volume of the figure enclosed by the resulting eight triangles and the two squares is given by

$$\frac{c}{3}(a^2 + \sqrt{2}ab + b^2),$$

where a and b are the lengths of the sides of the squares, and c is the distance between their planes.

7C8. A waste paper basket is in the form of a frustum of a square pyramid surmounted by a congruent inverted frustum, whose slant edges would, if produced, intersect in the centre of the base. If every edge with the exception of those at the waist is of length $2a$, show that the capacity of the basket is given by

$$\frac{7\sqrt{14}}{3} a^3.$$

7C9. If two regular polygons, each having n sides of length a, are arranged in parallel planes so that the joins of alternate vertices are equal to one another, show that the volume enclosed by the polygons together with the resulting $2n$ isosceles triangles, is given by

$$\frac{na^2d}{12}\left(\cot\frac{\pi}{n}+\cot\frac{\pi}{2n}\right),$$

where d is the distance between the parallel planes.

7C10. Show that the word " regular " might be omitted from the statement of 7C9, as it follows from the remaining data that all the angles of the polygons are equal.

7C11. Show that the formula of 7C9 correctly gives the volume of a tetrahedron having a pair of equal opposite edges of length a at distance d apart. (Each of these edges should be regarded as a polygon of *two* sides.)

7C12. Show that the volume of a regular octahedron can be correctly calculated by means of the formula of 7C9.

7C13. By considering the volumes of four tetrahedra, find the locus of a point P whose distances p, q, r, from three given planes are such that

$$ap+bq+cr=v,$$

where a, b, c are any given numbers, positive or negative, and v is any given volume.

CHAPTER VIII

AREA AND VOLUME OF CONE AND SPHERE

DEF. : A cylinder is called a **right cylinder** if its ends are circles and each is the orthogonal projection of the other.

DEF. : A cone is called a **right cone** if its base is a circle whose centre is the orthogonal projection of the vertex.

DEF. : A straight line joining two points on a sphere is called a **chord**, and a chord which passes through the centre is called a **diameter**.

DEF. : A plane through the centre of a sphere is called a **diametral plane**.

DEF. : A plane divides a solid sphere into two **segments**, and its surface into two **caps**.

DEF. : Two parallel planes enclose a **frustum** of a solid sphere, and a **zone** of its surface.

DEF. : A single branch of a conical surface with its vertex at the centre of a sphere divides the latter into two **sectors**.

DEF. : The section of a sphere by a diametral plane is called a **great circle**, and any other plane section of a sphere is called a **small circle**.

(For proof of the fact that any plane section of a sphere *is* a circle, see 4W1.)

DEF. : The part of a spherical surface enclosed by the halves of two great circles is called a **lune** ; and the part enclosed by arcs of three great circles is called a **spherical triangle**.

DEF. : Three mutually perpendicular diametral planes divide a spherical surface into eight **octants**.

MAGNITUDE OF A FIGURE ; ELEMENTS

The theory of this chapter and the next is based on the following set of definitions :

DEF. : **Length, area,** and **volume** are called **magnitudes of 1, 2, and 3 dimensions** respectively.

DEF. : The **elements** of a curve are the **chords** of any set of arcs into which it may be divided.

DEF. : The **elements** of a surface are the **plane polygons** whose vertices coincide with those of any set of superficial polygons into which it is divided.

DEF. : The **elements** of a solid figure are parts of the **polyhedron** bounded by elements of its surface.

NOTATION : If m stands for an element, then Σm stands for the total magnitude of all the elements of the same set.

DEF. : If, by insisting on a sufficiently small maximum distance between vertices of the same element, we can make every possible value of Σm differ as little as we please from some definite magnitude M, then M is said to be the **limiting value** of Σm.

NOTATION : Lt Σm stands for " the limiting value of Σm ".

DEF. : If, for a given figure, Lt Σm exists, it is said to be the **magnitude** of that figure.

NOTE : As elements of a cylinder, we can take prisms, having, as ends, corresponding elements of the ends of the cylinder.

As elements of a cone, we can take pyramids, with the same vertex, and having, as bases, elements of the base of the cone.

It follows that Theorems 7T1-7T5 hold good if the words " *cylinder* " and " *cone* " are substituted for " prism " and " pyramid ".

Theorem 8T1

The area of the conical surface of the frustum of a right cone with slant height k and circumferences of ends c, c', is

$\frac{1}{2}k(c+c')$.   (Fig. 68.)

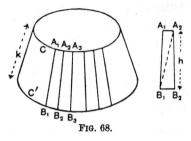

FIG. 68.

Let the surface of the frustum be divided into n equal parts by planes through the axis, and let A_1B_1, A_2B_2, ... be the lines of division.

The equal trapezia $A_1B_1B_2A_2$, $A_2B_2B_3A_3$, ... are elements; let h be the height of each.

$\therefore$ the area of the surface

$$= \text{Lt } \Sigma A_1B_1B_2A_2$$
$$= \text{Lt } \Sigma \tfrac{1}{2}h(A_1A_2 + B_1B_2)$$
$$= \text{Lt } \tfrac{1}{2}h\Sigma(A_1A_2 + B_1B_2).$$

But $\text{Lt } h = k$, $\text{Lt } \Sigma A_1A_2 = c$, and $\text{Lt } \Sigma B_1B_2 = c'$;

$\therefore$ area of surface $= \tfrac{1}{2}k(c+c')$.   (Q.E.D.)

Corollaries :

(1) If c be the average circumference of a conical frustum (i.e. the circumference mid-way between the circular ends), the area $= kc$.

(2) If r, r' be the radii of the ends, the area

$$= \tfrac{1}{2}k(2\pi r + 2\pi r') = \pi k(r + r').$$

(3) If r is the average radius, area $= 2\pi kr$.

(4) As a cone is a frustum with one end reduced to a point,

$\therefore$ the area of the surface of a right cone

$$= \tfrac{1}{2}kc = \pi kr.$$

(5) A cylinder is a frustum with equal ends ;

$\therefore$ the surface of a right cylinder

$$= kc = 2\pi kr.$$ (Q.E.D.)

Theorem 8T2

The volume of any conical frustrum with height h and areas of ends A, B, is $\frac{1}{3}h(A+\sqrt{AB}+B)$. (Fig. 69.)

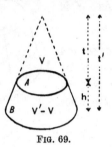

FIG. 69.

(*Unlike 8T1, this theorem is not restricted to frusta of right cones.*)

Let volume and height of the complete cone be V', t', and those of the part cut off V, t.

Then
$$\frac{A}{B}=\frac{t^2}{t'^2}.$$ (7T1)

Also
$$\frac{V}{V'}=\frac{\frac{1}{3}At}{\frac{1}{3}Bt'}$$ (7T4)
$$=\frac{t^3}{t'^3}.$$

Hence volume of frustum
$$=V'-V$$
$$=V'\left(1-\frac{V}{V'}\right)$$
$$=\tfrac{1}{3}Bt'\left(1-\frac{t^3}{t'^3}\right)$$
$$=\tfrac{1}{3}Bt'\left(1-\frac{t}{t'}\right)\left(1+\frac{t}{t'}+\frac{t^2}{t'^2}\right)$$
$$=\tfrac{1}{3}B(t'-t)\left(1+\sqrt{\frac{A}{B}}+\frac{A}{B}\right)$$
$$=\tfrac{1}{3}h(B+\sqrt{AB}+A). \qquad \text{(Q.E.D.)}$$

Theorem 8T3

Equal areas are intercepted on a sphere and its circumscribed cylinder by any two planes parallel to the circle of contact. (Fig. 70.)

Let AOB *be the diameter of the sphere at right angles to the plane of the circle of contact, and let* C *be any point on the latter.*

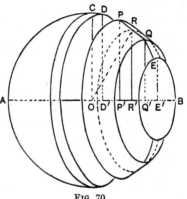

FIG. 70.

Let the given planes cut the semicircle ACB in the points D, E; let the arc DE be divided into n equal parts; and let PQ be one of them.

Draw OR $\perp$ PQ, and let P′, R′, Q′ be the projections of P, R, Q on OB.

Then the angle between PQ and OB $= \stackrel{\wedge}{\text{ORR}'}$;

$$\therefore \quad \text{P}'\text{Q}' = \text{PQ} \cos \text{ORR}' \qquad (5\text{T}6)$$

$$= \text{PQ} \cdot \frac{\text{RR}'}{\text{OR}};$$

$$\therefore \quad \text{PQ} \cdot \text{RR}' = \text{P}'\text{Q}' \cdot \text{OR}.$$

Hence the area of the conical surface carved out by PQ

$$= 2\pi \text{RR}' \cdot \text{PQ} \qquad (8\text{T}1)$$

$$= 2\pi \text{OR} \cdot \text{P}'\text{Q}'.$$

The n chords like PQ will all be equal, and at equal distances from the centre;

$\therefore$ the total surface carved out by the n chords like PQ

$$= 2\pi \text{OR} \cdot \Sigma \text{P}'\text{Q}'$$

$$= 2\pi \text{OR} \cdot \text{D}'\text{E}'.$$

As D′E′ is constant, the area of the surface carved out depends only on the length of OR.

By sufficiently reducing the length of each chord, we can make the difference between OR and OC, and, $\therefore$, the difference between

$$2\pi OR \cdot D'E' \quad \text{and} \quad 2\pi OC \cdot D'E'$$

as small as we please ;

$\therefore$ the area of the zone carved out by the arc DE

$= 2\pi OC \cdot D'E'$

= the area of the surface of a right cylinder with radius OC and length D′E′   (8T1)

= the area of the circumscribed cylinder between the given parallel planes.   (Q.E.D.)

COROLLARY 1. THE SURFACE OF A SPHERE OF RADIUS r

$$= 2r \cdot 2\pi r$$
$$= 4\pi r^2.$$

COROLLARY 2. THE SURFACE OF A CAP OR ZONE OF DEPTH h ON A SPHERE OF RADIUS r

$$= 2\pi rh.$$

DEF. : The **angle of intersection of two curves** is the angle between their tangents at their point of intersection.

It follows that the angle of intersection of two great circles of a sphere is equal to the dihedral angle between their planes ; for their tangents are at right angles to their common diameter, which is in the line of intersection of their planes ;

$\therefore$, if the angles of a lune are each equal to A radians, its area is $\dfrac{A}{2\pi}$ of the surface of the sphere.

COROLLARY 3. THE AREA OF A LUNE WITH ANGLE OF A RADIANS

$$= \frac{A}{2\pi} \cdot 4\pi r^2$$
$$= 2Ar^2.$$

Theorem 8T4

The area of a spherical triangle with angles A, B, C is

$$r^2(A + B + C - \pi)$$

where r is the radius of the sphere. (Fig. 71.)

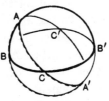

FIG. 71.

Let the diameters through A, B, C be AA′, BB′, CC′ respectively.

Although the spherical triangles ABC, A′B′C′ cannot, in general, be superposed, as one is " left-handed " and the other " right-handed ", it is evident that corresponding *elements* will be congruent ;

∴ sph. triangles ABC, A′B′C′ are equal in area.

These two triangles, together with the hemisphere C,ABA′B′, are equivalent to the three lunes ABA′C, BCB′A, CA′C′B′, the first two of which overlap to the extent of the triangle ABC.

The areas of the lunes are $2Ar^2$, $2Br^2$, $2Cr^2$ respectively, and that of the hemisphere is $2\pi r^2$;   (8T3)

$$\therefore \quad 2\triangle ABC + 2\pi r^2 = 2r^2(A + B + C) ;$$

$$\therefore \quad \triangle ABC = r^2(A + B + C - \pi). \qquad \text{(Q.E.D.)}$$

DEF. : Any figure drawn on the surface of a sphere subtends at the centre a **solid angle** whose **magnitude** is measured by the ratio of the area of the figure to that of the square on the radius.

COROLLARY : THE MAGNITUDE OF A TRIHEDRAL ANGLE WITH DIHEDRAL ANGLES A, B, C, IS $A + B + C - \pi$.

Theorem 8T5

If the spherical surface of a sector is of area A, and r is the radius of the sphere, then the volume of the sector is

$\dfrac{Ar}{3}$.   (Fig. 72.)

FIG. 72.

The elements of the sector are pyramids with a common vertex at the centre of the sphere, and with their bases forming the elements of the spherical surface A.

Let h be the height, and a the area of the base, of an element.

Let A′, $r′$ be any quantities very slightly smaller than A, r respectively.

By sufficiently reducing the maximum area of individual elements, and correspondingly increasing their number, we can ensure that

$$A′ < \Sigma a < A \ ;$$

and

$$r′ < h < r \ ;$$

$$\therefore \quad \Sigma r′a < \Sigma ha < \Sigma ra \ ;$$

$$\therefore \quad r′\Sigma a < \Sigma ha < r\Sigma a \ ;$$

$$\therefore r′A′ < r′\Sigma a < \Sigma ha < r\Sigma a < rA.$$

$$\therefore r′A′ < \Sigma ha < rA \ ;$$

$\therefore$ we can make $\dfrac{\Sigma ha}{3}$ as nearly equal to $\dfrac{rA}{3}$ as we please ;

$\therefore$ the volume of the sector $= \dfrac{rA}{3}$.   (Q.E.D.)

COROLLARY 1.   THE VOLUME OF A SPHERE OF RADIUS r

$$= \frac{4\pi r^2 r}{3} = \tfrac{4}{3}\pi r^3.$$

COROLLARY 2.   THE VOLUME OF A SECTOR ON A CAP OF DEPTH h

$$= \frac{2\pi rh \cdot r}{3} = \frac{2\pi r^2 h}{3}.$$

Theorem 8T6

If a segment of depth h is cut from a sphere of radius r, its volume is

$$\frac{\pi h^2}{3}(3r - h). \quad \text{(Fig. 73.)}$$

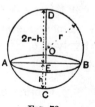

FIG. 73.

Let AB *be a diameter of the segment, and* CD *the perpendicular diameter of the sphere, cutting* AB *in* E.

Then $AE . EB = CE . ED$;

$\therefore AE^2 = h(2r - h)$;

$\therefore$ the volume of the cone with vertex at O, the centre of the sphere, and with the plane surface of the segment for base

$$\begin{aligned}
&= \tfrac{1}{3}\pi OE . AE^2 \\
&= \tfrac{1}{3}\pi (r - h) . h(2r - h) \\
&= \tfrac{1}{3}\pi h(2r^2 - 3rh + h^2).
\end{aligned}$$

The volume of the sector composed of the cone and the segment

$$\begin{aligned}
&= \tfrac{2}{3}\pi r^2 h \qquad\qquad\qquad\qquad (8\text{T}5) \\
&= \tfrac{1}{3}\pi h(2r^2) \ ;
\end{aligned}$$

$\therefore$ the volume of the segment

$$\begin{aligned}
&= \tfrac{1}{3}\pi h(3rh - h^2) \\
&= \tfrac{1}{3}\pi h^2(3r - h). \qquad\qquad (\text{Q.E.D.})
\end{aligned}$$

WORKED EXAMPLES

DEF. : If (x, y, z) are the coordinates of any point P on a sphere with respect to three mutually perpendicular planes through its centre, and if (ax, by, cz) are the coordinates of a point Q, then the locus of Q is called an **ellipsoid**, and its intercepts on the axes of coordinates are called its **semi-axes**.

DEF. : If $a = b$, the ellipsoid is called a **spheroid**, and is said to be **prolate** or **oblate** according as c is greater or less than a.

8W1. Show that, if a, b, c are the semi-axes of an ellipsoid, its volume is $\frac{4}{3}\pi abc$.

Let m, m' be corresponding elements of the ellipsoid and of the concentric unit sphere.

Linear measurements of m parallel to the axes are respectively a, b, c times those of m';

$$\therefore\ m = abcm'\ ;$$

$\therefore$ volume of ellipsoid $= abc$ times that of the unit sphere

$$= abc \cdot \tfrac{4}{3}\pi (1)^3$$
$$= \tfrac{4}{3}\pi abc. \hspace{2cm} \text{(Q.E.D.)}$$

8W2. Show that the area of the part of the earth's surface visible from a balloon at height h is

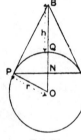

$$\frac{2\pi r^2 h}{r + h},$$

where r is the radius of the earth.   (Fig. 74.)

Let B be the balloon, O the centre of the earth, BP a tangent from B to any plane section of the earth through OB, N the foot of the perpendicular from P to OB, and Q the point of intersection of OB with the surface of the earth.

FIG. 74.

Then
$$\mathsf{ON} = \frac{\mathsf{OP}^2}{\mathsf{OB}} = \frac{r^2}{r+h}\ ;$$

$$\therefore\ \mathsf{QN} = r - \frac{r^2}{r+h} = \frac{rh}{r+h}\ ;$$

$\therefore$ the area of the cap visible from B

$$= 2\pi r \cdot \frac{rh}{r+h} = \frac{2\pi r^2 h}{r+h}. \hspace{1.5cm} \text{(8T3)}$$

(Q.E.D.)

8W3. A napkin ring is in the form of a sphere pierced by a cylindrical hole. Prove that its volume is the same as that of a sphere with diameter equal to the length of the hole.   (Fig. 75.)

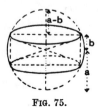

FIG. 75.

Let a be the radius of the sphere, and $2b$ the length of the hole.
The part removed consists of

two segments of depth $(a - b)$

+ two cylinders of height b and radius $\sqrt{(a^2 - b^2)}$,

i.e. two segments of depth $(a - b)$

+ six cones of height b and radius $\sqrt{(a^2 - b^2)}$,

i.e. two sectors on caps of depth $(a - b)$

+ four cones of height b and radius $\sqrt{(a^2 - b^2)}$.

The area of each cap $= 2\pi a(a - b)$;

$$\therefore \text{ volume of each sector} = \frac{a}{3} \cdot 2\pi a(a - b).$$

The volume of each cone $= \dfrac{b}{3} \cdot \pi(a^2 - b^2)$;

$\therefore$ volume of hole

$$= \tfrac{4}{3}\pi a^2(a - b) + \tfrac{4}{3}\pi b(a^2 - b^2)$$
$$= \tfrac{4}{3}\pi(a^3 - a^2 b + a^2 b - b^3)$$
$$= \tfrac{4}{3}\pi(a^3 - b^3).$$

The napkin ring

$$= \text{(original sphere)} - \text{(part removed)}$$
$$= \tfrac{4}{3}\pi a^3 - \tfrac{4}{3}\pi(a^3 - b^3)$$
$$= \tfrac{4}{3}\pi b^3$$
$$= \text{sphere with diameter equal to the length of}$$
$$\text{the hole.}   \text{(Q.E.D.)}$$

EXAMPLES 8A

8A1. Find approximately what per cent. of the earth's surface lies in the Tropics (i.e. between latitudes $23\frac{1}{2}°$ North and $23\frac{1}{2}°$ South).

8A2. Show that the area of a belt of the earth's surface between two parallels of latitude is proportional either to the difference between the sines of the latitudes, or to their sum.

8A3. Six equal cones are packed inside a cube with their vertices at the centre and their bases inscribed in the faces. Show that the volume of each unoccupied corner comprises nearly 2·7 per cent. of the volume of the cube.

8A4. Find the volume of a hollow cylinder open at the ends and having radii a, b, and height h.

8A5. Find the volume of a hollow sphere with radii a, b.

8A6. If r is the average of the inner and outer radii of a hollow sphere of thickness t, find its volume.

8A7. Find the number of cubic inches of lead per inch of piping, if d and t are respectively the internal diameter and the thickness of the wall, both in inches.

8A8. Verify the formula for the area of a spherical triangle (8T4), in the case of an octant.

8A9. If ABC is any spherical triangle, show that the area of the remainder of the surface of the sphere can be correctly calculated by treating it as a spherical triangle with angles $2\pi - $ A, $2\pi - $ B, $2\pi - $ C.

8A10. If a right cone, a hemisphere, and a cylinder have the same base and height, show that their volumes are in the ratios $1 : 2 : 3$, and their total surfaces in the ratios

$$1 + \sqrt{2} : 3 : 4.$$

EXAMPLES 8B

8B1. The annular space between two concentric cylinders of radii r, R, is divided into two parts with volumes P, Q, by a conical frustum with radii r, R, and height equal to that of each of the cylinders. Prove that

$$\text{P} : \text{Q} = \text{R} + 2r : 2\text{R} + r.$$

8B2. Four cones are packed into a regular tetrahedron with their vertices at the point of intersection of the medians and their bases inscribed in the faces. Prove that each unoccupied corner comprises nearly ten per cent. of the volume of the tetrahedron.

8B3. If eight cones are packed into a regular octahedron in the manner described in 8B2, show that the volume of each unoccupied corner is approximately 6·6 per cent. of that of the octahedron.

8B4. Show that approximately ·33 per cent. of the earth's surface is included between latitudes 45° and 60° North and longitudes 45° and 60° East.

8B5. The surface of a peg-top consists of a major spherical cap and its tangent cone. If these are equal in area, find the ratio in which their plane of contact divides the axis.

8B6. A right cylinder is carved by means of a lathe into a succession of conical frusta, each having ends with radii a and b. If the ends of the carved model are unequal, show that its volume is independent of the number of frusta, and of their individual heights, and that these need not be equal to one another.

8B7. A lead weight is in the form of a sphere surmounted by a tangent cone, and the total height is twice the diameter ; find the ratio of the total volume to that of the sphere.

8B8. A buoy is in the form of a hemisphere surmounted by a cone ; if the total height is twice the diameter, find the ratio of the total volume to that of the hemisphere.

8B9. Find the volume of a lens of diameter (or aperture) $2a$, and thickness $2d$, the two spherical surfaces being of equal curvature.

8B10. A cone with semi-vertical angle 30° is inscribed in a sphere ; find the ratio of its volume to that of the sphere.

8B11. Show that the ratio of the volumes of two cubes inscribed in, and circumscribed about, the same sphere is the same as the ratio of the volumes of two spheres inscribed in, and circumscribed about, the same cube.

8B12. Show that, if a paper cone be formed by joining the straight edges of a sector of a circle with radius r and angle $x°$, and pressing the curved edge on a plane, its total surface is

$$\frac{\pi x r^2}{360}\left(1+\frac{x}{360}\right).$$

8B13. Show that the volume of the cone of 8B12 is

$$\frac{\pi x^2 r^3}{3(360)^2}\sqrt{1-\left(\frac{x}{360}\right)^2}.$$

8B14. Show that, if a sphere can be inscribed in a frustum of a right cone, the ratio of their volumes is equal to that of their surfaces.

8B15. Assuming the earth to be a smooth sphere with radius r, find the volume of its atmosphere up to a height h between latitudes 45° north and south.

8B16. The rim of a right cone is pared away by means of a lathe until the remaining solid consists of a cylinder surmounted by a cone equal to it in volume. Find what fraction of the original volume is removed.

EXAMPLES 8C

8C1. A sphere is cut by two parallel planes at distances H and h from one extremity of the diameter at right angles to them. If r is the radius of the sphere, find the volume enclosed between the planes.

8C2. A segment of thickness h is removed from a sphere, and then a slice of thickness t. The longer edge of this slice is then trimmed off, leaving a right cylinder. Find the volume thus trimmed away, if r is the radius of the sphere.

8C3. Find the volume of a hollow cone with semi-vertical angle 30°, height H, and thickness t, and with a base of the same thickness.

8C4. The ends of a certain solid figure are segments of spheres, and the middle portion is a conical frustum, whose surface is tangential to the completed spheres. If the latter have radii a, b, and would just touch one another in the interior, show that the area of the surface is equal to that of a sphere with radius $\sqrt{(a^2 + b^2)}$.

8C5. If the volume of a cone is n times that of its inscribed sphere, show that the ratio of its height to the radius of the sphere has one of the values $2n \left(1 \pm \sqrt{1 - \dfrac{2}{n}} \right)$.

8C6. If the distance between the planes of two circles is k times the sum of their radii, show that the areas of the spherical and conical zones bounded by them are in the ratio

$$\sqrt{(1 + k^2)} : 1.$$

8C7. DEF.: The corners of a cube, cut off by a sphere which touches its twelve edges, are called **pendentives**.

If each straight edge of a pendentive is of length a, show that its volume is

$$a^3 - \pi a^3 \left(1\tfrac{1}{4} - \frac{2\sqrt{2}}{3} \right).$$

8C8. Show that the area of the curved surface of the pendentive in 8C7 is equal to

$$\tfrac{1}{2}\pi a^2 (3\sqrt{2} - 4).$$

8C9. A hemisphere and a right cone of semi-vertical angle $30°$ stand on the same side of the same circle, whose radius is $2a$. Show that the volume of the part of the hemisphere that is outside the cone is $\dfrac{2\pi a^3}{\sqrt{3}}$, and that the volume of the part of the cone which is outside the hemisphere is

$$\tfrac{1}{3}\pi a^3 (10\sqrt{3} - 16).$$

8C10. A spindle-shaped figure consists of two unequal right cones with a common circular base. Inside it is inscribed a right cylinder in which a cube is capable of being inscribed. Show that the ratio of the volumes of cylinder and spindle is as $3r^2(R - r) : R^3$, where r, R are their radii.

8C11. An hour-glass is bounded by parts of two equal spheres with radius a, and their common tangent double-cone, whose semi-vertical angle is $30°$. Find its surface and volume.

CHAPTER IX

CENTROIDS

Def. : If p is the distance of a plane α from any point of an element m of a given figure, and if Lt $\Sigma mp = 0$, then α is called a **centroidal plane** of the figure.

Theorem 9T1

Parallel to any given plane there is one and only one centroidal plane for any finite figure. (Fig. 76.)

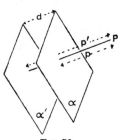

Let α' be any given plane, α any plane parallel to it at a distance d, and p', p their distances from any point P in any element m.

$$\text{Then} \qquad p = p' - d ;$$
$$\therefore \ \text{Lt } \Sigma mp = \text{Lt } \Sigma m (p' - d)$$
$$= \text{Lt } \Sigma mp' - \text{Lt } \Sigma md$$

FIG. 76.
$$= \text{Lt } \Sigma mp' - d . \text{Lt } \Sigma m.$$

The values of Lt $\Sigma mp'$ and Lt Σm are independent of our choice of the plane α.

We may, therefore, choose the plane α so that

$$d = \frac{\text{Lt } \Sigma mp'}{\text{Lt } \Sigma m}.$$

With this plane,

$$\text{Lt } \Sigma mp' - d . \text{Lt } \Sigma m = 0 ;$$
$$\therefore \ \text{Lt } \Sigma mp = 0 ;$$
$$\therefore \ \alpha \text{ is a centroidal plane.} \qquad (\text{q.e.d.})$$

Theorem 9T2

If three centroidal planes of a figure have a common point O, but not a common straight line, then every plane through O is a centroidal plane.
(Fig. 77.)

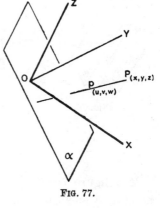

FIG. 77.

Let OX, OY, OZ be the lines of intersection of the given centroidal planes, α any other plane through O, and (u, v, w) the direction cosines of its normal with respect to the axes OX, OY, OZ ; and let (x, y, z) be the coordinates of any point P of any element m of the figure, and p its distance from α.

Then $p = ux + vy + wz$; (5T8)

$\therefore mp = m(ux + vy + wz)$.

Each element has its own x, y, z, and m ; but u, v, and w are the same for all ;

$\therefore$ Lt $\Sigma mp = u$. Lt $\Sigma mx + v$. Lt $\Sigma my + w$. Lt Σmz

$= \quad 0 \quad + \quad 0 \quad + \quad 0$

as the planes of the axes are centroidal planes ;

$\therefore$ Lt $\Sigma mp = 0$;

$\therefore \alpha$ is a centroidal plane. (Q.E.D.)

COROLLARY 1. ALL THE CENTROIDAL PLANES OF THE SAME FIGURE HAVE A COMMON POINT.

DEF. : The point common to all centroidal planes of a figure is called its **centroid**.

COROLLARY 2. EVERY FINITE FIGURE HAS A UNIQUE CENTROID.

Theorem 9T3

If R be the distance of the centroid G of a figure M from a plane β, and r the distance of any point P in an element m from the same plane, then

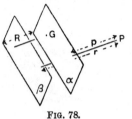

FIG. 78.

$$RM = Lt \, \Sigma rm. \quad \text{(Fig. 78.)}$$

Let α be the plane through G $\parallel \beta$, and let p be the distance of P from α.

Then $\qquad r = R + p \, ;$

$$\therefore \, Lt \, \Sigma rm = Lt \, \Sigma Rm + Lt \, \Sigma pm$$
$$= R \, . \, Lt \, \Sigma m + Lt \, \Sigma pm$$
$$= RM + 0. \quad \text{(Q.E.D.)}$$

Theorem 9T4

If a figure be divided into any number of portions (not necessarily small or equal), and if M_1, M_2, ... be their magnitudes and R_1, R_2, ... the distances of their centroids from any plane β, then the distance $\bar{R}$ of the centroid of the figure from β is such that

$$\bar{R}(M_1 + M_2 + ...)$$
$$= R_1 M_1 + R_2 M_2 + ... \quad \text{(Fig. 79.)}$$

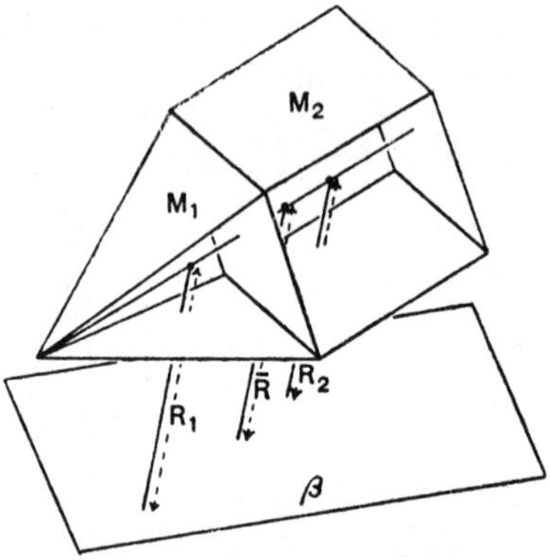

Let m_1 be any element of M_1, and m_2 any element of M_2, and so on; and let $r_1, r_2 ...$ be the distances of points of $m_1, m_2, ...$ from β.

FIG. 79.

Then $\quad R_1 M_1 + R_2 M_2 + ...$

$$= Lt \, \Sigma r_1 m_1 + Lt \, \Sigma r_2 m_2 + ... \qquad (9T3)$$
$$= Lt \, \Sigma rm,$$

since the elements of the M's are the elements of the figure.

But $\qquad \bar{R}(M_1 + M_2 + \ldots) = \text{Lt } \Sigma rm$; $\qquad$ (9T3)

$\therefore \ \bar{R}(M_1 + M_2 + \ldots) = R_1M_1 + R_2M_2 + \ldots$. (Q.E.D.)

COROLLARY : THE POSITION OF THE CENTROID OF A SET OF FIGURES DEPENDS ONLY ON THEIR MAGNITUDES AND THE POSITIONS OF THEIR CENTROIDS, AND NOT ON THEIR SHAPES.

Theorem 9T5

(Theorem of Pappus.)

If a one- or two-dimensional plane figure of magnitude M revolve through an angle α about an axis in its plane and at distance $\bar{r}$ from its centroid, then the area or volume swept out $\qquad = M\bar{r}\alpha.$

Let m be any element of M, and r the distance of any point of it from the axis of rotation.

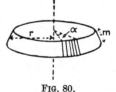

FIG. 80.

CASE 1. ONE-DIMENSIONAL FIGURE : (i.e. a straight line, or curve). (Fig. 80.)

Here m is a short straight line. Let r be the distance of its middle point from the axis of rotation.

In a complete revolution it carves out a conical zone of slant height m and average radius r ;

$$\therefore \text{ its area} = 2\pi rm ; \qquad (8T1)$$

$\therefore$ rotation through an angle α produces a portion of area

$\dfrac{\alpha}{2\pi} \cdot 2\pi rm$;

$$\text{i.e. } \alpha rm ;$$

$\therefore$ the area carved out by the whole figure

$$= \text{Lt } \Sigma \alpha rm$$
$$= \alpha \text{ Lt } \Sigma rm$$
$$= \alpha M\bar{r}. \qquad (9T3)$$

(Q.E.D. (i).)

CASE 2.   TWO-DIMENSIONAL FIGURE.   (Fig. 81.)

Take as elements rectangles with their sides parallel or perpendicular to the axis of rotation.

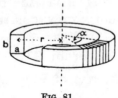

FIG. 81.

In any one rectangle let b, a be the lengths of sides respectively parallel and perpendicular to the axis, so that $m = ab$; and let r be the distance of the centre of the rectangle from the axis.

∴ each side of length a carves out an area $ar\alpha$.   (Case 1)

∴ the rectangle sweeps out a *cylinder* (in the general sense of the term) of height b and base area $ar\alpha$;

$$\therefore \text{ its volume} = b \cdot ar\alpha ; \tag{7T2}$$

$$= mr\alpha ;$$

∴ the volume swept out by the figure

$$= \text{Lt } \Sigma mr\alpha$$

$$= \alpha \text{ Lt } \Sigma mr$$

$$= \alpha M\bar{r}. \tag{9T3}$$

(Q.E.D. (ii).)

COROLLARY : IF THE ANGLE $\alpha = t°$, THE AREA OR VOLUME SWEPT OUT $= \dfrac{M\bar{r}t\pi}{180}$.

Theorem 9T6

If M, M′ are the areas or perimeters of right and oblique sections respectively of any cylinder, and C is the centroid of M and the projection of a point C′ in M′, then M . CC′ is the cylindrical volume or area between the sections. (Fig. 82.)

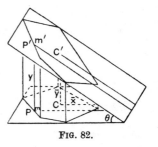

FIG. 82.

(Notice that C′ is not always the centroid of M′.)

Let m, m′ be corresponding elements of M, M′ ; *let* P, P′ *be any two of their corresponding points,* y, $\bar{y}$ *the lengths of* PP′, CC′, *and* x, $\bar{x}$ *the distances of* P, C *from the line common to the planes of section, and* θ *the dihedral angle between those planes.*

The element mm' is

either a rectangle with height y and base m,

or a right prism with height y and base area m ;

∴ in both cases, the magnitude of $mm' = my$;

∴ the cylindrical volume or area between the sections

$$= \text{Lt } \Sigma my$$
$$= \text{Lt } \Sigma mx \,.\, \tan \theta$$
$$= \tan \theta \,.\, \text{Lt } \Sigma mx$$
$$= \tan \theta \,.\, \text{M}\bar{x} \qquad (9\text{T3})$$
$$= \text{M}\bar{y}$$
$$= \text{M} \,.\, \text{CC}'. \qquad (\text{Q.E.D.})$$

WORKED EXAMPLES

9W1. Show that the centroid of a circular arc of radius r and angle 2α is at a distance $\dfrac{r \sin \alpha}{\alpha}$ from the centre.

The length of the arc is $2r\alpha$.

If rotated about the diameter of the circle parallel to its chord, the arc carves out a zone of a sphere.

Depth of zone $= 2r \sin \alpha$;

$\therefore$ its area $= 2r \sin \alpha \,.\, 2\pi r.$ \hfill (8T3)

By symmetry, the centroid of the arc lies on the radius that bisects it. Let x be its distance from the centre.

Then \qquad $2r\alpha \,.\, 2\pi x = 2r \sin \alpha \,.\, 2\pi r$; \hfill (9T5)

$$\therefore \; x = \frac{r \sin \alpha}{\alpha}.$$

(Q.E.D.)

9W2. Show that the centroid of a sector of a circle of radius r and angle 2α is at a distance $\dfrac{2}{3} \dfrac{r \sin \alpha}{\alpha}$ from the centre.

This problem may be solved by the same method as 9W1, but it is simpler to proceed as follows :

Let the sector be divided into n equal sectors.

By making n large enough, the ratio of the *segment* of each narrow sector to its *triangle* may be made as small as we please ;

$\therefore$ the distance of the centre of the circle from the centroid of each sector can be made as nearly equal to $\frac{2}{3}r$ as we please.

The position of the centroid of the sum of the sectors depends only on their magnitudes, (which are equal), and the positions of their centroids ; \hfill (9T4)

$\therefore$ it is the same as the centroid of the circular arc of radius $\frac{2}{3}r$ and angle 2α ;

$\therefore$ its distance from the centre is

$$\frac{2}{3} \frac{r \sin \alpha}{\alpha}.$$

(9W1)

(Q.E.D.)

9W3. A single bay of the vault of a crypt consists of two equal half-cylinders, of length and diameter $2a$, piercing one another at right angles, so that their lines of intersection, (the groins), terminate in the vertices of a square. Show that the area of the surface of this bay is $4a^2(\pi - 2)$.

(Fig. 83.)

Let ABCD *be the square,* E *the point of intersection of the groins;
and let* EF ∥ DA *meet the vertical plane through* AB *in* F.

Let G *be the centroid of arc* AF,
and draw GH ∥ AD *cutting the vertical plane through* AE *in* H. *Let*
E′, F′, G′, H′ *be the projections of*
E, F, G, H *on the plane* ABCD.

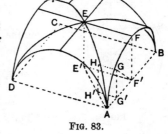

FIG. 83.

The surface of the vault is equal
to eight times the cylindrical triangle AEF.

This is the cylindrical area be-
tween the right and oblique sections AF, AE, of the *cylinder*
whose base is the arc AF;

$$\therefore \text{ its area} = \text{arc AF} \cdot \text{GH.} \qquad (9\text{T}6)$$

$$\text{GF}' = \frac{a \sin \frac{1}{4}\pi}{\frac{1}{4}\pi} \qquad (9\text{W}1)$$

$$= \frac{a}{\sqrt{2}} \frac{4}{\pi};$$

$$\therefore \text{ G}'\text{F}' = \text{GF}' \cos \tfrac{1}{4}\pi$$

$$= \frac{a}{\sqrt{2}} \frac{4}{\pi} \frac{1}{\sqrt{2}}$$

$$= \frac{2a}{\pi};$$

$$\therefore \text{ GH} = \text{G}'\text{H}' = \text{AG}' = \text{AF}' - \text{G}'\text{F}'$$

$$= a - \frac{2a}{\pi};$$

$\therefore$ the area of the surface of the bay

$$= 8 \cdot \frac{2\pi a}{4} \cdot a \left(1 - \frac{2}{\pi}\right)$$

$$= 4a^2(\pi - 2). \qquad (\text{Q.E.D.})$$

9W4. A radius OA of a circle is of length a, and is bisected at right angle by a chord BC. Show that the centroid of the minor segment cut off is at the distance

$$\frac{3\sqrt{3}a}{4\pi - 3\sqrt{3}}$$

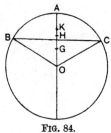

FIG. 84.

from the centre of the circle. (Fig. 84.)

As BC bisects OA at right angles,

$$\therefore \quad AB = OB = OA ;$$

$$\therefore \quad \hat{BOA} = 60°, \quad \text{and} \quad BC = a\sqrt{3}.$$

The area of the segment ABC

$$= \text{sector } O, BAC - \text{triangle } OBC$$

$$= \frac{\pi a^2}{3} - \frac{1}{2}\frac{a}{2}\cdot a\sqrt{3}$$

$$= \frac{a^2}{12}(4\pi - 3\sqrt{3}).$$

Let G, H, K be the centroids of the triangle, sector, and segment respectively.

$$OG = \frac{2}{3}\frac{a}{2} = \frac{a}{3},$$

$$OH = \frac{2 \cdot a \sin\frac{\pi}{3}}{3 \cdot \frac{\pi}{3}} \qquad (9T3)$$

$$= \frac{\sqrt{3}a}{\pi}.$$

$$OH \cdot O,BAC = OG \cdot OBC + OK \cdot BAC ; \qquad (9T4)$$

$$\therefore \quad OK \cdot BAC = OH \cdot O,ABC - OG \cdot OBC ;$$

$$\therefore \quad OK \cdot \frac{a^2}{12}(4\pi - 3\sqrt{3})$$

$$= \frac{\sqrt{3}a}{\pi}\frac{\pi a^2}{3} - \frac{a}{3}\frac{\sqrt{3}a^2}{4} ;$$

$$\therefore \quad OK(4\pi - 3\sqrt{3}) = 4\sqrt{3}a - \sqrt{3}a = 3\sqrt{3}a ;$$

$$\therefore \quad OK = \frac{3\sqrt{3}a}{4\pi - 3\sqrt{3}}. \qquad \text{(Q.E.D.)}$$

EXAMPLES 9A

9A1. Show that, if a chord divides a circle into two parts in the ratio $m : n$, the distances of their centroids from the centre of the circle are in the ratio $n : m$.

9A2. Use Pappus' Theorem to find the volume of a cone.

9A3. Use 9T4 to show that the point of intersection of the medians of a tetrahedron is its centroid.

9A4. Show that the centroid of a pyramid or cone divides the straight line joining the vertex to the centroid of the base in the ratio $3 : 1$.

9A5. Show that the centroid of the curved surface of a cone divides the axis in the ratio $2 : 1$.

9A6. If h is the height, and k the slant height, of a cone, show that the centroid of the total surface is at the distance

$$\frac{k(k - \sqrt{k^2 - h^2})}{3h}$$

from the base.

9A7. Two solid cones with heights a, b, stand on opposite sides of the same base. If a is greater than b, find the distance of the centroid of the combined figure from the common base.

9A8. A solid figure consists of a cylinder with height b surmounted by a cone with height a. Find the distance of the centroid from the vertex.

9A9. An anchor ring with mean radius a is made from an iron rod with circular section and radius b. Find its volume.

9A10. Find the area of the surface of the ring of 9A9.

9A11. Find the centroid of a semicircular arc of radius a.

9A12. Find the centroid of a semicircle of radius a.

9A13. Find the volume swept out by the revolution of a plane figure consisting of two parts with areas A, B, and their centroids at distances x, y, from the axis.

9A14. Find the centroid of a spherical zone.

9A15. Find the centroid of a spherical cap with height h on a sphere with radius r.

9A16. By regarding a semicircle as the sum of two quadrants, and making use of 9A12 and 9T4, find the centroid of a quadrant of a circle of radius a.

9A17. Find the centroid of a quadrant of an ellipse bounded by a semi-major axis of length a and a semi-minor axis of length b.

9A18. A right cone and a right cylinder have the same base and height, and the cone is inside the cylinder. Find the centroid of the remainder of the cylinder.

9A19. Find the centroid of a sphere of radius a having a spherical cavity of radius b, if c is the distance between the centres.

EXAMPLES 9B

9B1. Discuss whether C′ in 9T6 is the centroid of M′.

9B2. Show that the position of the centroid of a semi-ellipsoid can, but that of its curved surface cannot, be deduced from the positions of the centroids of a hemisphere and a hemispherical surface.

9B3. Use the method of 9W2 to find the distance of the centroid of a hemisphere from its centre.

9B4. Find the distance of the centroid of an octant from the centre of its sphere.

9B5. If an octant of a sphere of radius a is cut from a cube with edge of length a, show that the centroid of the remainder is at a distance

$$\frac{3\sqrt{3}(8-\pi)a}{8(6-\pi)}$$

from the right-angled corner.

9B6. If a quadrant of a circle of radius a is cut from a square constructed on its radii, show that the centroid of the remainder is at a distance

$$\frac{2\sqrt{2}a}{3(4-\pi)}$$

from the right-angled corner.

9B7. If a, b are the lengths of the parallel sides of a trapezium, and h is the distance between them, prove that the distance of the centroid from the side is given by

$$\frac{h}{3}\frac{2a+b}{a+b}.$$

(Regard the trapezium as either the sum or the difference of two triangles.)

9B8. From 9B7 prove that, if one side of a trapezium is of length h and at right angles to two others of lengths a, b respectively, its distance from the centroid is equal to

$$\frac{1}{3}\frac{a^2+ab+b^2}{a+b}.$$

9B9. Use 9B8 to find the volume of a frustum of a cone with radii a, b, and height h.

9B10. The top of a right cylinder is the base of a right cone of height a. If b is the height of the cylinder, and its base rests on a spheroid of depth c, show that the distance of its centroid from its point is equal to

$$\frac{3(a^2+2b^2+c^2)+4(2bc+2ca+3ab)}{4(a+3b+2c)}.$$

9B11. A section through the axis of an iron wheel consists of two capital T's of height h, width w, and thickness t, with their feet separated by a space t, corresponding to the hole of that diameter for the accommodation of the axle. Find the volume of the wheel.

9B12. A peg-top is in the form of a hemisphere and an inverted cone on opposite sides of a common base. Find the distance of its centroid from the common base, a being the radius of the hemisphere, and b the height of the cone.

9B13. By cutting up a spherical sector into elementary sectors, and applying 9T4, find the distance of the centroid from the centre of the sphere, if a is the radius of the sphere, and h the depth of the cap.

9B14. The central vertical section of the inner surface of a round salad-bowl consists of two equal semicircles with diameters at right angles to a straight line joining their lower ends. Show that the area of the inner surface is given by

$$\tfrac{1}{4}\pi(d^2-2dh+5h^2)+\tfrac{1}{2}\pi^2h(d-h),$$

where h is the height and d the inner diameter of the bowl.

9B15. The end of the horn of a loud-speaker is formed by the revolution of a quadrant of radius R about an axis parallel to the tangent at one corner, and at a distance r from it. Show that the area of its surface is given by

$$\pi^2R(R+r)-2\pi R^2.$$

9B16. A solitaire board has a circular groove of semi-circular section, flanked by an outer ridge of equal semi-circular section. If V is the volume of the largest marble that can touch the bottom of the groove, show that the volume of the ridge exceeds that of the groove by $\dfrac{3\pi V}{2}$.

9B17. Show that the volume of the spike formed by the revolution of a quadrant about the tangent at one corner is equal to

$$\frac{\pi r^3}{6}(10 - 3\pi),$$

where r is the radius.

9B18. Two cylinders with radius c and lengths a, b, intersect at right angles forming a cross. Show that its volume is equal to

$$\pi c^2\left(a + b - \frac{16c}{3\pi}\right).$$

9B19. Show that the curved surface of the cross described in 9B18 is equal to

$$2\pi c\left(a + b - \frac{8c}{\pi}\right).$$

9B20. In the centre of the base of a cone with height H, is bored a similar conical hole with height h. Show that the distance of the centroid of the remaining hollow cone is at the distance

$$\frac{H+h}{4}\ \frac{H^2+h^2}{H^2+Hh+h^2}$$

from the base.

9B21. Prove 8W3 by the methods of this chapter.

9B22. Find the centroid of a sector of a sphere of radius a if the plane of its rim is at a distance b from the centre.

9B23. Find the centroid of a minor segment of a sphere of radius a cut off by a plane at a distance b from the centre.

9B24. Show that the formula obtained in 9B22 gives the centroid of the remainder of the sphere if this is regarded as a sector whose rim is at a distance $(-b)$ from the centre.

9B25. Show that the centroid of the major segment in 9B23 is given by replacing b by $-b$ in the formula for the centroid of the minor segment.

EXAMPLES 9C

9C1. A solid of revolution is swept out by a minor segment of a circle with chord $\sqrt{3}a$, and radius a. Prove that its volume is equal to
$$\frac{\pi a^3}{12}(9\sqrt{3}-4\pi).$$

9C2. An anchor ring of mean radius p and thickness $2q$ is split into inner and outer rings of semi-circular section ; show that the ratio of the volumes of the parts
$$=3\pi p-4q : 3\pi p+4q.$$

9C3. A bay of a Gothic vault is formed by the intersection of circular cylinders with their axes along the sides of a horizontal square ABCD. (Alter Fig. 83 so that A, B are centres of arcs BF, AF respectively, and so on.) Show that the area of the surface of the vault is
$$\frac{4a^2}{3}(2\pi-3\sqrt{3}),$$
where a is the length of AB.

9C4. Show that the volume of the air-space in the bay of vaulting described in 9C3 is $\frac{2}{3}a^3(2\pi-3\sqrt{3})$.

9C5. Show that the distance of the centroid of a segment of a circle from the centre is
$$\frac{2r\sin^3\alpha}{3(\alpha-\sin\alpha\cos\alpha)},$$
where r is the radius, and 2α the angle subtended at the centre by the arc of the segment.

9C6. Show that, if a radius of a circle bisects a segment, its distance from the centroid of the half-segment is equal to
$$\frac{a}{3}\frac{(1-\cos\theta)^2(2+\cos\theta)}{\theta-\sin\theta\cos\theta},$$
where a is the radius of the circle, and θ the angle subtended at the centre by the arc of the half-segment.

9C7. If a segment of a circle is rotated successively about the tangents and diameter parallel to its chord, show that the difference between the volumes of the first two solids is equal to twice that of the third.

9C8. Show that the distance of the centre of a circle from the centroid of the figure bounded by an arc and the tangents at its ends is equal to
$$\frac{r\sin^3\alpha}{3\cos^2\alpha(\tan\alpha-\alpha)},$$

where r is the radius of the circle, and α the angle subtended at its centre by either tangent.

9C9. Show that, if the figure bounded by a circular arc and the tangents at its ends revolve about one of these tangents, the volume swept out is equal to

$$2\pi r^3 \cdot \frac{\sin\alpha(3 - \sin^2\alpha) - 3\alpha\cos\alpha}{3\cos\alpha},$$

where r is the radius of the circle, and α the angle subtended at the centre by either tangent.

9C10. A, B, C, D, E, are points of contact of pairs of four equal circles ABX, ACD, BCE, DEY, and r is the radius of each. The continuous curve XACDYECBX (like a figure-of-eight) revolves about the tangent at C carving out a solid resembling an hour-glass. Show that the area of its surface is equal to

$$4\pi r^2 \left(1 + \frac{\pi}{3}\right).$$

9C11. Show that the volume of the hour-glass described in 9C10 is given by

$$\frac{2\pi r^3}{3}(2 + 3\sqrt{3} - \pi).$$

9C12. XY is the axis of a circular cylinder, and A, B are two points on the right section through X. BC is a generator, and B′C′ its projection on the plane AXY. If the plane ACC′ cuts the cylinder in the arc AC, show that the area of the cylindrical triangle ABC is equal to

$$\frac{ac(\theta - \sin\theta)}{1 - \cos\theta},$$

where $a =$ XA, $c =$ BC, and $\theta =$ angle AXB.

9C13. Show that the volume of the solid ABB′,CC′ in 9C12 is equal to

$$\frac{a^2c(3\theta - 3\sin\theta\cos\theta - 2\sin^3\theta)}{6(1 - \cos\theta)}.$$

9C14. Show that the air-space in the bay of the crypt-vault discussed in 9W3 has the volume

$$\frac{2a^3}{3}(3\pi - 4).$$

9C15. Show that the major segment in 9C1 sweeps out a volume

$$\frac{\pi a^3}{12}(9\sqrt{3} + 8\pi).$$

CHAPTER X

RABATMENT

WHEN a set of *coplanar* lines of a solid figure has been *drawn*, it is often convenient to *imagine* a stiff sheet of cardboard projecting from the paper and hinged to it along one of the straight lines already drawn, and having another set of coplanar lines drawn upon it.

We then suppose this sheet of cardboard to be turned backwards or forwards about the crease until it lies flat on the paper, where its lines can now actually be *drawn*.

This process is called rabatment.

If A, B, C are points in a plane that cuts the paper in the straight line XY, we say "rabat ABC to $A_1B_1C_1$ about XY". If we then rabat the points D, E about ZW (with which they must be coplanar), their rabatted positions are called D_2, E_2; while for the third, fourth, and subsequent rabatments the suffixes 3, 4, ... are employed.

Theorem 10T1

If a point is rabatted about two different creases, its projection on the plane of the paper is the point of intersection of the perpendiculars drawn to the creases from its corresponding rabatments. (Fig. 85.)

Let P *be rabatted about* OB *and* OC *to* P_1, P_2 *respec-*

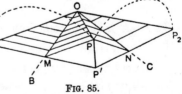

FIG. 85.

tively; let $P_1M \perp OB$, *and* $P_2N \perp OC$; *and let them meet in* P' ; *to* prove *that* P' *is the projection of* P *on the plane of the paper.*

121

As M and N are on the creases, they are unaltered by rabatment.

∴ PM ⊥ OB, and PN ⊥ OC ;

∴ OB ⊥ pl. P_1MP, and OC ⊥ pl. P_2NP ;   (4T1)

∴ plane OBC ⊥ planes P_1MP and P_2NP ;   (5T4)

∴ plane OBC ⊥ PP', their line of intersection ;   (5T4)

∴ P' is the projection of P on the plane of the paper.

(Q.E.D.)

COROLLARY : A STRAIGHT LINE PERPENDICULAR TO A CREASE DESCRIBES A PLANE PERPENDICULAR TO THE PLANE OF THE PAPER.

WORKED EXAMPLES

10W1. Given the base of a tetrahedron and the lengths of the oblique edges, find the length and position of the perpendicular from the vertex to the base. (Fig. 86.)

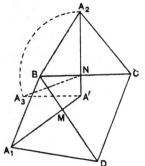

FIG. 86.

Let the triangle BCD *be the given base, and let the lengths of the remaining edges* AB, AC, AD *be given.*

Rabat the face ABD to A_1BD about BD, and the face ABC to A_2BC about BC (*i.e. in the plane of the paper construct triangles* A_1BD *and* A_2BC *congruent respectively to triangles* ABD *and* ABC).

Draw A_1M ⊥ BD and A_2N ⊥ BC, and produce them to meet in A'.

Then AA' is the normal from A to the plane BCD.   (10T1)

AN = A_2N, and AA' ⊥ NA' in plane BCD ;

∴ we can rabat triangle ANA' to A_3NA' (*i.e. construct triangle* A'NA$_3$ *making* NA'A$_3$ *a right angle, and* NA$_3$ = NA$_2$).

Then A' is the foot of the perpendicular from A to the base, and A$_3$A' is its length.   (Q.E.F.)

10W2. Find the centre and radius of the sphere circumscribing a tetrahedron whose base and altitude and the projection of whose vertex on the base are given. (Fig. 87.)

With the notation of 10W1, *let* P, Q, Q_2 *be circumcentres of the triangles* CBD, ABC, A_2BC, *and let* K *be the middle point of* BC.

Then KP, KQ, KQ_2 are all $\perp$ BC ;

$\therefore$ $Q\hat{K}P$ = dihedral angle between planes ABC, DBC

$$= A_3\hat{N}A' ; \quad (10W1)$$

$\therefore$ we can rabat PKQ to PKQ_4 by drawing

$KQ_4 \parallel NA_3$ and $= KQ_2$.

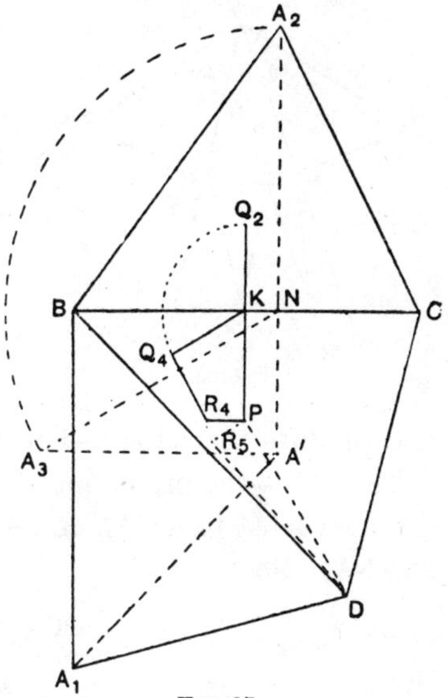

Let R be the centre of the sphere.

FIG. 87.

Then RP $\perp$ pl. BCD, and RQ $\perp$ pl. ABC ;   (4W1)

$\therefore$ BC is perpendicular to each of the connected straight lines KQ, KP, RQ, RP ;

$\therefore$ these straight lines are coplanar ;   (4T2)

$\therefore$ the point of intersection of straight lines drawn from P, $Q_4 \perp$ KP, KQ_4 respectively is the rabatment of R about KP.

As RP $\perp$ pl. BCD, $\therefore$ RP $\perp$ PD ;

$\therefore$ we can rabat RPD to R_5PD about PD.

Then R_5D is the radius of the sphere, R_4P and R_5P are equal to the distance of the centre from the plane of the base, and P is the projection of the centre on the base.   (Q.E.F.)

10W3. Given the face angles of a trihedral angle, find its dihedral angles ; *and, conversely,* given the dihedral angles, find the face angles. (Fig. 88.)

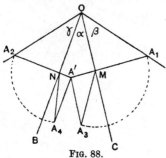

Let α, β, γ be the given face angles. Construct $\hat{BOC} = \alpha$, in the plane of the paper, and rabat β to $\hat{COA_1}$ and γ to $\hat{BOA_2}$. (N.B.—Make $OA_1 = OA_2$, as they are rabatments of the same line OA.)

Fig. 88.

Draw $A_1M \perp OC$, and $A_2N \perp OB$, and produce them to meet in A'.

Then A' is the projection of A.   (10T1)

Rabat A'MA to A'MA$_3$, and A'NA to A'NA$_4$, making MA$_3$ = MA$_1$, and NA$_4$ = NA$_2$.

Then $$OC \perp \text{pl. } AMA' \,; \tag{10T1}$$

$\therefore$ dihedral angle $\alpha\beta = \hat{A'MA} = \hat{A'MA_3}$. Similarly dihedral angle $\gamma\alpha = \hat{A'NA_4}$.

By a similar construction we could find dihedral angle $\beta\gamma$.

(Q.E.F.)

CONVERSE : Construct the supplements of the given dihedral angles.

These are equal to the face angles of the conjugate trihedral angle.   (6T1)

Find its dihedral angles.

Construct their supplements.

These are equal to the face angles of the given trihedral angle.   (6T1)

(Q.E.F.)

10W4. Given the face angles of a trihedral angle, find the locus of the points of contact of its faces with its inscribed spheres.

ANALYSIS : (Fig. 89). Let a sphere touch the faces of the given trihedral angle in the points P, Q, R, and let the plane PQR cut the edges in the points A, B, C.

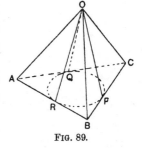

FIG. 89.

Then OP = OQ = OR (tangents to the sphere), and BP = BR (tangents to the circle PQR).

∴ triangles POB, ROB are congruent ;

∴ $P\hat{O}B = R\hat{O}B$, and two similar equalities.

∴ $A\hat{O}R + R\hat{O}B + P\hat{O}C =$ half the sum of the face angles ;

∴ $A\hat{O}B + P\hat{O}C$ is constant ;

∴ $P\hat{O}C$ is constant ;

∴ the required locus is the set of three infinite straight lines OP, OQ, OR.

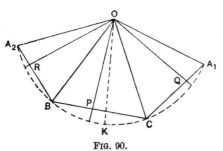

FIG. 90.

Hence the following construction :

CONSTRUCTION : (Fig. 90).

Rabat the angles BOA, COA, to BOA_2, COA_1, on plane of BOC ;

and let OK bisect $A_2\hat{O}A_1$.

From $B\hat{O}C$ cut off $B\hat{O}P = C\hat{O}K$,

from $B\hat{O}A_2$ cut off $B\hat{O}R = B\hat{O}P$,

and from $C\hat{O}A_1$ cut off $C\hat{O}Q = C\hat{O}P$.   (Q.E.F.)

10W5. Given the base and altitude of a tetrahedron, and the projection of its vertex on the base, construct the projection, and find the length, of the common perpendicular of two opposite edges.

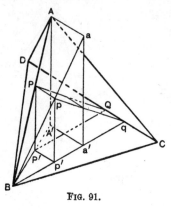

FIG. 91.

ANALYSIS: (Fig. 91). Let ABCD be the given tetrahedron, and let AB, CD cut their common perpendicular in P and Q; let A′, P′ be the projections of A, P on plane BCD, and let a, p, $a′$, $p′$, q be the projections of A, P, A′, P′, Q on the plane through B$\perp$CD.

Then Aa ∥ Pp ∥ Qq ∥ DC; and PQqp is a plane quadrilateral with three right angles;

∴ it is a rectangle;

∴ PQ = and ∥ pq.

But PQ $\perp$ AB and CD;   ∴ $pq \perp$ AB and Aa;   (3T6)

∴ $pq \perp$ Ba.   (4T1)

Hence the following construction:

CONSTRUCTION: (Fig. 92). Draw B$q \perp$ CD and A′$a′ \perp$ Bq.

Rabat qBa to qBa_1 (i.e. from $a′$A′ cut off $a′a_1$ = altitude of tet.).

Draw $qp_1 \perp$ Ba_1; $p_1p′ \perp$ Bq; $p′$P′ ∥ $a′$A′ (actually along $p′p_1$ in the diagram), cutting BA′ in P′; and draw P′Q $\perp$ CD.

Rabat BA′A to BA′A$_2$.

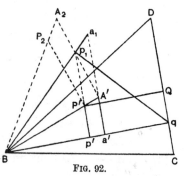

FIG. 92.

Draw P′P$_2$ ∥ A′A$_2$, cutting A$_2$B in P$_2$.

Thus the points P, Q, are found, and P′Q is the projection of PQ, and p_1q is equal to it in length.   (Q.E.F.)

NOTE ON THE GRAPHICAL SOLUTION OF
TRIHEDRAL ANGLES

Def. : If two trihedral angles have two common edges and their remaining edges in the same straight line, they are said to be **supplementary**.

E.g. if AV is produced to A', the trihedral angles V,ABC, and V,A'BC are supplementary.

It follows that the eight trihedral angles determined by three concurrent straight lines may be described as

> *a given trihedral angle,*
> *its three supplements,*
> *and the four trihedral angles vertically opposite to them.*

It is easy to see that supplementary trihedral angles have one face angle and its opposite dihedral angle in common, and the remaining corresponding angles supplementary.

Thus, if $\alpha\beta\gamma$, $\alpha'\beta'\gamma'$ are supplementary,

$$\alpha = \alpha', \qquad \beta\gamma = \beta'\gamma',$$
$$\beta = 180° - \beta', \qquad \gamma\alpha = 180° - \gamma'\alpha',$$
$$\gamma = 180° - \gamma', \qquad \alpha\beta = 180° - \alpha'\beta'.$$

Contrast these with conjugate trihedral angles. (6T1)

The method of 10W3 applies to all trihedral angles, whether the face angles are acute or obtuse. If β (Fig. 88), were obtuse, M would fall on CO produced, and A' would lie outside the angle BOC.

If β and γ were both obtuse, it would be more convenient to construct the supplementary trihedral angle $\alpha\beta'\gamma'$.

EXAMPLES 10A

10A1. Find graphically the length of the diagonal of a cube whose edge is 3 inches ; find also its inclination to a face. Check by calculation.

10A2. Find graphically the length of the diagonal of a regular octahedron whose edge is 3·5 inches. Find also the dihedral angles.

10A3. Find graphically the altitude of a regular tetrahedron, each edge of which is 3 inches long.

From your figure find the dihedral angles and the inclination of an edge to a face.

10A4. Find the distance between opposite edges of a tetrahedron, each edge of which is 2·5 inches long.

10A5. Find the radius and centre of the sphere which will cut the plane of the paper in a given circle of radius 3 inches, and pass through a point whose distances from the centre and plane of the circle are respectively 5 inches and 3 inches.

10A6. The sides of the base of a tetrahedron are respectively 3, 3·5, and 4 inches in length, and the inscribed sphere, the radius of which is 0·6 inch, touches the base 2·5 inches from its smallest angle and 1·5 inches from its largest angle. Find graphically the dihedral angle at the 3·5 inch edge.

10A7. Given the altitude of a tetrahedron and the sides of the base ($1\frac{1}{2}$, 3, $2\frac{1}{2}$, and 2 inches respectively), find the remaining edges so that the perpendiculars from the four corners to the opposite faces may be concurrent.

10A8. Given the three pairs of opposite edges of a tetrahedron (5, 4 ; 7, 8·4 ; 8, 6 cm. respectively), find the distance between the middle points of the last pair.

10A9. Construct the plane section of a cube through two given points on one face and one on an adjacent face.

10A10. Construct the plane section of a cube through two given points on one face and one on the opposite face.

10A11. Three edges of a tetrahedron are inclined at an angle of 30° to the base, which is an equilateral triangle. Compare the lengths of these edges with those of the base.

10A12. A frustum of a square pyramid has parallel edges 10 feet and 4 feet long, and oblique edges 5 feet. Find graphically the angles of the trapeziums that form the sloping faces, and also the inclination of the parallel faces to the others.

10A13. Find graphically the radius of a hemisphere that can be inscribed in a regular square pyramid, given that the edges at the base are 4 inches long, and the face angles at the vertex are 76°.

10A14. Find graphically the edge of a cube which can be inscribed in a hemisphere of given radius, say 3 inches.

10A15. Find graphically the length of the edge of a cube that can be inscribed in a sphere of radius 3 inches.

10A16. What restriction is imposed on the number of edges of a pyramid, if all the angles at its vertex are required to be obtuse ?

EXAMPLES 10B

10B1. If two opposite sides of a rectangle subtend equal obtuse angles at a given point in space, show that they determine with it a pair of planes equally inclined to the plane of the rectangle.

10B2. Show why the word " obtuse " cannot be omitted from 10B1.

10B3. If alternate vertical angles of a rectangular pyramid are equal to one another, prove that its oblique edges are equal.

10B4. Construct the plane section of a cube through one point on each of three faces which have a common vertex.

10B5. Construct the plane section of a cube through one given point on each of three consecutive faces.

10B6. O,ABCD is a square pyramid with the triangular faces equilateral. A plane through A bisects OC at Q, and cuts OB at P, where $BP = \frac{1}{4}OB$. Find graphically where it cuts OD.

10B7. In a right cone 4 inches high and with semi-vertical angle 25°, is inscribed a cube with its base on the base of the cone. Find graphically the length of an edge.

10B8. Four spheres, each of diameter 2 inches, rest in a hemispherical bowl, touching one another two by two, and just touching the surface of the water which fills the bowl. Find graphically the diameter of the bowl.

10B9. Show graphically that if a strip of bandage be wrapped round any convex pyramid, towards the point, it will, sooner or later, cross over itself, and continue to wind round the pyramid, but towards the base, and ultimately lie in one of the faces. What is the corresponding statement in the case of a cone ? Are these statements true if the base of the pyramid or cone is concave ?

10B10. The six oblique edges of a pyramid are equal, and each face angle at the vertex is 30°. Find graphically the angles between the base and the oblique edges and faces.

10B11. Given that the edges of the tetrahedron ABCD have the following lengths: AB = 3·04, BC = 2·61, CA = 2·13, CD = 1·93, AD = 3·52, BD = 3·95 units, find graphically the magnitude of the dihedral angle AB, and, if its plane bisector cuts CD in F, find by construction the length of CF.

10B12. The sphere inscribed in the tetrahedron ABCD touches the face ABC in the point S. Find graphically the length of SA, given the following measurements: BC = 2·97, CA = 4·12, AB = 2·25, AD = 3·94, BD = 2·71, CD = 2·32 units.

10B13. The lengths of the edges BC, CA, AB of the tetrahedron ABCD are respectively 2·92, 2·36, and 3·27 units, and those of its medians AP, BQ, CR are 2·04, 2·55, and 2·24 units. Find by construction the altitude DD′, and the lengths of the remaining edges, AD, BD, CD. (N.B. P, Q, R are *centroids* of faces.)

10B14. The plan of a field is a rectangle ABCD, with AB, BC, 600 and 500 yards long, and running respectively due north and due east. The corners A, B, C are respectively 200, 240, and 300 feet above sea-level. Find, graphically or by calculation, the direction of the line of slope.

10B15. ABCD,XYZW is a cube, and P is the middle point of AB. Find the length and position of the straight line ST which cuts PZ and DW at right angles.

10B16. If ABCD is a tetrahedron in which AC ⊥ BD, and BC = a, CA = b, AB = c, and CD = d, calculate the length of AD.

10B17. The straight lines joining the middle points of the opposite edges of a certain tetrahedron are mutually at right angles, and their lengths are x, y, z. Calculate the lengths of the edges.

10B18. Find by construction the lengths of the edges of a tetrahedron, if the joins of the middle points of opposite edges are 3·5, 4·5, and 5·5 units long, and the first two of these are inclined to one another at 48°, the second two at 70°, and the first and last at 56°.

10B19. Two opposite edges of a tetrahedron are at right angles to one another; their lengths are respectively 2·5 in., and 3·5 in., and they are 3 in. apart. Find the size and position of the square section parallel to them.

10B20. Find graphically the dihedral angles of a trihedral angle whose face angles are 30°, 45°, and 60°.

10B21. Find graphically the dihedral angles of a trihedral angle whose face angles are 90°, 108°, and 120°.

10B22. Find graphically the face angles of a trihedral angle whose dihedral angles are 135°, 120°, and 150°.

10B23. Find graphically the face angles of a trihedral angle whose dihedral angles are 72°, 90°, and 60°.

10B24. If α, β, γ are face angles of a trihedral angle, and $\beta\gamma$, $\gamma\alpha$, $\alpha\beta$ its dihedral angles, prove that

$$\cos\alpha\beta = \frac{\cos\gamma - \cos\alpha\cos\beta}{\sin\alpha\sin\beta}.$$

10B25. ABCD is a tetrahedron in which AB $= 10\cdot73$, BC $= 13\cdot90$, CA $= 10\cdot98$, AD $= 6\cdot04$, BD $= 14\cdot75$, and CD $= 12\cdot0$ units. Find the shortest distance between AB and CD, and the distance of C from their common perpendicular.

EXAMPLES 10C

10C1. A sphere of radius 1 inch rests in a trihedral angle whose face angles are each 40°. Find graphically the distance of the centre of the sphere from the vertex of the angle.

10C2. The jib of a crane is initially inclined at an angle of 30° to the vertical. It is swung about a vertical axis through an angle of 25°, and then lowered till its inclination to the vertical is 50°. Find graphically the angle between its initial and final positions.

10C3. Find graphically the dihedral angle between two roofs inclined at 40° and 50° respectively to the horizontal, if the angle between their ridges is 100°. Find also the angle between the horizontal plane and the gutter in the valley between the roofs. Does it make any difference whether the ridges or the eaves are on the inside of the 100° bend ?

10C4. Find graphically the radius of the sphere inscribed in a tetrahedron which has pairs of opposite edges of the following lengths : 3·0, 4·4 ; 3·6, 4·0 ; 4·8, 2·5 units.

10C5. ABCD is a tetrahedron in which AB $= 3\cdot3$, BC $= 3\cdot8$, CA $= 4\cdot2$, AD $= 3\cdot1$, BD $= 2\cdot7$, CD $= 2\cdot9$. P, Q are points on AD, BC respectively, such that AP $= 0\cdot9$, BQ $= 1\cdot5$ units. If G is the centroid of the tetrahedron, find graphically the points R, S, T, U, where the plane PQG cuts the edges AB, CD, AC, BD respectively.

10C6. Prove, either by construction, or by calculation, that any two skew edges of a regular octahedron are trisected by a straight line that cuts them both at right angles.

10C7. Find the ratio of the areas of the faces of cubes that can be inscribed in a given sphere and in one of its hemispheres.

10C8. ABCD,XYZW is a cube, and P is the centre of the face XYZW. Construct a straight line through P to cut CD and AY. Find its length in terms of that of AB.

10C9. P is the middle point of the edge WX of a cube ABCD,XYZW ; through P construct a straight line cutting AZ and DC. Find its length in terms of that of AB.

10C10. A cube is inscribed in a tetrahedron so that each face of the latter contains one edge of the former. Show that two edges of the tetrahedron are at right angles to one another, and that if there are two solutions there must also be a third.

10C11. Show that three cases of 10C10 arise according as the edges of the cube in contact with faces of the tetrahedron consist of

 (i) four separate edges ;
 (ii) two opposite edges and two parallel edges adjacent to one of
       them ;
(iii) two pairs of opposite edges not all parallel to one another.

10C12. If ABCD is a tetrahedron, and MN is the common perpendicular to the edges AB, CD, which are at right angles to one another, and if PQ is an edge of the inscribed cube which satisfies the conditions of 10C11 (i), show that

$$\frac{1}{PQ} = \frac{1}{AB} + \frac{1}{CD} + \frac{1}{MN}.$$

10C13. If, in 10C12, AB = 3·5, CD = 4·2, and MN = 3·0 units, calculate the length of PQ, and check by a practical construction.

10C14. With the notation of 10C12, find PQ if AB = 8, CD = 9·5, MN = 4·8, and N is in CD produced, and DN = 2·8.

10C15. With the notation of 10C12, find PQ if AB = 6·6, CD = 4·8, and MN = 12·0, and M, N are in AB, CD produced, and BM = 3·4, and DN = 4·0 units.

10C16. A wireless mast is kept in a vertical position on a hillside by means of three wire ropes equally inclined to the horizontal.

Two of them, each of length 55 feet, are inclined to the third, which is 45 feet long, at angles of 40°, and to one another at an angle of 30°. Find the slope of the ground.

10C17. A lamp-shade is in the form of a frustum of a hexagonal pyramid, whose parallel faces are inclined at 45° to the other six. If a hemisphere can be inscribed in this frustum, and each edge of the base is 9 inches long, find graphically the lengths of the remaining edges.

10C18. Three equal cones with semi-vertical angles 22° have a common vertex and touch one another along three generators. Find graphically the semi-vertical angles of the cones that will touch them externally and internally along three generators.

10C19. If each of the oblique edges of a tetrahedron is two-thirds of the length of a side of the equilateral base, show that the foot of the normal from the centre of the base to any other face is the centre of the inscribed circle of that face.

10C20. Three equal cones have a common vertex and touch a plane along three generators and each other along three others. Either construct or calculate their semi-vertical angle. (Use 10C19.)

10C21. If two face angles of a trihedral angle are respectively 50° and 36°, and the dihedral angle between them is 75°, find by construction the remaining face angle.

10C22. If two dihedral angles of a trihedral angle, and the included face angle are respectively 49°, 103°, and 84°, find graphically the remaining dihedral angle.

10C23. Three equal cones with semi-vertical angle θ touch a cone with semi-vertical angle φ along three generators, and touch one another along three other generators. Obtain an expression for θ in terms of φ.

10C24. Each face angle at the vertex of a square pyramid is equal to 50°. A plane cuts three consecutive edges at distances 4·0, 4·6, 5·8 units from the vertex. Find graphically its point of intersection with the fourth edge, and its inclination to the axis.

10C25. ABCD is a tetrahedron in which BC = 3·75, CA = 3·35, AB = 3·50, and the distances AP, BQ, CR, of A, B, C from the opposite faces are respectively 1·88, 1·96, 2·76. Find graphically the dihedral angles at the base, the altitude, and the lengths of the remaining edges.

CHAPTER XI

POLYHEDRA

DEF. : If a single portion of space not pierced by holes is bounded only by plane polygons, it is called a **polyhedral solid,** and its surface is called a **polyhedron.** (*Quoted from Chap. I.*)

A polyhedron is said to be **regular** if its faces and solid angles are regular.

It follows that all the face angles are equal to one another, and therefore that all the faces, and all the solid angles, are congruent to one another.

DEF. : Any plane net-work which adequately represents the arrangement of the faces, edges, and vertices of a polyhedron without regard to area, length, or angle, is called a **distorted representation.**

Imagine, for example, one face of a cube or octahedron opened like a window, so that the whole of the interior may be viewed through it (Fig. 93).

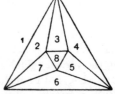

FIG. 93.—DISTORTED REPRESENTATION OF CUBE AND OCTAHEDRON
(FIRST METHOD).

The arrangement of the other faces may be represented by a plane net-work whose outline is that of the " window ", while

the " window-face " itself may be represented by the rest of
the plane *outside* the outline.

Alternatively (Fig.
94), imagine the in-
terior of each of these
solids viewed from a
point just inside one
of its vertices.

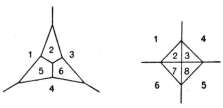

The faces that meet
at this vertex will be

FIG. 94.—DISTORTED REPRESENTATION OF CUBE
AND OCTAHEDRON (SECOND METHOD).

represented by parts of the plane outside of the rest of the
diagram, separated by diverging straight lines representing the
corresponding edges. The vertex itself cannot be represented.
(The numbering of the faces is the same in Figures 93 and 94.)

Theorem 11T1

(Euler's Theorem.)

**The number of faces of any polyhedron, together with the
number of vertices, is two more than the number of edges.**

*Let f, v, e be the numbers of faces, vertices, and edges respec-
tively ;* to prove that
$$f + v - e = 2.$$

Using either a model or a distorted representation of any
polyhedron, mark the edges in turn, starting with the outline
of a single face.

For any polygon, $v = e$, and, as it divides the polyhedron into
two parts, we may say that $f = 2$.

∴, when only one face is outlined,
$$f + v - e = 2.$$

As each new edge is marked, if it is attached at one end only,
it marks a new vertex without completing a new face ; if the
edge is attached at both ends, it completes a new face without
marking a new vertex.

$\therefore$ the difference between e and $f + v$ is unaltered.

$\therefore$, at every stage of the marking,

$$f + v - e = 2. \qquad \text{(Q.E.D.)}$$

NOTE : Instead of regarding the uncompleted part of the polyhedron at each stage as an additional face, we may prefer to count only the faces actually marked.

In this case, $f = 1$ at the beginning, and

$$f + v - e = 1$$

as long as the polyhedron is incomplete.

As the last face can be put in place without the addition of either edges or vertices, we have, for the complete polyhedron,

$$f + v - e = 2. \qquad \text{(Q E.D.)}$$

Theorem 11T2

If a regular polyhedron has m edges to each vertex, and n edges to each face, then

$$(m - 2)(n - 2) < 4.$$

If the sides of any polygon are produced in turn, the exterior angles so formed are together equal to $360°$;

$\therefore$ each angle of a regular polygon with n sides

$$= 180° - \frac{360°}{n}.$$

The sum of the face angles of any convex polyhedral angle is less than $360°$.   (6T3)

$$\therefore \text{ each angle} < \frac{360°}{m} \, ;$$

$$\therefore 180° - \frac{360°}{n} < \frac{360°}{m} \, ;$$

$$\therefore 1 < \frac{2}{n} + \frac{2}{m} \, ;$$

$$\therefore mn < 2m + 2n \, ;$$

$$\therefore mn - 2n - 2m + 4 < 4 \, ;$$

$$\therefore (m - 2)(n - 2) < 4. \qquad \text{(Q.E.D.)}$$

COROLLARY : It follows that EVERY REGULAR POLYHEDRON IS INCLUDED IN THE FOLLOWING TABLE :

$m-2$	$n-2$	m	n	Polyhedron
3	1	5	3	(11T4)
2	1	4	3	Octahedron
1	1	3	3	Tetrahedron
1	2	3	4	Cube
1	3	3	5	(11T3)

Theorem 11T3

There exists a regular polyhedron with five edges to each face and three to each vertex. (Fig. 95.)

In a model, or a distorted representation, start with a single pentagonal face ABCDE. Attach edges AA_1, BB_1, ... , making three edges at each of the vertices A, B, ... Complete the faces $A_1ABB_1D_2$, $B_1BCC_1E_2$, ... , making three edges at each of the vertices A_1, B_1, ... Attach edges A_2A_3, B_2B_3, ... and complete the faces $A_3A_2D_1B_2B_3$, $B_3B_2E_1C_2C_3$, ... ,

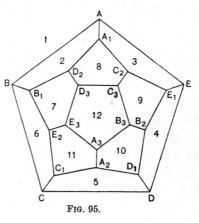

FIG. 95.

making three edges at each of the vertices A_3, B_3, ... , and enclosing a new face $A_3B_3C_3D_3E_3$.

Thus there exists a regular polyhedron with five edges to each face and three to each vertex, and it has 12 faces, 30 edges, and 20 vertices. (Q.E.D.)

DEF. : A polyhedron having twelve regular pentagonal faces is called a **regular dodecahedron**.

Theorem 11T4

There exists a regular polyhedron with five edges to each vertex and three to each face. (Fig. 96.)

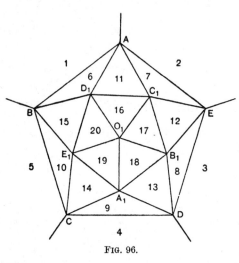

FIG. 96.

In a model, or a distorted representation, start with five concurrent edges, AO, BO, CO, DO, EO (represented by diverging straight lines, the vertex O not being represented). Complete the faces OAB, OBC, ... , and the adjacent faces ABD_1, BCE_1,..., making five edges at each of the vertices A, B, ... Complete the faces AC_1D_1, BD_1E_1, ... , making four edges at each of the vertices A_1, B_1, ... One new face is required adjacent to each of these faces, and one new edge at each of these vertices. All these are supplied by attaching five concurrent edges O_1A_1, O_1B_1, O_1C_1, O_1D_1, O_1E_1.

Thus there exists a regular polyhedron with five edges to each vertex and three to each face ; and it has 20 faces, 30 edges, and 12 vertices.

DEF. : A regular polyhedron having twenty triangular faces is called a **regular icosahedron**.   (Q.E.D.)

COR. : THERE ARE, IN ALL, FIVE REGULAR POLHHEDRA, NAMELY, THE TETRAHEDRON, OCTAHEDRON, ICOSAHEDRON, CUBE, AND DODECAHEDRON.

CARDBOARD MODELS OF REGULAR POLYHEDRA.

Suppose a model of a polyhedron made out of thin cardboard, and then cut along the edges so that it can be flattened without distorting the faces. The resulting plane figure is called a " **net** " of the polyhedron.

Conversely, to construct a cardboard model when the shape of a net is known, we cut out the net, score half-way through the thickness of the cardboard along the common edges of faces that are adjacent in the net, bend along each edge *with the cut side outermost*, and join up the free edges with adhesive tape.

If we have a distorted representation of a regular polyhedron, or of any polyhedron of which the size and shape of the faces are known, we can construct a net without any previous knowledge of the form. It is sufficient to number all the faces in the distorted representation, and to notice the *order* of faces adjacent to particular faces, and the *order* of faces at particular vertices. Notice, however, that this gives the *inner* surface of the net, which must therefore be turned over before scoring and making up.

Thus, in the distorted representation of the regular octahedron (Fig. 93), the faces adjacent to face 8, taken in clockwise order, are 3, 5, 7. We begin the net with the equilateral triangle 8, and equilateral triangles 3, 5, 7 drawn on its

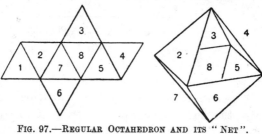

FIG. 97.—REGULAR OCTAHEDRON AND ITS " NET ".

sides. The faces at one vertex are 3, 8, 7, 2, in clockwise order. We accordingly construct equilateral triangle 2 on the proper edge of triangle 7, so that in the model another edge will join on to triangle 3. Proceeding in this way, we obtain the net shown in Fig. 97, or some equally good alternative.

Similarly the distorted representations in Figs. 95, 96 give the nets shown in Figs. 98, 99 respectively, in which the faces retain their former numbers.

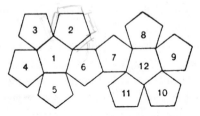

FIG. 98.—" NET " OF REGULAR DODECAHEDRON.

DEF. : If every figure that satisfies certain data is congruent to one or other of a *finite* set of figures, each is said to be **determined** by the data ; if all these figures are congruent to one another, each is said to be **uniquely determined** by the data.

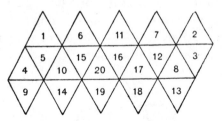

FIG. 99.—" NET " OF REGULAR ICOSAHEDRON.

It sometimes happens that, for particular values of a set of data, the figure *determined* by them is *impossible*. Thus, a triangle is uniquely determined by the lengths of its sides ; but if two of them are together less than the third, the triangle is impossible.

We have seen that a net is determined by its solid, but not uniquely. Indeed, the number of alternative nets to a given solid may be very great ; but it is always finite.

The question arises, whether a solid is determined by its net.

Clearly, a solid may not be *uniquely* determined by its net ; unless we exclude concave solids ; for a part of a polyhedron may be " turned inside out " without altering its net. The same net, for example, will serve a cube surmounted by a pyramid, and a cube with a pyramidal indentation.

It is also easy to show that a solid is determined by its net provided that all its solid angles are trihedral ; for the face angles of a trihedral angle determine its dihedral angles.

Certain other cases are considered in 11W4, and 11C22-24.

DEF. : The orthogonal projections of a figure on a given horizontal and a given vertical plane are called respectively its **plan and elevation.**

PLAN AND ELEVATION OF THE REGULAR DODECAHEDRON.

We see from the distorted representation (Fig. 95), that, in the projection of this polyhedron on the plane $A_3B_3C_3D_3E_3$,

(1) vertices with the same letter will be collinear ;

(2) vertices with the same suffix will be concyclic ;

(3) these circles will be concentric ;

(4) edges that appear to radiate from the centre of the distorted representation will have equal projections, because they will, in fact, be equally inclined to the plane $A_3B_3C_3D_3E_3$.   (5T6)

It follows from (3) and (4) that circles $A_1B_1C_1$ and $A_2B_2C_2$ will coincide.

The faces adjacent to $A_3B_3C_3D_3E_3$ can be rabatted upon it.

$$\therefore \ B_3C_2 \perp C_3D_3. \qquad (10T1)$$

∴ C_2 is the point of intersection of the radius through C_3 and the perpendicular from B_3 to C_3D_3.

It is therefore a simple matter to construct the plan as in Fig. 100.

Once the plan is drawn, all we need to know in order to construct any elevation or vertical section is the heights of the other three rings of vertices above the plane of the base.

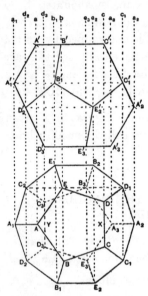

Let X, Y be the middle points of CD, C_3D_3 respectively. Then the height of A_1 will be one side of a right-angled triangle of which the other short side and hypotenuse are respectively equal to the lengths of A_1Y, A_3Y on the plan. Similarly the height of A_2 will be the third side of a right-angled triangle whose other short side and hypotenuse are equal to A_3A_2, A_3B_3 on the plan. The sum of these two heights is equal to that of A, i.e. the height of the dodecahedron.

FIG. 100.—PLAN AND ELEVA-
TION OF REGULAR DODECA-
HEDRON.

We therefore draw straight lines, parallel to one another, in any direction through all points of the plan, naming them with the corresponding small letters. The elevation of the plane of the base $A_3B_3C_3D_3E_3$ is a straight line parallel to XY, and cutting a_3, e_3, d_3, in A_3', E_3', D_3'. With centre D_3' and radius YA_3, describe an arc cutting a_1 in A_1'. With centres A_3' and A_1', and radius A_3B_3, describe arcs cutting a_2, a in A_2', A' respectively. Through A_2', A_1', A', draw straight lines parallel to XY cutting d_2, e_2; b_1, c_1; b, c respectively in the pairs of points D_2', E_2'; B_1', C_1'; B', C'.

PLAN AND ELEVATION OF THE REGULAR ICOSAHEDRON. (Fig. 101.)

It follows from the definition of a regular solid angle that the extremities of the five edges of a regular icosahedron that meet at a vertex are vertices of a regular pentagon. We see, further, from the distorted representation, Fig. 96, that there are two regular pentagonal pyramids, $O, ABCDE$ and $O_1, A_1B_1C_1D_1E_1$ joined by a girdle of ten equilateral triangles alternately upright and inverted, and that the pentagons $ABCDE$, $A_1B_1C_1D_1E_1$ are in parallel planes, and have the sides of one opposite to vertices of the other and parallel to the sides opposite to those vertices.

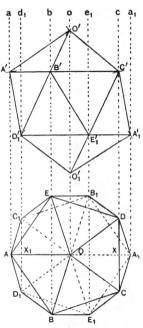

Accordingly (Fig. 101), we construct these pentagons in the plan with a common centre, O, or O_1. Joining their alternate vertices, we get the plan of the " girdle ", and joining A, B, C, D, E to O, and A_1, B_1, C_1, D_1, E_1 to O_1, we get the plans of the pyramidal ends.

Fig. 101.—Plan and Elevation of Regular Icosahedron.

To draw the vertical section OAO_1A_1, we notice that it bisects CD and C_1D_1 in the points X, X_1, say, and that the true length of AX_1 is equal to the height of an equilateral triangle on base AB; hence the distances of the planes $ABCDE$, $A_1B_1C_1D_1E_1$ from O, O_1 respectively, and from each other, can easily be constructed.

PICTORIAL REPRESENTATION. (Fig. 102.)

A Plan and Elevation convey all the information we need in order to deduce any required geometrical fact about a solid figure ; but, to get a vivid impression of its form, what we want is some means of representing length, breadth and height *simultaneously*.

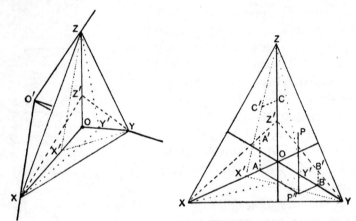

FIG. 102.—PICTORIAL REPRESENTATION.

The Plan and Elevation are orthogonal projections of the solid on two perpendicular planes. Let these, and a third plane at right angles to them, intersect the plane of the paper in the triangle XYZ, and let O be the projection on the paper of their common point O'.

Then   O'Z ⊥ O'X and O'Y ;

                 ∴ O'Z ⊥ XY.   (4T1)

Also   O'O ⊥ XY ; ∴ OZ ⊥ XY.   (4T1)

It follows that O is the orthocentre of triangle XYZ.

Rabat O' about YZ, ZX, XY to X', Y', Z' on OX, OY, OZ respectively.   (10T1)

The Plan and Elevation give us the coordinates (x, y, z) of any point P' of the solid.

From Z'X, Z'Y, X'Z cut off Z'A', Z'B', X'C' equal respectively to x, y, z. Then the projections of P' on O'X, O'Y, O'Z are represented by the points A, B, C on OX, OY, OZ respectively, such that A'A and B'B are ∥ ZO, and C'C ∥ XO.

Complete the parallelogram AOBP'', and draw P''P = and ∥ OC. Then P is the representation of the given point P', and P'' that of its projection on the plane XOY. Thus P' is *determined* by P and P''.

Figs. 103 and 104 have been prepared in this way from the plans and elevations in Figs. 100 and 101 respectively. The number-

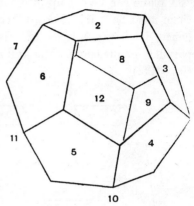

FIG. 103.—REGULAR DODECAHEDRON.

ing of the faces is the same as in the earlier figures, face 1 being removed in each case to reveal part of the interior.

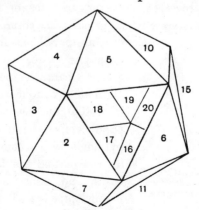

FIG. 104.—REGULAR ICOSAHEDRON.

DEF. : $A_1'A_2'$, $B_1'B_2'$, $C_1'C_2'$ are called the **axial lengths** of a straight line P_1P_2.

PARALLELOHEDRA

DEF. : Congruent polyhedra that can be stacked together so as to fill space completely are called **parallelohedra.**

A plane can be cut up into congruent triangles, but half of them must be " upside down " compared with the other half ; hence, if they are bases of prisms with equal heights and parallel oblique edges, these will not, in general, be congruent. (Fig. 105.)

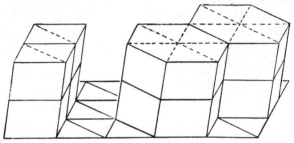

FIG. 105.—*Parallelohedra* :
STACK OF PARALLELEPIPEDS OR HEXAGONAL PRISMS.

Associated together, however, in twos or in sixes, they form congruent **parallelepipeds** or **hexagonal prisms**. These, there-fore, are parallelohedra.

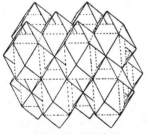

FIG. 106.—*Parallelohedra* :
RHOMBOIDAL DODECAHEDRA.

Suppose space cut up into con-gruent parallelepipeds that are alternately opaque and transparent (Fig. 106), and let each transparent parallelepiped be divided into six pyramids with a common vertex at its centre and its faces for their bases, and associate each opaque parallelepiped with the six trans-parent pyramids standing on its faces. It is not difficult to see that the triangular faces unite in pairs forming parallelo-grams with the edges of the opaque parallelepiped for diagonals, so that the resulting figure has twelve faces, opposite pairs of which are congruent, and opposite edges of which are parallel. Thus the whole of space may be divided up into congruent twelve-faced solids which may be called **rhomboidal dodecahedra.** If the original parallelepipeds had been cubes, the resulting figures would have been **rhombic dodecahedra.** We see that each of these parallelohedra is equivalent to two of the original parallelepipeds. (Notice that, in the figure, only *four* faces of each dodecahedron are made *opaque*.)

Next imagine each face that is parallel to a given edge of the original parallelepipeds to be *stretched* so that it acquires an extra pair of edges in the given direction, the other edges re-

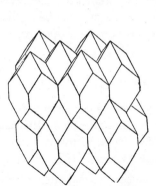

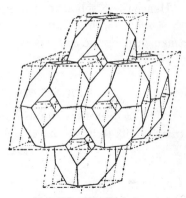

FIG. 107.—*Parallelohedra* :
RHOMBO-HEXAGONAL DODECAHEDRA.

FIG. 108.—*Parallelohedra* :
TRUNCATED OCTAHEDRA.

taining their length and direction. (Fig. 107.) The resulting figures will still be congruent dodecahedra completely filling space, but four faces of each will be hexagons while the other eight remain parallelograms. These parallelohedra may be described as **rhombo-hexagonal** dodecahedra.

Lastly (Fig. 108), the vertices and centres of a stack of congruent parallelepipeds are centres of another kind of parallelohedra. Let each parallelepiped be divided into eight congruent parallelepipeds by three planes through its centre. It is easy to prove that the middle points of the six edges of any one of the smaller parallelepipeds that do not meet a given diagonal of the larger are coplanar, and that their plane bisects the volume of the smaller. It follows that the part of the original parallelepiped inside these eight planes is a solid having half its volume and bounded by eight hexagonal and six rhomboidal faces (parallelograms), the latter lying in the six original faces. Further, the centres of the original stack of parallelepipeds are the vertices of a congruent stack; and the adjacent corners cut from any eight parallelepipeds at a point form a solid that bears the same relation to the new stack as the solid already described bears to the old.

Hence these solids are parallelohedra. They are called **truncated octahedra,** those formed from cubes and cuboids being distinguished by the epithets **regular** and **rectangular** respectively.

WORKED EXAMPLES.

11W1. Show that there exists a solid bounded by congruent isosceles triangles with their base angles grouped in eights at some vertices, and their vertical angles grouped in threes at the remaining vertices. (Fig. 109.)

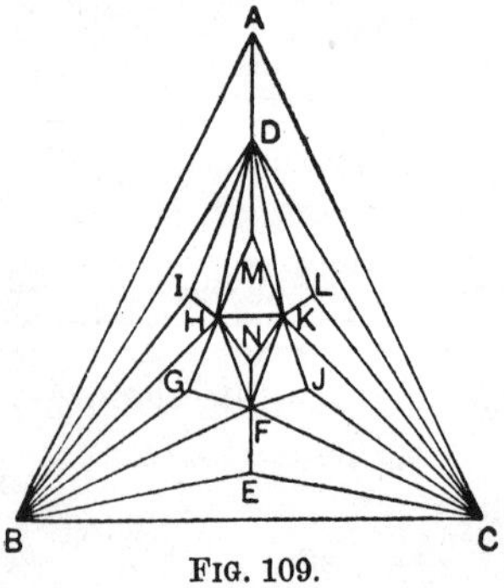

FIG. 109.

Let A be the vertical angle of the " window " ABC in the distorted representation. Draw AD, the third edge at A, the triangle BCE with base angles at B and C, and EF, the third edge at E.

We now have five edges each at B and C. Draw BG, BH, BI at B, and CJ, CK, CL at C, and complete the triangles with vertical angles at G, I, J, and L. Three new edges are required at each of the vertices H and K, and one at each of the vertices F and D. Draw DM, FN, making vertical angles at M and N, and supply the last edge at each of the vertices H and K by drawing the straight line HK.

We see that there are eight trihedral angles, which are vertices of triangular pyramids on equilateral bases. By symmetry, these equilateral triangles are faces of an inscribed regular octahedron, whose vertices are at the six octahedral vertices of the solid. (This solid is called a triakis octahedron; see No. 8 in the Table of Cubic Forms, at the end of Chapter XV.)

11W2. If all the solid angles of the figure of 11W1 are regular, show that the ratio of a pair of its unequal edges is as $2 + \sqrt{2} : 2$. (Fig. 110.)

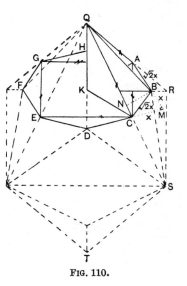

FIG. 110.

Let B be any trihedral vertex, Q, R, S the adjacent octahedral vertices, QDS the face adjacent to QBS, and QT a diagonal of the octahedron. Let a symmetrical section of the regular octahedral angle at Q cut QR, QB, QS, QD, QT respectively in the points A, B, C, D, K. Let N be the middle point of SQ, produce AB, DC to meet in M, and let $BM = x$.

Then ACQ is an equilateral triangle, and AKQ, BMC are right-angled isosceles triangles.

$$\therefore \quad AB = BC = \sqrt{2} \, . \, x \, ;$$
$$\therefore \quad AC^2 = AM^2 + CM^2,$$
$$= x^2(\sqrt{2} + 1)^2 + x^2 \, ;$$
$$\therefore \quad BQ^2 = AQ^2 = AC^2 = x^2(4 + 2\sqrt{2}).$$

As $BN \perp CQ$,
$$\therefore \quad BC^2 = BQ^2 + CQ^2 - 2 \, CQ \, . \, NQ \, ;$$
$$\therefore \quad 2 \, CQ \, . \, NQ = 2 \, BQ^2 - BC^2 \, ;$$

$$\therefore \ BQ \cdot SQ = 2\,BQ^2 - BC^2\,;$$

$$\therefore \ \frac{SQ}{BQ} = 2 - \frac{BC^2}{BQ^2}$$

$$= 2 - \frac{2x^2}{x^2(4 + 2\sqrt{2})}$$

$$= 2 - \frac{1}{2 + \sqrt{2}}$$

$$= 2 - \frac{2 - \sqrt{2}}{4 - 2}$$

$$= \frac{4 - (2 - \sqrt{2})}{2}$$

$$= \frac{2 + \sqrt{2}}{2}.$$

(Q.E.D.)

11W3. Construct a " net " for the solid described in 11W1.

(Fig. 111.)

We have first to construct one face. This may be done with

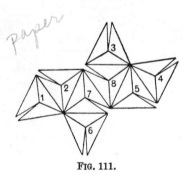

Paper

FIG. 111.

the help of the numerical result of 11W2, or as follows: Construct an isosceles triangle with the base and one side equal respectively to sides of a regular octagon and a square inscribed in the same circle (c.f. ABCDEFGH and ACEG in Fig. 110). The vertical angle of this triangle is equal to each base angle of the required face.

One of these, joined to two others along its shorter sides, forms a net of the oblique faces of one of the triangular pyramids whose bases are the faces of the inscribed regular octahedron. Each face, therefore, in the net of Fig. 99, has to be replaced by one of these subordinate, three-faced nets, which may be similarly numbered.

(Q.E.F.)

11W4. Show that the size and shape of any pyramid are uniquely determined by the lengths of its edges and the order of their arrangement.

(Fig. 112.)

Let V be the vertex, VN the altitude, and $A_1A_2A_3 \ldots A_n$ the base of any pyramid, and let the length of each edge be given.

Let $VP_1 \perp A_1A_2$, $VP_2 \perp A_2A_3$, and so on.

Then $A_1A_2 \perp VP_1$ and VN ;

$\therefore A_1A_2 \perp P_1N$, and so on. (4T1)

Also the lengths of VP_1, $VP_2 \ldots$ are determined, as they are altitudes of triangles whose sides are given.

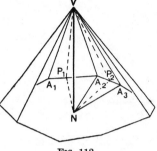

FIG. 112.

If possible, let VN increase, in response to some change in the shape of the pyramid.

As $P_1N^2 = VP_1^2 - VN^2$, it follows that P_1N decreases ;

$\therefore$ angles P_1A_1N, P_1A_2N decrease ;

$\therefore$ angle A_1NA_2 increases.

Similarly it may be proved that every angle at N increases.

But this is impossible, as their sum is equal to four right angles ;

$\therefore$ VN cannot increase ; and in the same way it can be proved that it cannot decrease ;

$\therefore$ the length of VN is constant.

But $A_1N^2 = A_1V^2 - VN^2$;

$\therefore A_1N$ is determined.

It follows that the sides of the triangles A_1NA_2, A_2NA_3, $\ldots$ are determined.

$\therefore$ the angles of the base of the pyramid are determined, and also the position of the foot of the perpendicular from the vertex, and the altitude.

$\therefore$ the shape and size of the pyramid are uniquely determined. (Q.E.D.)

11W5. The plane of the paper cuts three mutually perpendicular axes in the points X, Y, Z. O′ is their common point, and O is its projection on

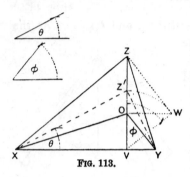

the paper. Given θ, the inclination of O′X to XY, and ϕ, the dihedral angle between plane O′XY and the paper, construct OX, OY, OZ, and rabat O′ about YZ, ZX, XY to X′, Y′, Z′ respectively. (Fig. 113.)

Rabat O′XY to Z′XY, making $Y\hat{X}Z' = \theta$, and $X\hat{Z}'Y = 90°$. Draw Z′V $\perp$ XY.

FIG. 113.

As shown in the discussion of Pictorial Representation, Z′ lies on OZ ;

$$\therefore \ XY \perp \text{plane } Z'VO'.$$

Rabat Z′VO′ to Z′VW, making $Z'\hat{V}W = \phi$, and VW = VZ′. Draw WZ $\perp$ VW cutting VZ′ produced in Z, and draw WO $\perp$ VZ.

(Q.E.F. (i).)

As X′, Y′, Z′ are all rabatments of the same point O′, XY′ = XZ′, and YX′ = YZ′ ; hence arcs through Z′ with centres X, Y cut OY, OX in Y′, X′ respectively. (Q.E.F. (ii).)

EXAMPLES 11A

11A1-5. New figures may be obtained by cutting the corners from known solids, which are then said to be " truncated ". Let every corner so removed be a pyramid with each slant edge of length x, and let a be the length of each edge of the original solid.

Find, by distorted representation, or by means of a rough sketch, the number and shapes of the faces of the new figure obtained from each of the following solids in the two cases where (i) $x = \frac{1}{2}a$, (ii) $x < \frac{1}{2}a$.

(11A1) Regular tetrahedron.
(11A2) Cube.
(11A3) Regular octahedron.
(11A4) Regular dodecahedron.
(11A5) Regular Icosahedron.

11A6. Tabulate the numbers of vertices, faces, and edges in the series of pyramids having 4, 5, 6, ... n vertices. (Cf. 1W4.)

11A7. Tabulate the numbers of vertices, faces, and edges in the series of prisms having 6, 8, 10, ... $2n$ vertices.

11A8. How many differently shaped pyramids have all their edges equal ?

11A9. Tabulate the numbers of vertices, faces, and edges in the solids obtained by cutting the corners from the series of pyramids having 4, 5, 6, ... n vertices, so that every edge is bisected.

11A10. Tabulate the numbers of vertices, faces, and edges in the solids obtained by cutting the corners from the series of prisms having 6, 8, 10, ... $2n$ vertices, so that every edge is bisected.

11A11. Show that the centres of the faces of every regular solid are vertices of a regular solid.

11A12. Show that only two *new* solids have their vertices at the middle points of the edges of the five regular solids.

11A13. Show that a regular tetrahedron can be inscribed in a cube so that each edge of the former lies in one face of the latter.

11A14. Show that a regular tetrahedron can be inscribed. in a regular octahedron with each vertex of the former at the centre of one face of the latter.

11A15. Show that the lengths of the edges of the tetrahedron and octahedron in 11A14 are in the ratio 2 : 3.

11A16. Tabulate the number of vertices, faces, and edges in the solids formed by constructing pyramids on the faces of the five regular solids.

11A17. Draw the plan and elevation of a cube with one edge vertical and in the plane of the paper, and the faces adjacent to this edge inclined to the paper at angles of 60° and 30°.

11A18. With the help of the figure of 11A17, draw the plan and elevation of the figure obtained by cutting off the corners of the cube by planes bisecting its edges.

11A19. Construct the axes for a pictorial representation, such that plane OXY is at an angle of 80° to the paper, and angle OXY *represents* an angle of 40°.

11A20. Construct the pictorial representation of a cube with its edges parallel to the axes of 11A19.

11A21. With the help of 11A20, construct the pictorial representation of the solid formed by constructing pyramids on the faces of the cube so that all the vertices are at the same distance from the centre.

11A22. If the axes in a pictorial representation are equally inclined to one another, show that the plane of the paper cuts off equal intercepts from the actual axes.

11A23. Repeat 11A9, with the edges trisected, and the cuts not overlapping.

11A24. If two faces of a prism are rectangles, and not parallel to one another, prove that all but two of the faces must be rectangles.

EXAMPLES 11B

11B1. Find the distance between two opposite edges of a regular tetrahedron, if a is the length of an edge.

11B2. Find the distance between two opposite faces of a regular octahedron, a being the length of an edge.

11B3. Show, by means of the two methods of distorted representation, or by means of a rough sketch, that two equal regular tetrahedra may be constructed with corresponding edges bisecting each other at right angles.

11B4. Find what solid has its vertices at the vertices of two regular tetrahedra whose edges bisect one another at right angles.

11B5. Describe the figure common to the two tetrahedra of 11B3. (Give the number of edges, and the number and shapes of vertices and faces.)

11B6. Show by means of a rough sketch, or by means of the two methods of distorted representation, that every edge of a cube can be bisected at right angles by one edge of another regular solid.

11B7. Describe the figure common to the two interpenetrating solids of 11B6.

11B8. Describe the solid whose vertices coincide with those of the two interpenetrating solids of 11B6.

11B9. Show that every edge of a regular dodecahedron can be bisected at right angles by one edge of another regular solid.

11B10. Describe the figure common to the two solids of 11B9.

11B11. Describe the figure whose vertices are those of the two solids of 11B9.

11B12. Show, by means of distorted representation, that a cube can be inscribed in a regular icosahedron, so that each vertex of the cube is at the centre of a face of the icosahedron.

11B13. Show that a regular dodecahedron can be inscribed in a cube, so that there is one edge of the dodecahedron in each face of the cube, parallel to two edges, and half-way between them.

11B14. Show that a cube can be inscribed in a regular dodecahedron, so that each vertex of the former coincides with one vertex of the latter.

11B15. Show that a regular icosahedron can be inscribed in a cube, so that one edge of the former lies in each face of the latter.

11B16. If ABCDEF is a regular plane hexagon, and ACEG a regular tetrahedron, find the ratio of AB to AG.

11B17. If one of the base angles of an isosceles triangle is equal to the angle AGB in 11B15, find the ratios of its three sides.

11B18. Tetrahedra are constructed on the faces of a regular tetrahedron so as to form a new solid with all its solid angles regular. Prove that its faces are congruent isosceles triangles.

11B19. Find the ratio of two unequal edges of the solid of 11B18.

11B20. Find the ratio of the total length of the longer edges of the solid of 11B18 to that of the shorter edges.

11B21. Find by construction the mutual inclination of the axes of a pictorial representation, given that their inclinations to the plane of the paper are $84° 20'$, $37°$, and $43°$.

11B22. If three mutually perpendicular axes are inclined at angles ξ, η, ζ to the plane of the paper, show that the mutual inclinations of their projections are the supplements of the angles of a triangle whose sides are of lengths $\sqrt{(\operatorname{cosec}^2\eta + \operatorname{cosec}^2\zeta)}$, etc.

11B23. Given the points X, Y, Z, where the paper is cut by three mutually perpendicular axes O'X, O'Y, O'Z, show how to find the inclinations of these lines to the plane of the paper.

11B24. If α, β, γ are the mutual inclinations of the axes in a pictorial representation, show that their inclinations to the plane of the paper are equal to

$$\cos^{-1}\sqrt{\frac{-\cos\alpha}{\sin\beta\sin\gamma}}, \text{ etc.}$$

11B25. Given five points A, B, C, D, E, in pictorial representation, find the point of intersection of the straight line AB with the plane CDE.

11B26. Given, in pictorial representation, the points A, B, C on the axes OX, OY, OZ respectively, these being equally inclined to one another, construct the normal from O to the plane ABC.

11B27. Given any two straight lines in pictorial representation, cut off from one a part equal to the other.

11B28. Construct the bisector of the angle between any two intersecting straight lines in pictorial representation.

11B29. Given the pictorial representation of a straight line, and the centre and radius of a sphere, find their two points of intersection.

11B30. A polyhedron has f faces, e edges, and v vertices. If every edge is bevelled (i.e. cut off by a plane parallel to itself), leaving a new figure with F faces, E edges, and V vertices, find expressions for F, E and V in terms of f, e, v.

11B31. Find expressions for F, E and V if the polyhedron of 11B30 is not *bevelled*, but *truncated* as in 11A1-5.

EXAMPLES 11C

11C1. Show that there exists a solid bounded by congruent rhombuses, and having some solid angles bounded by three obtuse angles, and the rest by four acute angles.

11C2. Find the ratio of the diagonals of a rhombus in 11C1.

11C3. Find the volume of the solid in 11C1, if a is the length of an edge.

11C4. Show that there exists a solid bounded by squares and equilateral triangles, and such that each square is adjacent to four triangles, and each triangle is adjacent to three squares.

11C5. Find the volume of the solid in 11C4, if a is the length of an edge.

11C6. Show that there exists a solid bounded by equilateral triangles and regular octagons, so that each triangle is adjacent to three octagons, and each octagon to four triangles and four other octagons on alternate sides.

11C7. Find the volume of the solid in 11C6, if a is the length of an edge.

11C8. Show that there exists a solid bounded by squares and hexagons, such that two hexagons and one square meet at every vertex.

11C9. Find the volume of the solid in 11C8, if a is the length of an edge.

11C10. Show that a solid can be constructed with its surface consisting of thirty congruent rhombuses, the long diagonals of which form the edges of a regular dodecahedron.

11C11. Show that the solid in 11C10 is the part common to five interpenetrating cubes.

11C12. Show that the lengths of the edges of the cube and icosahedron in 11B15 are in the ratio $2 : \sqrt{5} - 1$.

11C13. Given that the ratio of the length of the diagonal of a regular pentagon to that of the base is as $\sqrt{5} + 1 : 2$, prove that the ratio of the length of the edge of the cube in 11B13 to that of the edge of the inscribed dodecahedron is as $\sqrt{5} + 3 : 2$.

11C14. If ABC is a face of a regular icosahedron, and D, E, F are vertices of the adjacent faces, show that the plane DEF divides the remaining edges at A, B, C in the same ratio as that in which the diagonals of a regular pentagon divide one another.

11C15. Construct the section DEF (11C14).

11C16. Show that there exists a solid bounded by congruent isosceles triangles with their base angles grouped in sixes at some vertices, and their vertical angles grouped in threes at the remaining vertices.

11C17. If all the solid angles in the figure of 11C16 are regular, show that the ratio of the lengths of two unequal edges is as $3 : 5$.

11C18. Show that there exists a solid bounded by congruent isosceles triangles with their base angles grouped in sixes at some vertices, and their vertical angles grouped in fours at the remaining vertices.

11C19. If all the solid angles in the figure of 11C18 are regular, show that the ratio of the lengths of any pair of unequal edges is as $3 : 4$.

11C20. Show that there exists a solid bounded by congruent rhombuses and having four of its solid angles bounded each by one obtuse and three acute angles, and each of the others either by three obtuse, or by four acute, or by two obtuse angles and one acute.

11C21. Show that the ratio of the diagonals of each rhombus in 11C20 is as $2 : \sqrt{5}+1$.

11C22. Prove that a polyhedron, consisting of eight equilateral triangles arranged four at each vertex, must have three equal diagonals bisecting one another at right angles.

11C23. Show that the shape of the base of a pyramid is determined if the base angles of the other faces are given.

11C24. Show that, if two vertices of a solid figure are equidistant from the remaining vertices, and if the lengths and order of all the edges are given, then the shape and size of the figure are fully determined.

11C25. ABCDE is a regular pentagon with the vertices C, E on opposite faces of a cube, the side AB in the centre of another face, and the vertex D in another. Without any assumption as to the ratio of the side of a regular pentagon to its diagonal, prove that the edge of the cube $=\dfrac{\sqrt{5}+1}{2}$ AB, thus establishing the ratio given in 11C13.

11C26. Show that A, B, C, D, E in 11C25 are vertices of a regular solid inscribed in the cube.

11C27. Show that a section of a rhombic dodecahedron mid-way between two opposite trihedral vertices is a regular polygon.

11C28. If each edge of a regular solid is of length a, and the corners are cut off by planes cutting each edge at a distance x from the vertex, where x is greater than $\frac{1}{2}a$, so that all the edges of the resulting solid are equal, show that

$$\frac{x}{a} = \frac{1}{2} \cdot \frac{1 + \cos \varphi \sin \theta}{\cos \varphi (\sin \varphi + \sin \theta)},$$

where 2φ and 2θ are the magnitudes of face- and dihedral-angles of the original solid.

11C29. Evaluate the ratio $x : a$ of 11C28 in the cases of a cube, a regular tetrahedron and a regular octahedron.

CHAPTER XII

SEMI-REGULAR AND STAR POLYHEDRA

DEF. : If, in a pair of definitions, or propositions, the words
" point ", " vertex ", " n-hedral angle ", can be interchanged
with the words " plane ", " face", " n-gon " respectively, each
definition or proposition is said to be the **dual** of the other,
and the existence of a dual pair is said to be an instance of the
principle of duality.

Thus the cube is the dual of the regular octahedron, the
former having 6 regular 4-gonal faces forming 8 regular 3-
hedral angles, and the latter 6 regular 4-hedral angles forming
8 regular 3-gonal faces. Similarly the regular dodecahedron is
the dual of the regular icosahedron, and the regular tetrahedron is self-dual.

DEF. : If all the faces of a polyhedron are regular, and all
its solid angles are congruent to one another, it is said to be
facially regular.

The dual of a facially regular polyhedron is, by the above
definition of duality, a **vertically regular polyhedron.**

By transposing the expressions " face " and "solid angle ",
we get the definition :

If all the solid angles of a polyhedron are regular, and all its
faces are congruent to one another, it is said to be **vertically regular.**

The term " **semi-regular** " may appropriately be applied to
both facially and vertically regular polyhedra ; but it is often
used exclusively of the former.

NOTATION : If a facially regular solid has at each vertex
p faces with a sides each, q with b sides, and so on, the solid

may be given the reference symbol $Fa_pb_qc_r\,...\,$. Thus a regular hexagonal prism, which has two squares and one hexagon at each vertex, has the reference symbol $F4_26_1$.

If every face of a vertically regular solid forms p a-hedral angles, q b-hedral, and so on, the solid can be distinguished by the reference symbol $Va_pb_qc_r\,...\,$.

Theorem 12T1

If at each vertex of a facially-regular solid there are m_3 3-gons, m_4 4-gons, m_5 5-gons, and so on, then the number of vertices

$$=v=\frac{4}{2-\tfrac{1}{3}m_3-\tfrac{2}{4}m_4-\tfrac{3}{5}m_5-...}.$$

Each solid angle has m_n n-gon face-angles, making $v\,.\,m_n$ in all ;

each n-gon has n of these ;

∴ the number of n-gons

$$=f_n=\frac{v\,.\,m_n}{n}\,;$$
$$\therefore\ f=f_3+f_4+f_5+...$$
$$=v\,(\tfrac{1}{3}m_3+\tfrac{1}{4}m_4+\tfrac{1}{5}m_5+...).$$

Each solid angle has $\varSigma m$ edges, making $v\,\varSigma m$ in all ; but each edge of the solid coincides with two of these ;

∴ the number of edges of the solid

$$=e=\tfrac{1}{2}v\,\varSigma m.$$

By Euler's Theorem,

$$v-e+f=2\,;\qquad\qquad\text{(11T1)}$$
$$\therefore\ 2-\left(\frac{2e}{v}-\frac{2f}{v}\right)=\frac{4}{v}\,;$$
$$\therefore\ 2-(\varSigma m-\tfrac{2}{3}m_3-\tfrac{2}{4}m_4-\tfrac{2}{5}m_5-...)=\frac{4}{v}\,;$$
$$\therefore\ 2-(\tfrac{3-2}{3}\,m_3-\tfrac{4-2}{4}\,m_4-\tfrac{5-2}{5}\,m_5-...)=\frac{4}{v}.$$

Hence the proposition. (Q.E.D.)

COROLLARY 1. $2 > \frac{1}{3}m_3 + \frac{2}{4}m_4 + \frac{3}{5}m_5 + \dots$.

COROLLARY 2.   A FACIALLY-REGULAR SOLID CANNOT HAVE MORE THAN FIVE FACES AT EACH VERTEX.   (For m_3 has the least coefficient, and, if $m_3 = 6$, $\frac{1}{3}m_3 = 2$.)

COROLLARY 3.   A FACIALLY-REGULAR SOLID CANNOT HAVE FACES OF MORE THAN THREE DIFFERENT SHAPES.   (For if there were four, there would exist four terms of the " m series " ; the least possible value of their sum $= \frac{1}{3} + \frac{1}{2} + \frac{3}{5} + \frac{2}{3} = 2\frac{1}{10}$.)

Theorem 12T2

If a certain polygon occurs only once or twice at each vertex of a facially-regular solid, the faces sharing edges with it must either be all of the same kind, or of two kinds alternating with one another.

If there were three or more faces congruent to one another at a vertex, they might not all occur in the same way ; for example, if the faces at a vertex were arranged $xxxy$, the middle x would be adjacent to two x's, while each of the others would be adjacent to one x and one y.

If, however, a polygon occurs only once or twice at a vertex, the faces that share edges with it at one vertex must appear in the same way at every vertex, since all the solid angles are congruent.

Hence these faces must be either all alike, or of two kinds attached to alternate sides.   (Q.E.D.)

COROLLARY 1.   IF THE GIVEN FACE HAS AN ODD NUMBER OF SIDES, THE FACES SHARING ITS EDGES MUST ALL BE CONGRUENT TO ONE ANOTHER.

COROLLARY 2.   IF TWO CONGRUENT FACES WITH AN ODD NUMBER OF SIDES HAVE A COMMON EDGE, THERE MUST BE AT LEAST THREE OF THEM AT EACH VERTEX, FOR EACH MUST SHARE ALL ITS EDGES WITH LIKE FACES.

COROLLARY 3. IF THERE ARE THREE FACES AT EACH VERTEX OF A FACIALLY-REGULAR SOLID, AND ONE OF THEM HAS AN ODD NUMBER OF SIDES, THE OTHERS ARE EITHER CONGRUENT TO IT (giving a *regular* solid), OR CONGRUENT TO ONE ANOTHER AND BOUNDED BY AN EVEN NUMBER OF SIDES.

COROLLARY 4. FACIALLY-REGULAR SOLIDS MAY BE CLASSIFIED AS FOLLOWS :

(1) the series of **regular prisms**, $F4_2n_1$;
(2) the series of **regular prismoids**, $F3_3n_1$;
(3) solids with **one odd** and **two even faces** at each vertex ;
(4) solids with **three even faces** at each vertex ;
(5) solids with **more than three faces** at each vertex.

Theorem 12T3

With the exception of prisms, there are not more than four facially-regular solids with one odd and two even faces at each vertex.

As prisms are excluded, $m_4 = 0$. $\hfill$ (12T2)

$$\therefore\ 2 > \tfrac{1}{3}m_3 + \tfrac{3}{5}m_5 + \dots . \hfill (12T1)$$

$\therefore$, if $m_3 = 1$, the other faces being even,

$$1\tfrac{2}{3} > \tfrac{2}{3}m_6 + \tfrac{3}{4}m_8 + \tfrac{4}{5}m_{10} + \tfrac{5}{6}m_{12} + \dots .$$

$$\therefore\ m_{12},\ m_{14},\ \text{etc., cannot} = 2 ;$$

$$\therefore\ \text{we are left with } F3_16_2,\ F3_18_2,\ F3_110_2.$$

If $m_5 = 1$, the other faces being even,

$$1\tfrac{2}{5} > \tfrac{2}{3}m_6 + \tfrac{3}{4}m_8 + \dots .$$

$$\therefore\ m_8,\ m_{10},\ \text{etc., cannot} = 2 ;$$

$$\therefore\ \text{we are left with } F5_16_2.$$

If $m_7 = 1$, $1\tfrac{2}{7} > \tfrac{2}{3}m_6 \dots$;

$$\therefore\ \text{no } m \text{ can} = 2.$$

Hence there are no other solids satisfying the conditions.

$\hfill$ (Q.E.D.)

Theorem 12T4

With the exception of prisms, there are not more than three facially-regular solids with three even faces at each vertex.

As odd faces are excluded,

$$2 > \tfrac{1}{2}m_4 + \tfrac{2}{3}m_6 + \tfrac{3}{4}m_8 + \tfrac{4}{5}m_{10} + \dots .$$

As prisms are excluded, m_4 cannot $= 2$.

If $m_6 = 2$, $\tfrac{2}{3} > \tfrac{1}{2}m_4 + \tfrac{3}{4}m_8 + \dots .$

$\therefore$ m_8, m_{10}, etc., cannot $= 1$;

$\therefore$ we are left with $F4_16_2$.

If $m_8 = 2$, $\tfrac{1}{2} > \tfrac{1}{2}m_4 + \tfrac{2}{3}m_6 + \dots .$

$\therefore$ no m can $= 1$.

If $m_4 = m_6 = 1$, $\tfrac{5}{6} > \tfrac{3}{4}m_8 + \tfrac{4}{5}m_{10} + \tfrac{5}{6}m_{12} + \dots .$

$\therefore$ m_{12}, m_{13}, etc., cannot $= 1$;

$\therefore$ we are left with $F4_16_18_1$, $F4_16_110_1$.

If $m_4 = m_8 = 1$, $\tfrac{3}{4} > \tfrac{4}{5}m_{10} + \dots .$

$\therefore$ no other m can $= 1$;

$\therefore$ there is no other solid satisfying the conditions.

(Q.E.D.)

Theorem 12T5

With the exception of prismoids, there are not more than seven facially-regular solids with more than three faces at each vertex.

There must be either 4 or 5 faces at each vertex, and they must be of either 2 or 3 kinds.   (12T1)

We therefore classify according to congruent faces.

$$2 > \tfrac{1}{3}m_3 + \tfrac{2}{4}m_4 + \tfrac{3}{5}m_5 + \tfrac{4}{6}m_6 + \dots . \qquad (12T1)$$

If $m_3 = 4$, $\frac{2}{3} > \frac{2}{4}m_4 + \frac{3}{5}m_5 + \ldots$.

$\therefore$ m_6, m_7, etc., cannot occur.

$\therefore$ we are left with $F3_44_1$, $F3_45_1$.

If $m_3 = 3$, $1 > \frac{2}{4}m_4 + \frac{3}{5}m_5 + \ldots$.

$\therefore$ no *two* m's can occur, and no m can occur twice ;

$\therefore$ we have only the series of prismoids, $F3_3n_1$.

If $m_3 = 2$,

the triangles cannot have a common edge ;   (12T2)

and the three faces adjacent to either of them are congruent to one another ;   (12T2)

$\therefore$ there is only one other type of face.

Also, $\frac{4}{3} > \frac{2}{4}m_4 + \frac{3}{5}m_5 + \frac{4}{6}m_6 + \ldots$.

$\therefore$ m_6, m_7, etc., cannot occur twice ;

$\therefore$ we are left with $F3_24_2$, $F3_25_2$.

If $m_4 = 3$, $\frac{1}{2} > \frac{1}{3}m_3 + \frac{3}{5}m_5 + \frac{4}{6}m_6 + \ldots$.

$\therefore$ m_5, m_6 cannot occur ;

$\therefore$ we are left with $F3_14_3$.

If $m_4 = 2$, and m_3 is not > 1,

$$1 > \frac{1}{3}m_3 + \frac{3}{5}m_5 + \frac{4}{6}m_6 + \ldots \, .$$

$\therefore$ m_3, m_5, m_6 cannot $= 2$, and m_3 and m_6 cannot both $= 1$ at the same time ;

$\therefore$ we are left with $F3_14_25_1$.

If $m_5 = 2$, and m_3 is not > 1,

$$\frac{4}{5} > \frac{1}{3}m_3 + \frac{2}{4}m_4 + \frac{4}{6}m_6 + \frac{5}{7}m_7 + \ldots \, .$$

$\therefore$ no m can $= 2$, and no two m's can $= 1$.

$\therefore$ there are no other solids satisfying the conditions.

(Q.E.D.)

COROLLARY : EXCLUDING PRISMS, PRISMOIDS, AND REGULAR SOLIDS, THERE ARE NOT MORE THAN THIRTEEN FACIALLY REGULAR SOLIDS.

From their reference symbols their numbers of vertices, edges, and faces of each kind may be calculated by means of the formulae

$$v = \frac{4}{2 - \frac{1}{3}m_3 - \frac{1}{2}m_4 - \frac{3}{5}m_5 - \frac{2}{3}m_6 - \ldots}, \qquad (12\text{T}1)$$

$$e = \tfrac{1}{2}v\, \Sigma m, \qquad (12\text{T}1)$$

$$f_n = \frac{v}{n}\, m_n, \qquad (12\text{T}1)$$

and
$$f = e + 2 - v. \qquad (11\text{T}1)$$

Reference Symbol.	f	v	e	f_3	f_4	f_5	f_6	f_8	f_{10}
$F3_3$	4	4	6	4					
$F3_4$	8	6	12	8					
$F3_5$	20	12	30	20					
$F4_3$	6	8	12		6				
$F5_3$	12	20	30			12			
$F3_1 6_2$	8	12	18	4			4		
$F3_1 8_2$	14	24	36	8				6	
$F3_1 10_2$	32	60	90	20					12
$F4_1 6_2$	14	24	36		6		8		
$F5_1 6_2$	32	60	90			12	20		
$F4_1 6_1 8_1$	26	48	72		12		8	6	
$F4_1 6_1 10_1$	62	120	180		30		20		12
$F3_4 4_1$	38	24	60	32	6				
$F3_4 5_1$	92	60	150	80		12			
$F3_2 4_2$	14	12	24	8	6				
$F3_2 5_2$	32	30	60	20		12			
$F3_1 4_3$	26	24	48	8	18				
$F3_1 4_2 5_1$	62	60	120	20	30	12			
$F3_3 n_1$	$2n+2$	$2n$	$4n$	$2n$		and $f_n=2$			
$F4_2 n_1$	$n+2$	$2n$	$3n$		n	and $f_n=2$			

NOTE : The only pyramid which satisfies the definition of either a facially or a vertically regular solid is the regular tetrahedron ; but a **pyramid** whose base is a regular polygon may be called **regular** if the other faces are *equilateral*, and **semi-regular** if they are *isosceles*.

Theorem 12T6

There exists a facially regular solid corresponding to every reference symbol in the table of 12T5. (Fig. 114.)

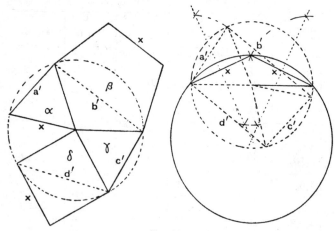

FIG. 114.

Let Fa_pb_q ... be any reference symbol in the table, and let $\alpha, \beta, \gamma, ...$ be the faces at one vertex, arranged in accordance with 12T2; e.g., for $F3_24_2$, α, γ would be triangles, and β, δ squares, like faces alternating.

Let x be the length of an edge of the solid, and let $a', b', c', ...$ be the distances between alternate vertices of $\alpha, \beta, \gamma, ...$ respectively.

By trial, or with the help of trigonometry, construct a cyclic polygon with sides equal to $a', b', c', ...$. On the diameter of its circumcircle, construct an isosceles triangle with two sides of length x. This is an axial section of the right cone circumscribing the given regular polyhedral angle, and its circum-circle is a great circle of the sphere circumscribing the solid.

For it is evident that this sphere is such that one set of concurrent edges corresponding to $Fa_p b_q$ ... may be inscribed in it. We may therefore imagine the polyhedron being built up, corner by corner, the set of polygons $\alpha, \beta, \gamma, ...$ being completed at every vertex of each preceding polygon.

As the network of faces grows, the unoccupied portion of the spherical surface diminishes, but as long as there is any space left, every corner will be congruent to each of the others. Hence the vacant space must ultimately reduce to a regular polygon completing the set of congruent solid angles at its vertices.

$\therefore$ every reference symbol in the table corresponds to an actual polyhedron.   (Q.E.D.)

COROLLARY 1. EVERY FACIALLY REGULAR SOLID CAN BE INSCRIBED IN A SPHERE.

COROLLARY 2. IN A FACIALLY REGULAR SOLID, VERTICES ADJACENT TO THE SAME VERTEX ARE COPLANAR AND CONCYCLIC, AND THEIR PLANE IS NORMAL TO THE LINE JOINING THE VERTEX TO THE CENTRE OF THE CIRCUMSCRIBED SPHERE.

Theorem 12T7

The dual of every facially regular solid exists.

The radius of the circumscribed sphere at any vertex is normal to the plane through the extremities of the edges that meet in that vertex.   (12T6)

$\therefore$ it is normal to the plane which bisects them.

$\therefore$ the plane which bisects the n edges at a vertex is cut by similar neighbouring planes in the sides of an n-gòn ; and all such n-gons are congruent to one another, and form regular polyhedral angles in front of the regular polygonal faces of the original solid.

∴ the planes which bisect concurrent edges of Fa_pb_q ... form the faces of Va_pb_q ... .   (Q.E.D.)

COROLLARY 1. EVERY VERTICALLY REGULAR POLYHEDRON MAY BE CIRCUMSCRIBED ABOUT A SPHERE.

COROLLARY 2. IN A VERTICALLY REGULAR POLYHEDRON, FACES ADJACENT TO A GIVEN FACE ARE CONCURRENT IN THE NORMAL TO THE GIVEN FACE FROM THE CENTRE OF THE IN-SCRIBED SPHERE ; for they meet the inscribed sphere at points on a circle, and, ∴, touch the tangent cone through this circle along a set of generators.

COROLLARY 3. THE POINTS OF CONTACT OF A VERTICALLY REGULAR POLYHEDRON WITH ITS INSCRIBED SPHERE ARE THE VERTICES OF A FACIALLY REGULAR SOLID ; for every polyhedral angle is regular, ∴ its faces touch the inscribed sphere at the vertices of a regular polygon ; and, all the faces of the orginal figure being congruent, these polygons meet in congruent solid angles.

COROLLARY 4. EVERY VERTICALLY REGULAR SOLID IS THE DUAL OF ONE OF THE FACIALLY REGULAR SOLIDS IN THE TABLE OF 12T5 ; for, by Cor. 3, every vertically regular solid touches its inscribed sphere in the faces of its dual ; and its dual is a facially regular solid ; and every possible facially regular solid is included in the table.

Theorem 12T8

Any dual pair of semi-regular solids can be so placed, with a common centre, that every two corresponding edges are at right angles to one another and to the common radius by which they are intersected.   (Fig. 115.)

Let O be the common centre, XY any edge of the facially regular solid, C its middle point, and A, B ; D, E the middle points of other edges at X, Y respectively.

Planes ABC, CDE are perpendicular to OX, OY respectively, and intersect in PCQ, one of the edges of a dual of the given facially regular solid.   (12T7)

∴ CP⊥plane OXY ;   (5T4)

∴ CP⊥OC and XY.

Also OX = OY ;

∴ OC⊥XY.

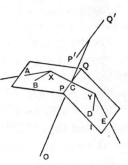

FIG. 115.

But CP is one of the edges of the vertically regular solid ; and any similar solid, similarly placed with the same centre, will have an edge P'Q' parallel to CP and intersecting the radius OC.

∴ P'Q'⊥OC and XY, and OC⊥XY.

(Q.E.D.)

COROLLARY 1. EVERY SEMI-REGULAR SOLID HAS THE SAME NUMBER OF EDGES AS ITS DUAL.

This also follows directly from the definition of duality ; for an edge can be regarded either as the straight line joining two vertices, or as the line of intersection of two faces.

COROLLARY 2. ANY EDGE OF A FACIALLY REGULAR SOLID SUBTENDS AT THE CENTRE AN ANGLE WHICH IS SUPPLEMENTARY TO ANY DIHEDRAL ANGLE OF THE DUAL (vertically regular) SOLID.

COROLLARY 3. THE EDGES OF ANY VERTICALLY REGULAR SOLID ARE TANGENTS TO A SPHERE CONCENTRIC WITH THAT WHICH TOUCHES THE FACES.

STAR POLYGONS, STAR POLYHEDRAL ANGLES, AND STAR POLYHEDRA

DEF. : The straight lines joining alternate vertices of a regular polygon form the sides of a **star polygon,** whose vertices coincide with those of the original polygon.

The two points in which each side crosses two others are not vertices, but **diagonal points** of the star polygon, and correspond to the points in which non-adjacent sides of an ordinary regular polygon meet when produced.

It is easy to see that a star polygon must have at least five sides, and that, if every side of a regular polygon is produced till it meets the alternate side on either hand, a star polygon is formed.

DEF. : The angles between alternate edges of a regular polyhedral angle form the face angles of a **star polyhedral angle.**

The edges of the star polyhedral angle coincide with those of the original angle, and the lines in which the planes of the face angles of the star polyhedral angle cross one another are **diagonal edges,** corresponding to the lines in which the planes of non-adjacent face angles of an ordinary regular polyhedral angle meet when produced.

A star polyhedral angle must have at least five edges, and, if the plane of every face angle of a regular polyhedral angle is produced until it meets that of the alternate face angle on either hand, a star polyhedral angle is formed.

DEF. : A set of congruent regular star polygons whose angles form the face angles of regular polyhedral angles is called a **star-faced polyhedron.**

A set of congruent regular polygons whose angles form the face angles of regular star polyhedral angles is called a **star-pointed polyhedron.**

Star-faced and star-pointed polyhedra are both called **star polyhedra.**

Theorem 12T9

There are only two regular star-faced polyhedra.

(Fig. 116.)

Suppose that there are m star n-gons at each vertex; i.e., suppose that SFn_m exists, where SF stands for *star-faced*.

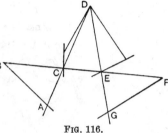

FIG. 116.

Let ABCDEF... be a face, B, D, F being consecutive vertices, and A, C, E the diagonal points alternating with them, so that ACE ... is the inscribed n-gon.

The m triangles, like CDE, at each vertex, are oblique faces of m-gonal pyramids.

If these were all removed, we should have a regular polyhedron with each face an m-gon, and its edges also forming

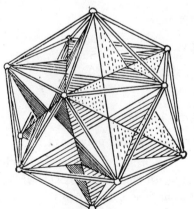

FIG. 117.—SF5$_5$, GREAT DODECAHEDRON.

regular n-gons like ACE ... .

A star polygon must have at least 5 sides; and the only regular polyhedra whose edges form regular polygons (as faces or sections) with more than 4 sides are the dodecahedron and the icosahedron, which give pentagons only.

The former makes $m=5$, and the latter makes $m=3$.

∴ the only star-faced polyhedra have the reference symbols SF5$_5$, SF5$_3$. (Figs. 117, 118.)   (Q.E.D.)

COROLLARY 1. In each case the faces are obtained by producing the edges of twelve regular pentagons;

∴ THE STAR-FACED POLYHEDRA HAVE TWELVE STAR-PENTAGONAL FACES EACH.

COROLLARY 2. IN EACH CASE THERE ARE AS MANY EDGES AS IN A REGULAR DODECAHEDRON OR ICOSAHEDRON ; i.e., 30.

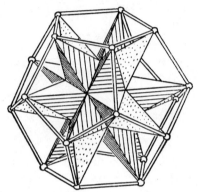

FIG. 118.—SF5₃, GREAT STELLATED DODECAHEDRON.

COROLLARY 3. The identity

$$f = \frac{v \cdot m}{n}, \text{ (12T1), gives } 12 = \frac{v \cdot m}{5},$$

whence SF5₅ HAS **12** VERTICES, AND SF5₃ HAS **20**.

Theorem 12T10

There are only two regular star-pointed polyhedra.

Suppose that there are m star n-hedral angles to each regular polygonal face; i.e., suppose that SPn_m exists, where SP stands for star-pointed. (Each face is an m-gon.)

Let α, β, γ be the planes of the faces at any vertex.

They will meet π, the plane of the vertices adjacent to it, in the sides of a star n-gon.

∴ the vertices adjacent to any vertex are vertices of a **regular n-gon,** where n must be at least 5.

∴ the vertices are vertices of a regular polyhedron, which must, therefore, be an icosahedron, as the vertices of a pentagon formed by edges of a regular dodecahedron are not equidistant from the same vertex.

Two vertices of a regular icosahedron are equidistant from the vertices of a given pentagon formed by its edges ; they are at the extremities of the diagonal normal to the plane of the pentagon.

The inscribed star-pentagon subtends star-pentahedral angles at both these vertices.

Choosing the nearer vertex, we get a star-pointed polyhedron with pentagonal faces ; if the farther vertex is chosen, the faces of the star-pointed polyhedron are equilateral triangles.

∴ the only star-pointed polyhedra have the reference symbols SP5$_5$, SP5$_3$. (Figs. 119, 120.)   (Q.E.D.)

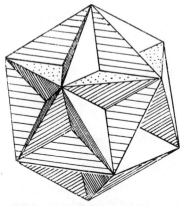

FIG. 119.—SP5$_5$, SMALL STELLATED DODECAHEDRON.

FIG. 120.—SP5$_3$, GREAT ICOSAHEDRON.

COROLLARY 1. IN EACH CASE THE VERTICES ARE THOSE OF A REGULAR ICOSAHEDRON, AND, ∴, 12 IN NUMBER.

COROLLARY 2. There are five edges at each vertex, but each edge serves two vertices ; ∴, IN EACH CASE THE NUMBER OF EDGES $= \frac{5}{2} . 12 = 30$.

COROLLARY 3. The *dual* of the identity of 12T1 is

$$v = \frac{f \cdot m}{n}, \text{ and gives } 12 = \frac{f \cdot m}{5},$$

whence SP5$_5$ HAS TWELVE FACES, AND SP5$_3$ HAS 20.

WORKED EXAMPLES

12W1. Discuss the facially regular solid F3$_2$5$_2$.

By calculation, $v = 30$, $e = 60$, $f_3 = 20$, and $f_5 = 12$.　　(12T5)
We notice that $f_5 = 12 = f$ for a regular dodecahedron ; and that $v = 30 = e$ for a regular dodecahedron.

∴ we have to construct pentagons on the faces of a regular dodecahedron, and fill in the intervals with equilateral triangles, and, at the same time, place one vertex of the new figure on each edge of the old.

∴ the vertices of F3$_2$5$_2$ must be the middle points of the edges of a regular dodecahedron. (See 12W7, p. 180.)

12W2. Discuss the facially regular solid F5$_1$6$_2$.

By calculation, $f_5 = 12 = f$ for a regular dodecahedron ; $f_6 = 20 = v$ for a dodecahedron ; and $v = 60 = 2e$ for a dodeca-hedron.　　(12T5)

∴ we have to construct pentagons on the faces of a regular dodecahedron, and fill in the intervals with regular hexagons so that there are two hexagons and one pentagon at each vertex. Clearly, the hexagons must have alternate edges in common, and pentagons on adjacent faces of the dodecahedron cannot have common vertices. ∴ the pentagons must be smaller than those of the figure of 12W1, having their vertices on the lines joining the centres of the dodecahedron faces to the middle points of their sides.

Experiment with a distorted representation confirms this reasoning.

12W3. Discuss the facially regular solid F3₄4₁. (Fig. 121.)

By calculation, $f_4 = 6 = f$ for a cube; and $f_3 = 32 = 4v = v + 2e$ for a cube.   (12T5)

FIG. 121.

∴ we have to arrange one square on each face of a cube, and fill in the intervals with one equilateral triangle at each vertex and two across each edge.

Experiment with a distorted representation shows that this is impossible if the sides of the squares are parallel to the sides or diagonals of the cube-faces.

We accordingly give the squares all a right-hand (or all a left-hand) twist, so that their vertices fall at the extremities of similar " **swastika** " devices : $\left(\begin{array}{c}\llcorner\ulcorner\\\urcorner\lrcorner\end{array}\text{ or }\begin{array}{c}\ulcorner\urcorner\\\llcorner\lrcorner\end{array}\right).$

Two distinct solids are possible ; for, if ABC be any corner triangle, and P, Q, R the remaining vertices of the adjacent triangles, the three squares adjacent to them may be attached either to PB, RA, QC, or to PC, QA, RB.

Each polyhedron may thus be regarded as the other turned inside out.   Such left- and right-handed pairs are said to be **enantiomorphous** (Gr. *enantios* = opposite).

These solids are called **snub cubes.**

12W4. Calculate the positions of the vertices of F3₄4₁ on the faces of its circumscribed cube. (Fig. 122.)

Let $2a$ be the length of a cube-edge, and b, c the lengths of a leg and a foot of a swastika.

Let PQR be a face of the snub cube, Q and R being in the same cube-face.

Then
$$PQ^2 = (2c)^2 + 2(a-b)^2$$
$$= 2(2c^2 + a^2 + b^2 - 2ab) \, ;$$
$$QR^2 = (b+c)^2 + (b-c)^2$$
$$= 2(b^2 + c^2) \, ;$$
$$RP^2 = (b-c)^2 + (a-c)^2 + (a-b)^2$$
$$= 2(a^2 + b^2 + c^2 - bc - ca - ab).$$

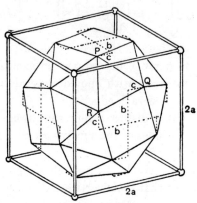

FIG. 122.—Snub Cube (F3₄4₁) inscribed in Cube (F4₃).

As $PQ^2 - QR^2 = 0$,
$$\therefore \; c^2 + a^2 - 2ab = 0 \, ;$$
$$\therefore \; c^2 = a(2b - a).$$

As $RP^2 - QR^2 = 0$,
$$\therefore \; a^2 - bc - ca - ab = 0 \, ;$$
$$\therefore \; c = \frac{a(a-b)}{a+b} \, ;$$
$$\therefore \; a(2b - a) = \frac{a^2(a-b)^2}{(a+b)^2}.$$

Cross-multiplying and simplifying, we get
$$x^3 + x^2 + x - 1 = 0,$$
where $x = \dfrac{b}{a}$.

An approximate solution may be found by trial as shown in the following table :

x	0	1	·5	·6	·55	·54
x^2	0	1	·25	·36	·3025	·2916
x^3	0	1	·125	·216	·1664	·1575
$x^3 + x^2 + x$	0	3	·875	1·176	1·0189	·9891

Explanation of the tabular solution :

For x to be equal to a root, $x^3 + x^2 + x$ must be equal to 1. We find that a root lies between 0 and 1, and try $x = ·5$. This gives rather too small a total, so we try ·6. This being found too large, we try ·55. A further trial shows that the root lies between ·54 and ·55.

This result is sufficiently accurate to enable us to draw the solid. It is, of course, capable of extension, but if several places of deci-mals were re-quired it would be better to em-ploy Horner's Method, to be found in books on the Theory of Equations.

We can now calculate c from the equation

$$c = a \cdot \frac{a - b}{a + b}.$$

It is found to be ·29a approx.

(Q.E.F.)

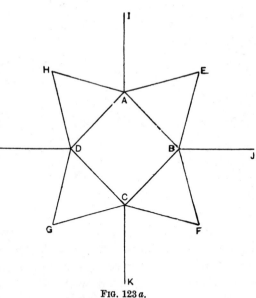

FIG. 123 a.

12W5. Devise a purely graphical method of constructing a face of a snub cube together with the coplanar face of its circumscribed cube, one side of the former being given. (Figs. 123 a, b, c, d.)

Let ABCD be any square face of the snub cube, E, F, G, H the vertices of the triangles on AB, BC, CD, DA, and I, J, K, L the extremities of the remaining edges at A, B, C, D. (Fig. 123 a.)

Draw the faces at A laid out in a plane (Fig. 123 b, dotted lines and dashed letters). By trial, draw a concentric circle in which can be inscribed the polygon DHIEB. (Cf. 12T6.)

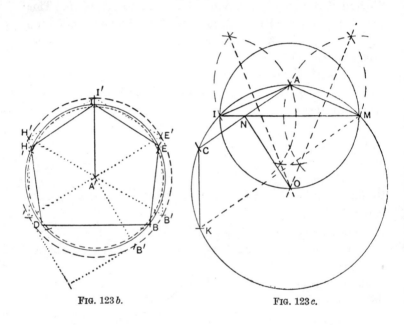

FIG. 123 b.　　　　　FIG. 123 c.

In a new figure (Fig. 123 c), draw the diameter IM of this circle, and find A, so that MA = IA = the true length of IA.

The circum-circle of triangle AIM is a great circle of the circumscribed sphere; in it draw the chords AC, CK, and ON, the perpendicular from the centre to AC. Then ON is equal to half the height of the cube.

Draw the cube-face PQRS (Fig. 123 d) and, using its centre, T, and radius = $\frac{1}{2}$IK (= $\frac{1}{2}$MK in Fig. 123 c), describe a circle cutting

PQ, RS at the ends of a diameter UV (as well as in the ends of another diameter).

Then U, V are the projections on PQRS of I, K, which are on faces adjacent to it and opposite to one another.

∴ AC lies in UV, and is bisected at T.

The square ABCD may now be drawn.

(Q.E.F.)

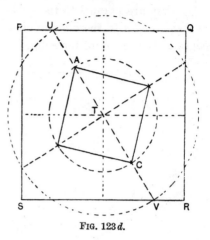

Fig. 123 d.

12W6. Show that there are just two vertically regular solids bounded by rhombuses.

The angles of a rhombus are alternately acute and obtuse ; and the solid angles of a vertically regular solid are regular ;

∴ each face must form 2 acute-angled, and 2 obtuse-angled solid angles.

The face angles at a vertex must together be less than 360°.

(6T3)

∴ obtuse-angled solid angles must be trihedral.

∴ every vertically regular solid bounded by rhombuses must have a reference symbol of the form $V3_2a_2$.

∴ their duals are given by $F3_2a_2$.

Reference to the table of 12T5 shows that the only facially regular solids with reference symbols of this form are $F3_24_2$ and $F3_25_2$.

∴ the only vertically regular solids bounded by rhombuses are $V3_24_2$, $V3_25_2$. (The former is the rhombic dodecahedron.) (Cf. Fig. 106.)   (Q.E.D.)

12W7. Construct one face of the solid V3₂5₂.   (Fig. 124.)

This is the dual of F3₂5₂, whose vertices are the middle points of the edges of a regular dodecahedron.   (12W1)

The faces of V3₂5₂ bisect the edges of F3₂5₂ ;

∴ they are parallel to the edges of the dodecahedron, and at right angles to the lines joining the middle points of those edges to the centre of the solid.   (12T8)

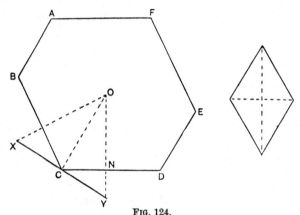

FIG. 124.

∴ the edges of the dodecahedron are themselves the short diagonals of the faces of a similar concentric V3₂5₂.

To find the length of a long diagonal, take a central section ABCDEF containing any two opposite edges AB, DE, and bisecting two other edges at C and F. (The section can be copied from Fig. 100.)

Draw perpendiculars from the centre, O, to BC, CD, and let them meet the line through C at right angles to OC in the points X, Y.

Then XY is the long diagonal of a rhombus whose plane is at right angles to that of the paper.

The required face may now be constructed with diagonals, equal to AB, XY, bisecting one another at right angles.

(Q.E.D.)

12W8. Show that the pentagonal faces of the facially regular solid F3₄5₁ lie on the faces of a regular dodecahedron, and construct a pair of concentric pentagons to show the arrangement. (Figs. 125 a, b.)

Proceeding as in 12W3, we find that the vertices of F3₄5₁ lie on the faces of a regular dodecahedron at the extremities of

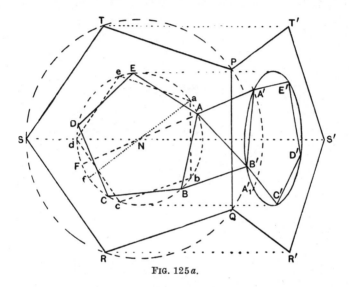

FIG. 125 a.

five-legged swastikas. It is therefore called a snub dodeca-hedron, and exists, like the snub cube, in two enantiomorphous forms.

Draw a regular pentagon *abcde* (Fig. 125 a), equal to any face of the snub dodecahedron ; and let *af* be a diameter of its circumscribed circle.

As in 12W5, we obtain the circle through vertices B, E, G, A″, B″, adjacent to a given vertex A (Fig. 125 b), and, by rabatting A about the diameter A″M, we construct the great circle A″AM of the circumscribed dodecahedron, and place in it a chord AF = *af*. Its distance, ON, from the centre, is half of the height of the circumscribed dodecahedron.

From Fig. 124 we get the ratio of the altitude of a regular dodecahedron to the radius of the circle circumscribing one of its faces ; it is the ratio 2 ON : ND.

Hence, concentric with *abcde*, we can construct a face PQRST of the dodecahedron, together with its circumscribed circle, and

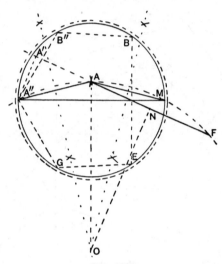

FIG. 125 *b*.

PQR'S'T', A'B'C'D'E', the projections of an adjacent face, and of the circle circumscribing the corresponding face A″B″C″D″E″ of the snub dodecahedron.

To find the position of A' on the ellipse A'B'C'D'E' (Fig. *a*), we describe an arc with centre N and radius equal to NA' (Fig. *b*), where A' is the projection of A″ on FA produced.

This gives two points, A', A_1', which are projections of vertices of the two enantiomorphous snub dodecahedra that can be inscribed in the regular dodecahedron.

Then NA' cuts the circle *abcde* in the point A, and the face ABCDE can be drawn in its proper position on the face PQRST.

(Q.E.F.)

12W9. Construct a pictorial representation of a snub dodecahedron.

(Figs. 126, 127.)

Construct a single face ABCDE of the snub dodecahedron, inscribed in the corresponding face PQRST of a circumscribed regular dodecahedron.   (12W8 ; Fig. 126 *a*.)

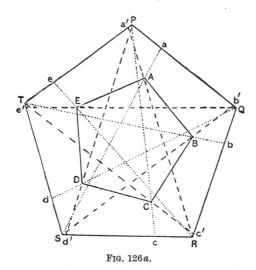

FIG. 126*a*.

Let straight lines joining each vertex of ABCDE to the two farthest vertices of PQRST meet the opposite sides of the latter in the two sets of points *a*, *b*, *c*, *d*, *e* and *a'*, *b'*, *c'*, *d'*, *e'* respectively.

Construct a pictorial representation of a regular dodecahedron, showing all the faces, both front and back.   (For sake of clearness in indicating the method followed, only a few faces are treated in Fig. 126 *b*.)

Divide each edge in the ratios P*a* : *a*Q, P*b'* : *b'*Q, measuring from each end in turn so as to obtain four points of division. (If a slide rule is available, this may be done most expeditiously by calculation and measurement ; otherwise graphical methods may be employed in a subsidiary diagram.)

On every face in turn construct the two sets of lines corresponding to SA*a* and RA*a'* in Fig. 126 *a*, and obtain the pentagonal faces of the snub dodecahedron by joining up the proper

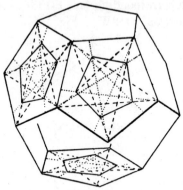

FIG. 126 *b*.

points of intersection. (Notice that the rear faces appear to be left-handed ; e.g., the *base* in Fig. 126 *b*.)

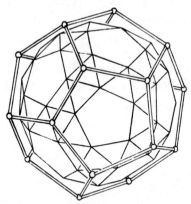

FIG. 127.—SNUB DODECAHEDRON (F3$_4$5$_1$) INSCRIBED IN REGULAR
DODECAHEDRON (F5$_3$).

Fig. 127 shows the snub dodecahedron as a solid figure, and the regular dodecahedron as a framework of rods.

(Q.E.F.)

TABLE OF COMMON NAMES OF SEMI-REGULAR AND STAR POLYHEDRA

("C.F." refers to the Table of Cubic Forms, pp. 242-245.)

$F3_16_2$	Truncated Tetrahedron.	(C.F. 9.)
$F3_18_2$	,, Cube.	(C.F. 8.)
$F3_110_2$	,, Dodecahedron.	
$F4_16_2$	,, Octahedron.	(p. 147 ; C.F. 6.)
$F5_16_2$	,, Icosahedron.	
$F4_16_18_1$	Great Rhombicuboctahedron.	(C.F. 11.)
$F4_16_110_1$	,, Rhombicosidodecahedron.	
$F3_44_1$	Snub Cube.	(p. 176 ; C.F. 13.)
$F3_45_1$	,, Dodecahedron.	(p. 184.)
$F3_24_2$	Cuboctahedron.	(C.F. 2.)
$F3_25_2$	Icosidodecahedron.	
$F3_14_3$	Small Rhombicuboctahedron.	(C.F. 10.)
$F3_14_25_1$	,, Rhombicosidodecahedron.	
$F3_3n_1$	n-gonal Prismoid.	
$F4_2n_1$	n-gonal Prism.	
$SF5_5$	Great Dodecahedron.	(p. 171.)
$SF5_3$	,, Stellated Dodecahedron.	(p. 172.)
$SP5_5$	Small Stellated Dodecahedron.	(p. 173.)
$SP5_3$	Great Icosahedron.	(p. 173.)
$V3_16_2$	Triakis Tetrahedron.	(C.F. 9.)
$V3_18_2$	Triakis Octahedron.	(C.F. 8.)
$V3_110_2$	Triakis Icosahedron.	
$V4_16_2$	Tetrakis Hexahedron.	(C.F. 6.)
$V5_16_2$	Pentakis Dodecahedron.	
$V4_16_18_1$	Hexakis Octahedron.	(C.F. 11.)
$V4_16_110_1$	Hexakis Icosahedron.	
$V3_44_1$	Pentagonal Icositetrahedron.	(C.F. 13.)
$V3_45_1$	Pentagonal Hexecontahedron.	
$V3_24_2$	Rhombic Dodecahedron.	(p. 146 ; C.F. 2.)

$V3_25_2$ Rhombic Triacontahedron.

$V3_14_3$ Icositetrahedron.   (C.F. 10.)

$V3_14_25_1$ Rhombic Hexecontahedron.

$V3_3n_1$ n-gonal Trapezohedron.

$V4_2n_1$ n-gonal Bipyramid.

EXAMPLES 12A

12A1. Show that, with the exception of prisms, prismoids, and the snub cube and dodecahedron, all the facially regular solids may be obtained by cutting the corners from regular solids, or from solids so obtained.

12A2. Describe the series of vertically regular solids that are the duals of the prisms.

12A3. Describe the series of vertically regular solids that are the duals of the prismoids.

12A4. Show that five vertically regular solids can be obtained by erecting pyramids on the faces of the five regular solids.

12A5. Which vertically regular solids are bounded by pentagons ?

12A6. Which vertically regular solids are bounded by kites, i.e., by quadrilaterals with two pairs of equal adjacent sides ?

12A7. Which regular solids are bounded by scalene triangles, i.e., triangles with three unequal sides ?

12A8. State and discuss the duals of the following statements : (*a*) " Regular polygons with the same number of sides are congruent." (*b*) " The facially regular solid Fa_pb_q has p congruent regular a-gons at each vertex."

DEF. : Two congruent semi-regular pyramids on opposite sides of the same base are said to form a **bipyramid**.

12A9. Is it true to say that every bipyramid bounded by congruent isosceles triangles is a vertically regular solid ?

12A10. What are the duals of vertically regular bipyramids ?

12A11. Make faint tracings of drawings of the regular solids, and using them as foundations, draw facially regular solids by the method of 12A1.

12A12. Make a faint tracing of a drawing of a cube, and use the figures of 12W5 to convert the cube into a snub cube.

12A13. Using a tracing of a projection of a regular dodecahedron and the figures of 12W8, construct a pictorial representation of a snub dodecahedron.

12A14. Show that a regular octahedron can be circumscribed about a snub cube, so that one face of the latter lies in each face of the former.

12A15. How many snub cubes can be inscribed in a regular octahedron, so that each face of the latter contains one face of the former ?

12A16. How many regular octahedra can be circumscribed about a snub cube ?

12A17. Show that every star polyhedron can be inscribed in one regular solid and circumscribed about another.

12A18. Show that the planes containing vertices of a facially regular solid adjacent to the same vertex enclose a vertically regular solid.

12A19. Interpret 12A18 in the case of *regular* solids.

12A20. State the duals of the first five theorems of this chapter, and their corollaries.

12A21. Show that all the dihedral angles of a vertically regular solid are equal to one another.

12A22. Show that the volume of a vertically regular solid is equal to that of a set of congruent pyramids, and that that of a facially regular solid is equal to that of two or three sets of congruent regular pyramids.

12A23. The edges of a facially regular solid are all equal ; what is the corresponding property of a vertically regular solid ?

EXAMPLES 12B

12B1. Show that Euler's Theorem (11T1) breaks down in the case of certain star polyhedra, and point out where the proof of that theorem fails to apply to star polyhedra.

12B2. If a plane-faced hole is bored through any polyhedral solid, show that the numbers of faces, edges, and vertices of the resulting solid no longer satisfy Euler's Theorem, and point out how this fact is provided for in the definition of a polyhedral solid (Chap. XI).

12B3. If a polyhedral solid is pierced by n holes in succession, so that the faces of the resulting solid are all plane, show that the numbers of faces, edges, and vertices satisfy the equation

$$f - e + v - 2 + 2n = 0.$$

12B4. To what does a vertically regular bipyramid approximate as the number of its vertices is continually increased ?

12B5. State the dual of 12B4 and its solution.

12B6. Show that each dihedral angle of any vertically regular solid is equal to the supplement of the angle subtended by an edge of its dual at the centre of the latter.

12B7. Show that a circle can be inscribed in any face of any vertically regular solid.

12B8. If two adjacent faces of a facially regular solid are inclined at angles α, β to the diametral plane coaxal with them, show that, in the dual solid whose edges touch a sphere of radius r, the corresponding edge is of length $r(\cot \alpha + \cot \beta)$.

12B9. Show that the angle between any two edges of a vertically regular solid is equal to one of the dihedral angles between the central planes containing the corresponding edges of the dual solid.

12B10-18. Taking an edge as unit of length, tabulate, for each of the following solids, (i) the distance of each face from the centre, (ii) the radius of the circle inscribed in each face, and, hence (iii) the inclination φ of each face to the central plane containing one of its sides ; also (iv) the angle θ subtended by any edge at the centre :

> (12B10.) Tetrahedron.
>
> (12B11.) Octahedron.
>
> (12B12.) Truncated tetrahedron.
>
> (12B13.) Truncated cube.
>
> (12B14.) Truncated octahedron.
>
> (12B15.) Great rhombicuboctahedron.
>
> (12B16.) Cuboctahedron.
>
> (12B17.) Prismoid with $2n$ vertices.
>
> (12B18.) Prism with $2n$ vertices.

12B19. If four triangular faces of a snub cube are adjacent to squares, and have their remaining vertices in common with a fifth square, the tetrahedral angle formed by their planes is congruent to that of a regular octahedron.

CHAPTER XIII

SPACE LATTICES

DEF. : The infinite array of parallelepipeds bounded by three infinite systems of equidistant parallel planes may be called a **partition**, and each parallelepiped may be called a **cell**.

DEF. : The cell-vertices of a partition constitute a **space-lattice**, which is said to be **determined** by the partition or any one of its cells. A point is said to be **on** a lattice if it is a *vertex* of one of its determining cells.

Theorem 13T1

If three vertices of a parallelogram are points on a lattice, so is the fourth vertex. (Fig. 128.)

Let ABCD *be a parallelogram whose vertices* A, B, C *are points on a lattice.*

Let a partition plane γ through C cut AB in C′, and let the parallel plane δ through D cut AB in D′.

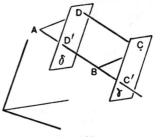

Then   DD′ ∥ CC′ ;   (3T4)

    ∴   C′D′ = CD = BA.

But consecutive parallel partition planes intercept equal intervals on any transversal ;   (3T5)

FIG. 128.

∴ there is, on each side of γ, a partition plane which, with γ, cuts off an intercept equal to AB ; i.e., = D′C′.

∴ δ is one of these partition planes.

Similarly D lies on two other partition planes ;

∴ it is a point on the lattice.   (Q.E.D.)

COROLLARY 1. IF THE EXTREMITIES OF THREE CONCURRENT EDGES OF A PARALLELEPIPED ARE FOUR POINTS OF A LATTICE, THE REMAINING VERTICES ARE ON THE LATTICE.

COROLLARY 2. IF THE EXTREMITIES OF THREE CONCURRENT EDGES OF A DETERMINING CELL OF ONE LATTICE ARE FOUR POINTS ON ANOTHER, THEN EVERY POINT OF THE FIRST LATTICE IS ON THE SECOND.

DEF. : If all points of a lattice are corresponding points of a system of congruent and similarly situated figures, the system is called a **space-pattern**, and each figure is called a **pattern-unit**. It follows that a lattice is a simple pattern. We shall generally use the single words " lattice " and " pattern " instead of " space-lattice " and " space-pattern ".

Theorem 13T2

The pattern formed by the vertices and centres of one set of parallel cell-faces of a partition is a lattice, and may therefore be called a *base-centred lattice*. (Fig. 129.)

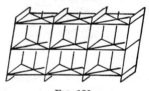

FIG. 129.

If we retain the planes of the cell-bases, and replace the other partition planes by two sets of diagonal planes containing the base-diagonals, the resulting partition determines a lattice.

(Q.E.D.)

Theorem 13T3

The pattern formed by the vertices and centres of the cells of a partition is a lattice, and may therefore be called a *cell-centred lattice.* (Fig. 130.)

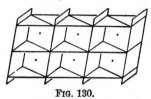

FIG. 130.

If we replace one set of partition planes by one set of diagonal planes, and retain the others, we get a base-centred lattice; (lying on its side, in Fig. 130). (Q.E.D.)

Theorem 13T4

The pattern formed by the vertices and centres of all the cell-faces of a partition is a lattice, and may therefore be called a *face-centred lattice.* (Fig. 131.)

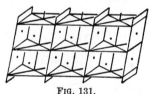

FIG. 131.

The centres of two sets of faces are cell-centres of the partition determining the remaining base-centred lattice. (13T2)

∴ they form a lattice. (13T3)

(Q.E.D.)

DEF. : A parallelepiped with three equal edges equally inclined to one another is called a **rhombohedron,** and the diagonal through their common vertex is called its **principal axis.**

A lattice determined by rhombohedra is called a **rhombic lattice.**

Theorem 13T5

The vertices and points of trisection of one set of cell-diagonals of any partition form a lattice, which may therefore be called a *diagonal-trisected lattice*. (Fig. 132.)

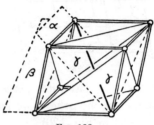

FIG. 132.

The given cell-diagonals are the lines of intersection of two sets of diagonal planes, α, β, which contain two sets of face-diagonals.

These are bisected by another two sets of face-diagonals, lying in a set of planes, γ, which ∴ trisect the given cell-diagonals. (3T5)

∴ the given points are the vertices of the partition $\alpha\beta\gamma$.

∴ they form a lattice. (Q.E.D.)

COROLLARY 1. IF THE PATTERN-UNIT OF A DIAGONAL-TRISECTED LATTICE IS A RHOMBOHEDRON, ITS DETERMINING CELL IS A RIGHT PRISM WHOSE BASE CONSISTS OF TWO EQUILATERAL TRIANGLES.

COROLLARY 2. A DIAGONAL-TRISECTED RHOMBIC LATTICE FORMS THE VERTICES AND BASE-CENTRES OF A STACK OF REGULAR RIGHT HEXAGONAL PRISMS; IT MAY THEREFORE BE CALLED A (base-centred) hexagonal lattice. (See Fig. 105.)

COROLLARY 3. THE VERTICES OF A RHOMBIC LATTICE LIE ON A (BASE-CENTRED) HEXAGONAL LATTICE.

SYMMETRY

DEF. : A pattern is said to have a **centre of symmetry**, O, if every straight line, drawn from a point of the pattern to O, and produced an equal distance beyond it, is terminated by another point of the pattern.

DEF. : A pattern is said to have a **plane of symmetry**, α, if every straight line, drawn from a point of the pattern normal to α, and produced an equal distance beyond it, is terminated by another point of the pattern.

DEF. : A pattern is said to have an **n-fold axis of symmetry**, x, if a rotation of $\dfrac{360°}{n}$ about x brings the pattern into self-coincidence. When n is 2, 3, 4, or 6, the axis is called **dyad, triad, tetrad**, or **hexad** respectively.

DEF. : For **symmetry in a plane**, retain the word " **centre** ", and replace the words " plane " and " axis " by the words " **line** " and " **pole** " respectively.

DEF. : Centres, planes, and axes of symmetry are all referred to as **elements of symmetry**.

SYSTEMS OF LATTICES

DEF. : A lattice whose determining cell is

(1) a cube,

(2) a square prism,

(3) a cuboid,

(4) a parallelepiped with two unequal edges at right angles to the third,

(5) a rhombohedron, or,

(6) a parallelepiped with three unequal edges not perpendicular to its faces,

is said to be

    (1) **cubic,**

    (2) **tetragonal,**

    (3) **orthorhombic,**   (*i.e. right-angled rhombic*)

    (4) **monoclinic,**   (*i.e. one oblique angle at a vertex*)

    (5) **rhombic,** or,

    (6) **anorthic,**

respectively ; and each of these lattices gives its name to the system of lattices which has the *same elements of symmetry* as itself.

It will be noticed that only the second and last of the above *names* refer to symmetry, all the others describing the form of the determining cell.

Every lattice has a centre of symmetry at every vertex and cell-centre.

The principal axis of a rhombohedron is a triad axis, the diagonal planes in which it lies are planes of symmetry, and normal to each is a dyad axis.   (Fig. 133.)

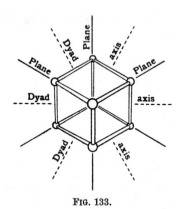

FIG. 133.

The symmetry of the other lattice-systems depends on the following proposition, the truth of which is evident from the definitions :

Theorem 13T6

If a partition-plane is perpendicular to a partition-edge, it is a plane of symmetry of the lattice ; and there is, perpendicular to it, a *plane* or an *n-fold axis* of symmetry of the lattice through every *line* or *n-fold pole* of symmetry of the faces that lie in it; also, every *line* of symmetry of the plane is at least a *dyad* axis of symmetry of the lattice.

COROLLARY : The elements of symmetry of lattices in, and normal to given planes may be tabulated as follows :

Type of Lattice.	Cell-Section Parallel to Given Plane.	Elements of Symmetry.			
		In Plane.		Normal to Plane.	
		Pl.	No. of Dyad Axes.	Type of Axis.	No. of Planes.
Hexagonal	Hexagon	Pl.	6	Hexad	6
Rhombic — Cubic ⎬	Equilat. triangle		3	Triad	3
Tetragonal ⎬	Square	Pl.	4	Tetrad	4
Orthorhombic ⎬	Rectangle	Pl.	2	Dyad	2
Monoclinic	Parallelogram	Pl.	0	Dyad	0

NOTES : (1) Except in the case of the rhombic lattice, the given plane is a plane of symmetry. This is indicated by the " Pl." in the first column for elements of symmetry *in* the given plane.

(2) In the case of the cubic lattice, the four dyad axes become tetrad.

(3) The anorthic lattice has no element of symmetry apart from its centre of symmetry.

Theorem 13T7

Cell-centred anorthic and rhombic lattices are indistinguishable from the corresponding ordinary lattices.

(Fig. 134.)

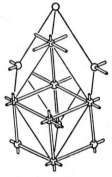

This is evidently true in the case of the anorthic lattice, whose centre is its only element of symmetry.

A rhombohedron has three equal diagonals equally inclined to one another ;

∴ three sets of cell-diagonals of a rhombic lattice determine a second rhombic lattice whose points are the vertices and cell-centres of the first.   (Q.E.D.)

FIG. 134.

COROLLARY : THE ONLY CELL-CENTRED LATTICES WHICH FORM DISTINCT TYPES ARE THE CELL-CENTRED CUBIC, TETRAGONAL, ORTHORHOMBIC AND MONOCLINIC LATTICES.

Theorem 13T8

Face-centred tetragonal, monoclinic, anorthic and rhombic lattices are indistinguishable from cell-centred tetragonal and monoclinic, and ordinary anorthic and rhombic lattices respectively. (Fig. 135.)

This follows, in the first two cases, from 13T4, and, in the third, from 13T4 and 13T7.

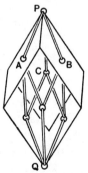

Let PQ (Fig. 135), be the principal axis of a rhombic cell, and A, B, C the centres of the faces concurrent in P.

PA, PB, PC determine a lattice ;   (13T4)

But they are equal, and equally inclined to one another ;

FIG. 135.

∴ the lattice is rhombic.   (Q.E.D.)

COROLLARY 1. THE ONLY FACE-CENTRED LATTICES WHICH FORM DISTINCT TYPES ARE THE FACE-CENTRED CUBIC AND ORTHORHOMBIC LATTICES.

COROLLARY 2. A 60° RHOMBIC LATTICE IS A FACE-CENTRED CUBIC LATTICE.

Theorem 13T9

The only base-centred lattice which forms a distinct type is the base-centred orthorhombic.

Base-centred cubic and rhombic, and rectangle-centred tetragonal lattices lose those axes of symmetry which do not pass through the centres in question ;

∴ they are, by definition, excluded from the corresponding systems of symmetry.

The method of 13T2 shows that base-centred anorthic, square-centred tetragonal, and parallelogram-centred monoclinic lattices are indistinguishable from the corresponding ordinary lattices.

Reversing the method of 13T3, we see that a rectangle-centred monoclinic lattice is indistinguishable from a cell-centred monoclinic lattice.

The only base-centred lattice left to form a distinct type is therefore the base-centred orthorhombic.　(Q.E.D.)

COR. : THERE ARE THUS ONLY 14 TYPES OF LATTICE.

They are named after Bravais, whose symbols explain themselves. (Γ_r, for example, stands for the simple *regular*, or cubic lattice.)

1, 2, 3, Cubic: simple, cell-centred, face-centred ($\Gamma_r, \Gamma_r', \Gamma_r''$) ;

4, 5, Tetragonal : simple, and cell-centred (Γ_t, Γ_t') ;

6, 7, 8, 9, Orthorhombic : simple, base-centred, cell-centred, and face-centred ($\Gamma_o, \Gamma_o', \Gamma_o'', \Gamma_o'''$) ;

10, 11, Monoclinic : simple, and cell-centred (Γ_m, Γ_m') ;

12, Rhombohedral (Γ_{rh}) ;　　13, Hexagonal (Γ_h) ;

14, Anorthic (or Triclinic), (Γ_{tr}).

WORKED EXAMPLES

13W1. Show that a pattern can be formed by regular octahedra arranged so that every vertex is common to three octahedra, two of which have a common edge in line with a diagonal of the other. (Fig. 136.)

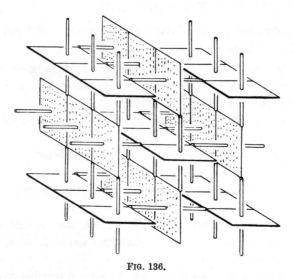

FIG. 136.

Consider a very large portion of space containing n octahedra. Each has 6 vertices, each of which is common to 3 octahedra ;

∴ there must be approximately $2n$ vertices.

At each vertex there is one common edge, making $2n$ in all.

∴ each octahedron has 2 edges in common with neighbouring octahedra.

The simplest supposition is that these are *opposite* edges, and that the square sections containing the common edges of neighbouring octahedra are coplanar.

This gives us a chain of octahedra with their adjacent square sections forming a flat ribbon, and their remaining diagonals at right angles to it.

At the end of these " free " diagonals, and in their plane, we must attach two similar ribbons, one on each side of the first, and with their common edges in line with its free diagonals.

Continuing in this way, we can build up the required pattern, with all the ribbons at right angles to one plane, which we take as the plane of the paper.

13W2. Determine the pattern-unit and lattice-system of the pattern described in 13W1. (Fig. 136.)

It is easy to see from the figure that the centres of the octa-hedra belong to two systems with horizontal and vertical ribbons respectively ; and that each system constitutes a tetragonal lattice with its base diagonals parallel to the edges of the paper, and its cell-centres occupied by the other system.

The lattice is therefore cell-centred tetragonal, and the pattern-unit consists of one octahedron of one system and parts of eight octahedra of the other.

EXAMPLES 13A

13A1. What is the proper description of a monoclinic lattice, if those cell-edges that are not at right angles to one another are equal ?

13A2. Show that the face-centring of any lattice increases the number of lattice-points in a given volume in a certain ratio.

13A3. Show that the centres of any *one, two,* or *three* systems of parallel faces of any given lattice (without its vertices) form a lattice.

13A4. Show that the cell-centres of any lattice, together with the middle points of its edges, form a lattice.

13A5. Show that a new lattice can be formed from any given lattice by obliterating alternate points from each set of partition-edges.

13A6-14. Enumerate the elements of symmetry of :

        (13A6) a cubic lattice ;

        (13A7) a tetragonal lattice ;

        (13A8) an orthorhombic lattice ;

        (13A9) a rhombic lattice ;

      (13A10) a monoclinic lattice ;

  (13A11) an anorthic lattice ;

  (13A12) a stack of semi-regular hexagonal prisms ;

  (13A13) a stack of rhombic dodecahedra ;

  (13A14) a stack of truncated cubes.

13A15. Show that there are just three ways in which a plane can be divided into congruent regular rectilinear figures.

13A16-18. Show that a plane can be filled by a pattern consisting entirely of one of the following sets of regular figures :

  (13A16) triangles and hexagons ;

  (13A17) squares and octagons ;

  (13A18) triangles, squares, and hexagons.

13A19. Enumerate the elements of symmetry of the three patterns of 13A15.

13A20. Enumerate the elements of symmetry of the patterns of 13A16-18.

13A21. What difference is made in the symmetry of a tetragonal lattice by placing a small sphere inside each cell in contact with the centre

  (a) of the base ;

or (b) of one of the rectangular faces ;

so that the spheres occupy corresponding positions in all the cells ?

13A22. Regular tetrahedra are similarly inscribed in the cells of a cubic lattice. Enumerate the elements of symmetry of the resulting pattern.

13A23. Show that a pattern may be formed by regular octahedra, arranged two at a vertex, so that all their edges form continuous infinite straight lines.

13A24. Assign the pattern of 13A23 to its appropriate lattice, and enumerate the elements of symmetry of the pattern.

13A25. Find the ratios of the edges of a cell of the lattice of 13W2.

EXAMPLES 13B

13B1. Show that, if the cell-edges of a tetragonal lattice are proportional to $1 : 1 : \sqrt{2}$, it should be classed in a higher system of symmetry.

13B2. What is the proper description of a rhombohedral lattice with angles of 60° and 120° ?

13B3. Show that a pattern can be formed by cubes arranged so that there are four at each vertex, and that the edges of adjacent cubes are collinear.

13B4. Show that a pattern can be formed by cubes arranged so that each vertex is common to two cubes, and that corresponding edges at the same vertex are collinear.

13B5. Show that a pattern can be formed by cubes so that four non-adjacent edges of each cube belong to it in common with four adjacent cubes, corresponding edges at the same vertex being collinear.

13B6. Show that cubes can be arranged two at a vertex so that each is adjacent to four (not eight) others, corresponding edges at the same vertex being collinear.

13B7. Show that a pattern can be formed by congruent, similarly placed tetrahedra arranged four at each vertex so that the edges form continuous straight lines.

13B8. Show that a pattern can be formed by regular tetrahedra, arranged so that every vertex is common to two tetrahedra, corresponding edges at the same vertex being collinear.

13B9. Show that a pattern can be formed by regular octahedra, six at a vertex, so that every edge is common to two octahedra.

13B10. Show that a pattern can be formed by regular tetrahedra, eight at a vertex, corresponding edges at the same vertex being collinear.

13B11. Show that regular tetrahedra can be arranged two at a vertex so as to form a pattern with a system of planes of symmetry at right angles to a system of triad axes.

13B12. Show that a pattern can be formed by cubes so that each meets one other at each of four vertices, and the projection of the pattern in a certain direction consists solely of squares, equilateral triangles, and regular hexagons.

13B13. Show that a pattern can be formed by regular tetrahedra, arranged two at a vertex, so that the projection on a certain plane consists solely of regular hexagons, equilateral triangles, and squares with their diagonals.

13B14. Assign each of the patterns 13B3-10 to its appropriate lattice, and describe its unit of pattern.

13B15. Show that the pattern of 13B11 may be assigned to either of three different lattices, and describe the corresponding units of pattern.

13B16. Show that the pattern of 13B12 may be assigned to either of three different lattices, and describe the corresponding units of pattern.

CHAPTER XIV

SPHERE-PACKS

Def. : If an infinite number of equal spheres are arranged so that every sphere is similarly related to the rest and in contact with at least four of them, they are said to form a **sphere-pack**.

Def. : The **density** of a sphere-pack is the ratio of the volume of the spheres to that of the continuous space occupied.

Theorem 14T1

If a rhombic lattice has no angle less than 60°, its vertices are centres of a sphere-pack ; and the density is given by the formula

$$\frac{\pi}{12\sqrt{\sin^3\theta \cdot \sin 3\theta}},$$

where 2θ is an acute angle of the lattice. (Figs. 137, 138.)

Let ABCD be a cell-face of a rhombic lattice, every point of which is the centre of a sphere with radius equal to half of a cell-edge. (Fig. 137.)

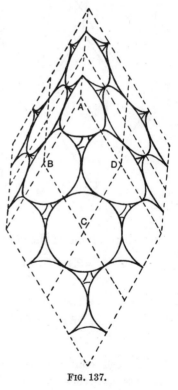

Fig. 137.

Then the spheres A, B, C, D touch one another at the middle points of the sides of the rhombus ABCD.

203

If the spheres B and D touch one another, BAD is an equi-lateral triangle ;

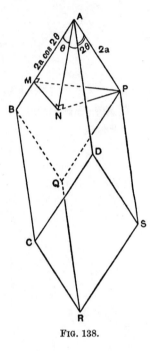

∴ they intersect or miss one another according as the angle BAD is less or greater than 60°.

(Q.E.D. (i).)

Let ABCD,PQRS be a cell (Fig. 138), with acute angles equal to 2θ at A, and let a be the radius of a sphere so that $2a$ is the length of an edge.

Draw

PM $\perp$ AB, and PN $\perp$ plane ABCD.

Then

AB $\perp$ PM and PN ;

∴ AB $\perp$ MN.   (4T1)

Clearly, $\stackrel{\wedge}{\text{PAM}} = 2\theta$, and $\stackrel{\wedge}{\text{MAN}} = \theta$.

Hence   AM $= 2a \cos 2\theta$;

∴ AN $=$ AM $\sec \theta = 2a \cos 2\theta \,.\, \sec \theta$;

∴ PN$^2 = 4a^2 - 4a^2 \,.\, \cos^2 2\theta \,.\, \sec^2 \theta$;

FIG. 138.

∴ the volume of the cell

$$= \text{PN} \,.\, \text{AB} \,.\, \text{AD} \,.\, \sin 2\theta$$
$$= 8a^3 \,.\, 2 \sin \theta \,.\, \cos \theta \sqrt{1 - \cos^2 2\theta \,.\, \sec^2 \theta}$$
$$= 16a^3 \,.\, \sin \theta \sqrt{\cos^2 \theta - \cos^2 2\theta}$$
$$= 16a^3 \,.\, \sin \theta \sqrt{\tfrac{1}{2} \cos 2\theta - \tfrac{1}{2} \cos 4\theta}$$
$$= 16a^3 \,.\, \sqrt{\sin^3 \theta \,.\, \sin 3\theta}.$$

The cell contains fragments of the eight spheres at its corners, and these are equal to the fragments into which any sphere is broken by the eight cells which meet in its centre ;

∴ their volume $= \tfrac{4}{3}\pi a^3$.

∴ the density of the sphere-pack

$$= \frac{\frac{4}{3}\pi a^3}{16a^3\sqrt{\sin^3\theta \cdot \sin 3\theta}} = \frac{\pi}{12\sqrt{\sin^3\theta \cdot \sin 3\theta}}. \qquad \text{(Q.E.D. (ii).)}$$

COROLLARY 1. IF EVERY ANGLE OF THE LATTICE $> 60°$, EACH SPHERE TOUCHES SIX OTHERS AT THE MIDDLE POINTS OF THE CELL-EDGES THAT MEET AT ITS CENTRE.

IF EVERY ACUTE ANGLE $= 60°$, EACH SPHERE TOUCHES ALSO ANOTHER SIX SPHERES AT THE CENTRES OF THE SIX FACES WHOSE ACUTE ANGLES MEET AT ITS CENTRE.

NOTE : To represent the internal structure of a sphere-pack, we replace the actual spheres by small knobs concentric with them. These knobs may be connected with one another by rods (Fig. 142), or rods and plates (Fig. 140) indicating the boundaries of the cells, or by links (Fig. 143) calling attention to some other property of the pack.

COROLLARY 2. THE DENSEST RHOMBIC SPHERE-PACK HAS $2\theta = 60°$, and the least dense has $2\theta = 90°$.

Their centres, therefore, constitute *face-centred* and *simple cubic lattices* respectively.

DEF.: Spheres whose centres form a simple cubic lattice are said to be **cubic-packed**, and to form a **cubic pack**.

If the lattice is face-centred cubic (i.e., 60°

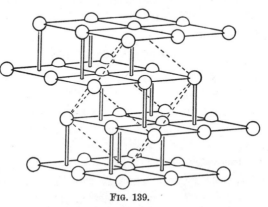

FIG. 139.

rhombic), the spheres are said to be **cubic-close-packed**, and to form a **close cubic pack**. (Figs. 137, 139.)

Theorem 14T2

If the edges of a monoclinic lattice are all equal, and its acute angles not less than 60°, its vertices are centres of a sphere-pack ; and the density is given by the formula

$$\frac{\pi}{6 \sin 2\theta},$$

where 2θ is an acute angle of the lattice.   (Fig. 137.)

The middle point of each edge of the lattice will be a point of contact of the spheres at its extremities.

As in 13T10, spheres at the obtuse angles of a rhombus will intersect, touch, or miss one another according as the acute angles are less than, equal to, or greater than 60°.

∴ each sphere touches at least six others ;

∴ they form a sphere-pack.

(Q.E.D. (i).)

If $2a$ is the length of an edge, the volume of a sphere $= \frac{4}{3}\pi a^3$, and that of a cell $= 8a^3 . \sin 2\theta$.

As in 13T10, the fragments of spheres contained by a cell are exactly equal to one whole sphere.

∴ the density of the pack

$$= \frac{\frac{4}{3}\pi a^3}{8a^3 . \sin 2\theta}$$

$$= \frac{\pi}{6 . \sin 2\theta}. \qquad \text{(Q.E.D. (ii).)}$$

COROLLARY : IF EVERY ANGLE OF THE LATTICE $> 60°$, EACH SPHERE TOUCHES SIX OTHERS AT THE MIDDLE POINTS OF THE CELL-EDGES THAT MEET AT ITS CENTRE.

IF EVERY ACUTE ANGLE $= 60°$, EACH SPHERE TOUCHES ALSO ANOTHER TWO SPHERES AT THE CENTRES OF THE TWO FACES WHOSE ACUTE ANGLES MEET AT ITS CENTRE. In this case the centres of the pack form a regular base-centred hexagonal lattice, (cf. Fig. 105, Chapter XI).

DEF. : If the centres of a sphere-pack form a regular base-centred hexagonal lattice, the spheres are said to be **hexagonal-packed**, and to form a **hexagonal pack**.

DEF. : If the centres of a sphere-pack form two base-centred hexagonal lattices, arranged s that every sphere of one is in contact with six spheres of its own lattice and with three in each of two adjacent layers of the other, the spheres are said to be **hexagonal-close-packed**,

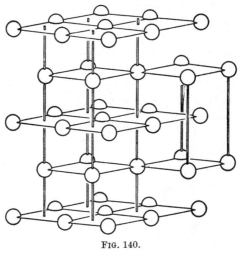

FIG. 140.

and to form a **close hexagonal pack**.   (Fig. 140.)

Theorem 14T3

Close cubic, and close hexagonal packs are equally dense, the density being $\frac{\pi}{3\sqrt{2}}$.   (Figs. 139, 140.)

In either of these packs any two adjacent hexagonal layers of spheres have their centres at the vertices of a single layer of 60° rhombohedra.

∴ the density in each case

$$= \frac{\pi}{12\sqrt{\sin^3 30° \cdot \sin 3 \cdot 30°}} \qquad (14T1)$$

$$= \frac{\pi}{12\frac{1}{\sqrt{8}}} = \frac{\pi}{3\sqrt{2}}. \qquad \text{(Q.E.D.)}$$

Note : If a base-centred hexagonal lattice were *not* base-centred, it would *not be a lattice* ; it would consist of the vertices of a stack of hexagonal prisms.

Def. : If the centres of a sphere-pack are the vertices of a stack of hexagonal prisms, the spheres are said to be **hexagonal-open-packed,** and to form an **open hexagonal pack.**

Theorem 14T4

Any two congruent, similarly placed lattices, displaced from one another by a quarter of a cell-diagonal, form the vertices of two open stacks of congruent, oppositely placed tetrahedra, each of which has its vertices at the centroids of the other. (Fig. 141.)

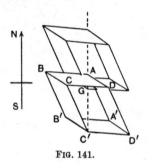

FIG. 141.

Let ABCD,A′B′C′D′ *be any parallelepiped, and* G *the centroid of the tetrahedron* AA′BD.

Then AG $=\frac{3}{4}$ of a median of the tetrahedron.   (2W2)

This median lies in the diagonal planes through A, and is therefore in AC′.

The planes A′BD, CD′B′ belong to a set of lattice-planes, two of which pass through A and C′ ;

∴ they trisect AC′.   (3T5)

∴ AG $=\frac{3}{4}$ of $\frac{1}{3}$ of AC′ $=\frac{1}{4}$ of AC′.

Let AC′ be placed north and south.

Then the centroids of the lattice-tetrahedra at the northern ends of the cells of the lattice determined by ABCD,A′B′C′D′ form a congruent, similarly placed lattice on which G lies.

The second lattice has points of the first as centroids of its *southern* lattice-tetrahedra.   (Q.E.D.)

COROLLARY : IF THE ORIGINAL LATTICES ARE FACE-CENTRED CUBIC (i.e., by 13T8, 60° rhombic), THE TETRAHEDRA ARE REGULAR.

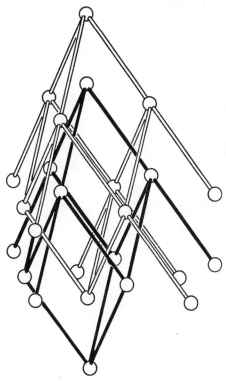

FIG. 142.

DEF. : If the centres of a sphere-pack form two face-centred cubic lattices displaced by a quarter of a cell-diagonal, the spheres are said to be **tetrahedral-packed**. (Fig. 142.)

DEF. : If a tetrahedral pack is formed, not with spheres, but with tetrahedral clusters of four spheres each, so that every two spheres of neighbouring clusters touch one another on the common altitude of their tetrahedra, the spheres are said to be **tetrahedral-open-packed**. (If a tracing be made of the four-way corners of Fig. 143, it may be fitted over Fig. 142, showing that these corners are centres of a tetrahedral pack.)

The above sphere-packs are themselves referred to as a **tetrahedral pack** and an **open tetrahedral pack** respectively.

DEF. : If a pattern is formed by spheres of two different sizes, so that equal spheres are similarly related to the rest, and only unequal spheres are in contact, the structure is called a **compound sphere-pack**.

If one set of equal spheres belong to two or more systems, such that all in the same system are similarly related to the whole pack, the pack is said to be **composite**.

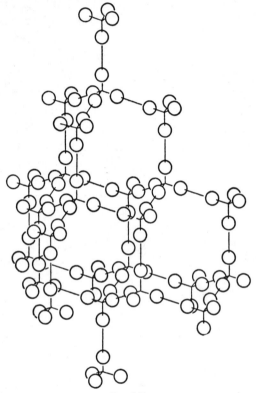

Fɪɢ. 143.

If every sphere is at the centre of a straight line, equilateral triangle, or regular polyhedron, the vertices of which are at the centres of the spheres in contact with it, the pack is said to be **regular**. If this can be said of only one set of equal spheres, the pack is **semi-regular**.

Complex sphere-packs with spheres of more than two different sizes lie outside the scope of this chapter.

We shall take the radius of one set of spheres as the unit of length, and the other as r; so that $r : 1$ is the **radius-ratio**.

If every unit sphere touches m spheres of radius r, and every sphere of radius r touches n unit spheres, the pack is said to have the **coordination-symbol m : n.**

Theorem 14T5

If the unit spheres of a compound sphere-pack are at the vertices, and those of radius r at the cell-centres, of a structure of regular n-cornered solids of which m meet at each vertex, and if ρ is the density of the structure of solids and V the volume of each, then the coordination-symbol and density of the pack are respectively

$$m : n$$

and $$\tfrac{4}{3}\pi \left(r^3 + \frac{n}{m} \right) \frac{\rho}{\mathsf{V}}.$$

The coordination symbol follows directly from the definition.

Corresponding to each solid there is *one* central sphere; its volume is $\tfrac{4}{3}\pi r^3$.

For each solid there are n corner-spheres, each of which is shared by m solids.

$\therefore$, corresponding to each solid, we have the equivalent of $\dfrac{n}{m}$ unit spheres, and one sphere of radius r; their volume is $\tfrac{4}{3}\pi \left(r^3 + \dfrac{n}{m} \right).$

$\therefore$ the ratio of the density of the sphere-pack to that of the structure of solids

$$= \frac{\tfrac{4}{3}\pi \left(r^3 + \dfrac{n}{m} \right)}{\mathsf{V}}.$$

$\therefore$ the density of the pack

$$= \tfrac{4}{3}\pi \left(r^3 + \frac{n}{m} \right) \frac{\rho}{\mathsf{V}}. \qquad \text{(Q.E.D.)}$$

Theorem 14T6

If a sphere of radius r at the centre of a regular tetra-hedron touches unit spheres at its vertices, the volume of the tetrahedron is

$$\frac{8\sqrt{3}}{27}(r+1)^3. \quad \text{(Fig. 144.)}$$

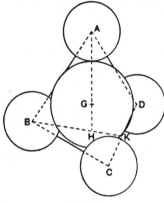

Let G be the centre of the regular tetrahedron ABCD, and let AG meet the plane BCD in H, and let BH meet CD in K. Let $CK = x$.

Then

$$AG = r+1, \quad \text{and} \quad AG = \tfrac{3}{4}AH\,;$$
$$\therefore \; AH = \tfrac{4}{3}(r+1).$$

FIG. 144.

Also $AB = 2x$, $AK = BK = \sqrt{3}x$, and $BH = \tfrac{2}{3}\sqrt{3}x$;

$$\therefore \; AH = x\sqrt{(4 - \tfrac{4}{3})} = 2\frac{\sqrt{2}}{\sqrt{3}}x\,;$$

$$\therefore \; x = \frac{\sqrt{3}}{2\sqrt{2}}\cdot\frac{4}{3}(r+1) = \frac{\sqrt{2}}{\sqrt{3}}(r+1).$$

The area of the base $BCD = CK \cdot BK$

$$= x^2\sqrt{3} = \tfrac{2}{3}(r+1)^2\sqrt{3}\,;$$

$\therefore$ the volume of the tetrahedron $= \tfrac{1}{3}AH \cdot BCD$

$$= \tfrac{1}{3}\cdot\tfrac{4}{3}(r+1)\cdot\tfrac{2}{3}(r+1)^2\sqrt{3}$$

$$= \frac{8\sqrt{3}}{27}(r+1)^3.$$

(Q.E.D.)

COROLLARY : IF THE SOLIDS OF 14T5 ARE REGULAR TETRA-HEDRA, THE DENSITY OF THE COMPOUND SPHERE-PACK IS

$$\frac{3\sqrt{3}}{2}\,\pi\,\frac{r^3 + \dfrac{4}{m}}{(r+1)^3}\,\rho.$$

Theorem 14T7

If the unit spheres of a compound sphere-pack are at the vertices, and those of radius r at the centres, of a structure of regular tetrahedra, octahedra, or cubes, the radius-ratio r must exceed

$$\frac{\sqrt{3}}{\sqrt{2}} - 1, \quad \sqrt{2} - 1, \quad \sqrt{3} - 1,$$

(i.e., ·225, ·414, ·732), respectively.

The spheres at the vertices must not be large enough to touch one another ;

∴ the length of an edge of the polyhedron must be greater than 2 units.

With a regular tetrahedron, an edge $= 2 \cdot \dfrac{\sqrt{2}}{\sqrt{3}} (r+1)$.   (14T6)

$$\therefore \ 2 \cdot \frac{\sqrt{2}}{\sqrt{3}} (r+1) > 2 ;$$

$$\therefore \ r > \frac{\sqrt{3}}{\sqrt{2}} - 1. \quad \text{(Q.E.D. (i).)}$$

With a regular octahedron, the diagonals bisect one another at right angles ;

$$\therefore \ \text{an edge} = (r+1)\sqrt{2} ;$$

$$\therefore \ (r+1)\sqrt{2} > 2 ;$$

$$\therefore \ r > \sqrt{2} - 1. \quad \text{(Q.E.D.(ii).)}$$

With a cube, an edge $= \dfrac{1}{\sqrt{3}}$ times a diagonal

$$= \frac{2(r+1)}{\sqrt{3}}.$$

$$\therefore \ \frac{2}{\sqrt{3}} (r+1) > 2 ;$$

$$\therefore \ r > \sqrt{3} - 1. \quad \text{(Q.E.D. (iii).)}$$

WORKED EXAMPLES

14W1. Find the density of a tetrahedral sphere-pack.

With the notation of 14T5, $\rho = \frac{1}{6}$, $n = m = 4$, and $r = 1$.

∴, by the Corollary of 14T6, the density

$$= \frac{3\sqrt{3}}{2}\,\pi \cdot \frac{1 + \frac{4}{4}}{2^3} \cdot \frac{1}{6}$$

$$= \frac{\sqrt{3}}{16}\,\pi = \cdot 340 \text{ approx.}$$

14W2. Find the density of an open tetrahedral sphere-pack.

(Fig. 145.)

By definition, each sphere of a tetrahedral pack is replaced

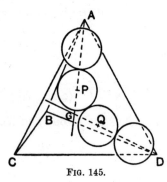

by four spheres with their centres at the vertices of a tetrahedron and the points of contact of neighbouring clusters are the same as those of the original spheres.

Let ABCD be one of the original tetrahedra, and G its centroid; and let P on AG, and Q on GD be the centres of two new spheres in contact with one another.

Fig. 145.

Volume of 4 new spheres $= 4 \cdot \frac{4}{3}\pi(\frac{1}{2}PQ)^3$,

and volume of 1 old sphere $= \frac{4}{3}\pi(\frac{1}{2}AG)^3$;

∴ ratio of density of open to that of simple tetrahedral pack $= 4(PQ/AG)^3$.

$$\frac{PG}{PQ} = \frac{AG}{AD} = \frac{3}{4}\sqrt{\frac{2}{3}} = \frac{1}{2}\sqrt{\frac{3}{2}};$$

$$\tfrac{1}{2}AG = PG + \tfrac{1}{2}PQ = \tfrac{1}{2}\sqrt{\tfrac{3}{2}}PQ + \tfrac{1}{2}PQ;$$

$$\therefore \frac{AG}{PQ} = \sqrt{\tfrac{3}{2}} + 1.$$

As density of old pack $=\dfrac{\sqrt{3}}{16}\,\pi$, that of the open pack

$$=\frac{\sqrt{3}}{16}\,\pi\cdot\frac{4}{(\sqrt{\frac{3}{2}}+1)^3}=\frac{\sqrt{3}}{4}\,\pi\left(\frac{\sqrt{2}}{\sqrt{3}+\sqrt{2}}\right)^3$$

$$=\sqrt{\tfrac{3}{2}}\,\pi\,(\sqrt{3}-\sqrt{2})^3=\cdot123\text{ approx.}$$

14W3. Describe a regular compound sphere-pack with coordination-symbol 2 : 4, and find its density. (Fig. 146 *a*, *b*.)

The spheres must clearly be
at the centres and vertices of
a structure of regular tetrahedra, arranged two at a
vertex so that each vertex is
in line with the centres of the
two tetrahedra to which it is
common.

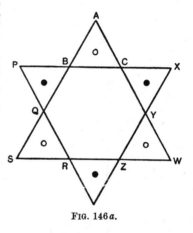

As equal spheres must be
similarly related to the rest,
it is simplest to join up the
pairs of tetrahedra so that
their corresponding adjacent
edges are collinear.

FIG. 146 *a*.

To find the pattern formed by the vertices of the tetrahedra,
consider the plane of any face ABC. (Fig. 146 *a*.)

Beyond B we have the vertices P, Q, corresponding to C, A ;
and beyond C, the vertices X, Y, corresponding to B, A respectively. Beyond Q we have R, S, corresponding to P, B ; and
beyond Y, the vertices Z, W, corresponding to X, C.

Then BCYZRQ must be a regular hexagon, as the sides are all
equal, and each angle is 120°.

∴ the vertices in the plane of any face form a pattern of
equilateral triangles and regular hexagons which separate one
another.

Further, as corresponding edges at the same vertex are collinear, the tetrahedra standing on contiguous triangles must be on opposite sides of the plane.

FIG. 146 b.

Each hexagon is adjacent to six triangles, each of which is shared by three hexagons ;

∴, corresponding to each hexagon there are two tetrahedra, one above, and one below the plane.   (Fig. 146 b.)

The area of a triangle is one-sixth of that of a hexagon, or one-eighth of that of the hexagon and two triangles combined.

∴ the space effectively occupied by each tetrahedron is a prism with equal height and eight times its base-area, and, ∴, twenty-four times its volume.

Hence the density of the structure of tetrahedra $= \frac{1}{24}$.

Volume of a tetrahedron

$$= V = \frac{8\sqrt{3}}{27}(r+1)^3. \tag{14T6}$$

$\therefore$ Density of the pack $= \frac{4}{3}\pi \left(r^3 + \frac{n}{m} \right) \frac{\rho}{V}$ \hfill (14T5)

$$= \frac{4}{3}\pi (r^3+2) \frac{1}{24} \frac{27}{8\sqrt{3}(r+1)^3}$$

$$= \frac{\sqrt{3}}{16} \pi \frac{r^3+2}{(r+1)^3}.$$

NOTE 1 : If double layers of tetrahedra similar to those described above are joined up so that each is the mirror-image of the next, the resulting pattern of spheres is a *regular composite* sphere-pack having the same density as the above *regular compound* sphere-pack.

NOTE 2 : Fig. 146 b shows three double layers of tetrahedra. It is not difficult to recognise that, below the inverted tetrahedra of the bottom layer there must be upright tetrahedra corresponding to those of the top layer.

Thus each double layer is a repetition of the third double layer directly above or below it, the intermediate layers being congruent to them but laterally displaced.

NOTE 3 : See also the " Hint " on 13B4 (Answers and Hints).

14W4. Describe a compound sphere-pack with coordination symbol 2 : 4, but denser than that of 14W3. (Fig. 147.)

Construct a plane pattern of squares separated by equilateral triangles and regular hexagons on alternate sides.

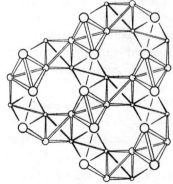

FIG. 147.

Each hexagon is adjacent to six squares, each of which is shared by two hexagons ;

∴ each hexagon corresponds to three squares.

These three squares are adjacent to six triangles, each shared by three squares ;

∴ each hexagon corresponds to two triangles.

We find that the plane can be divided into congruent, similarly placed cells, each consisting of one hexagon, two triangles, and three squares.

If $2a$ is the length of a side, the area of three squares is $12a^2$, that of a hexagon is $6\sqrt{3}a^2$, and that of a whole cell is

$$8\sqrt{3}a^2 + 12a^2.$$

∴ the density of the pattern of squares $= \dfrac{3}{2\sqrt{3}+3} = 2\sqrt{3}-3.$

The squares form three systems α, β, γ, having their bases parallel to the sides of any equilateral triangle. On each square construct a pile of cubes, and let the planes of their bases be named consecutively ξ, η, ζ, ξ, η, ζ, … .

In these planes draw the diagonals through the points $\xi\beta\gamma$, $\eta\gamma\alpha$, $\zeta\alpha\beta$, where $\xi\beta\gamma$ stands for any point common to a β square and a γ square in a ξ plane.

These diagonals taken in pairs determine regular tetrahedra inscribed in one-third of the total number of cubes, and meeting one another two at each vertex. (The tetrahedra are arranged like spiral staircases round the triangular wells.)

Each tetrahedron occupies one-third of the volume of its cube ;   (7T6)

∴ the tetrahedra occupy one-ninth of the volume of all the cubes ;

∴ the density of the structure of tetrahedra

$$= \tfrac{1}{9}(2\sqrt{3}-3) = \cdot 0516 ;$$

and its ratio to that of the structure in 14W3

$$= \cdot 0516 : \tfrac{1}{2\cdot 4}$$
$$= 1\cdot 238.$$

∴ the density of the compound sphere-pack with centres at the vertices and centres of these tetrahedra

$$= \tfrac{4}{3}\pi \left(r^3 + \frac{n}{m} \right) \frac{\rho}{V}, \qquad (14\text{T}5)$$

where $\rho = \cdot 0516,$

and $$V = \frac{8\sqrt{3}}{27}(r+1)^3 ; \qquad (14\text{T}6)$$

∴ density of pack $= \cdot 422 \dfrac{r^3 + 2}{(r+1)^3}.$

EXAMPLES 14A

14A1. Describe a regular compound sphere-pack with coordination-symbol 2 : 2.

14A2. Describe a regular compound sphere-pack with coordination-symbol 3 : 3. (Let its centres be coplanar.)

14A3. By analogy with the three-dimensional sphere-packs discussed in this chapter, define a *plane* regular compound "circle-pack".

14A4-9. Describe *plane* regular compound circle-packs with the following coordination-symbols :

(14A4) 2 : 2. (14A5) 2 : 3. (14A6) 3 : 3.

(14A7) 4 : 4. (14A8) 2 : 4. (14A9) 3 : 6.

14A10. Show that there are only three plane regular circle-packs.

EXAMPLES 14B

14B1. Find the density of a simple cubic sphere-pack.

14B2. Find the density of an open hexagonal sphere-pack (i.e. one whose centres form the vertices of a stack of semi-regular hexagonal prisms).

14B3. Find the density of a hexagonal sphere-pack (i.e. one whose centres form the vertices of a stack of semi-regular triangular prisms, and, ∴, form a hexagonal lattice).

14B4. Find the density of a centred cubic sphere-pack.

14B5. Calculate to three places of decimals the densities of the following sphere-packs, and arrange them in order of density :

Cubic, Close-cubic, Centred cubic, Hexagonal, Open-hexagonal, Close-hexagonal, Tetrahedral, Open-tetrahedral.

14B6. Describe a regular compound sphere-pack with coordination-symbol 8 : 8.

14B7. Find the density of a regular compound sphere-pack with coordination-symbol 8 : 8.

14B8. To what simple sphere-pack does the compound pack of 14B6 degenerate when $r = 1$?

14B9. Describe a regular compound sphere-pack with coordination-symbol 6 : 6.

14B10. Find the density of the pack in 14B9.

14B11. To what simple sphere-pack does the regular compound pack of 14B9 degenerate when $r = 1$? Show that its density is correctly given by the formula obtained in 14B10, if r is put equal to 1.

14B12. Describe a regular compound sphere-pack with coordination-symbol 8 : 4.

14B13. Find the density of the pack in 14B12.

14B14. Show that the centres of the two sets of equal spheres of the pack described in answer to 14B12 are the centres of two different simple sphere-packs.

14B15. Describe a regular compound sphere-pack with coordination-symbol 2 : 8.

14B16. Find the density of the pack in 14B15.

14B17. Show that the centres of one set of equal spheres in the pack of 14B15 are the centres of a simple regular sphere-pack.

14B18. Describe a regular compound sphere-pack with coordination-symbol 2 : 6.

14B19. Find the density of the pack in 14B17.

EXAMPLES 14C

14C1. Describe a semi-regular compound sphere-pack with coordination-symbol 3 : 6.

14C2. Find the density of the pack in 14C1.

14C3. To what lattice system should the pack of 14C1 be referred?

14C4. Enumerate the elements of symmetry of the pack in 14C1.

14C5. Describe a regular compound sphere-pack with coordination-symbol 4 : 4.

14C6. Find the density of the pack in 14C5, and show that the density of the corresponding simple pack is correctly given when r is made $= 1$.

14C7. Enumerate the elements of symmetry of the pack in 14C5.

14C8. Describe the symmetry of the compound and composite packs in 14W3.

14C9. Show that the centres of each system of spheres in the pack of 14W3 are the centres of a simple sphere-pack. Are both these packs *regular* ?

14C10. Show that the centres of an open tetrahedral sphere-pack form thirty-two equal, interpenetrating cubic lattices.

14C11. Show that the centres of the sphere-pack in 14C1 lie at the vertices and circumcentres of a structure of isosceles triangles, with their planes parallel to two of three mutually perpendicular planes and the bisectors of their vertical angles parallel to the third.

14C12. Describe a semi-regular compound sphere-pack with coordination-symbol 2 : 4, such that each of one set of equal spheres is at the centre of a square formed by the centres of the spheres in contact with it, and each of the other set of spheres is in a straight line with its two immediate neighbours.

14C13. Describe the symmetry of the pack in 14C12.

14C14. Calculate the density of the pack in 14C12.

14C15. Describe a compound sphere-pack each of whose spheres lies at the centre of a square formed by the spheres in contact with it, and is as far removed as possible from the next nearest sphere.

14C16. Calculate the density of the pack in 14C15.

14C17. Describe the symmetry of the pack in 14C15.

14C18. Show that every black square on an infinite chessboard may be numbered 1, 2, 3, or 4, in such a way that the numbers of the squares adjacent to every white square fall in the order 1 2 3 4, either clockwise, or anti-clockwise.

On each black square erect a pile of cubes, and to consecutive layers of cubes assign the letters $a, b, c, d, a, b, c, \ldots$.

In the cubes a_1, b_2, c_3, d_4, inscribe regular tetrahedra having common vertices $a_1 b_2$, $b_2 c_3$, $c_3 d_4$, $d_4 a_1$.

Discuss the compound sphere-pack whose spheres have their centres at the centres and vertices of the above structure of tetrahedra.

14C19. Find the angle between the altitudes of neighbouring tetrahedra at any vertex of the structure described in 14W4.

CHAPTER XV

PATTERNS AND CRYSTALS

A PATTERN does not necessarily belong to the same system of symmetry as its lattice ; for example, a stack of cubical boxes, each containing one upright flower-pot just large enough to fit it, forms a *tetragonal*, not a *cubic* pattern, as its vertical axis, though equal in length to the other two, is differently related to the pattern.

DEF. : The three faces at any cell-vertex constitute a **cell-corner** ; and two opposite corners of the same cell are called a **double-corner**.

DEF. : A pattern belongs to the same **system of symmetry** as its lattice, if, and only if, the pattern can be brought into self-congruence with any pair of congruent cell-faces, and, alternatively, any pair of congruent double-corners, coinciding with one another.

It follows that the patterns belonging to a given system can be classified according to which elements of symmetry they share with their lattice.

DEF. : If a pattern retains the centre, all the axes, or the majority of the planes of symmetry possessed by its lattice, it is called **central, axial,** or **planar** respectively ; if it retains all of these, it is called **regular** ; if none, **irregular.**

The following definitions are employed in the subsequent discussion :

DEF. : If a pattern can be brought into self-congruence with an axis of symmetry in its original position, but with its sense reversed, the axis is said to be **non-polar**. Axes for which this is impossible are said to be **polar**.

A pattern is said to be polar or non-polar with respect to a polar or non-polar axis.

DEF. : Two superposable solid figures are said to exhibit **direct congruence**, while the congruence of an object and its image in a plane mirror is called **reflex**. Both cases are included in the term **general congruence**.

(E.g. a pair of shoes have reflex congruence, while two similar shoes for the same foot have direct congruence. Enantiomorphous figures have reflex congruence.)

NOTATION : Central, planar, axial, regular, and irregular patterns are denoted by the suffixes c, p, x, r, and o appended to the initial letter of its lattice-system ; thus we shall see that there are five classes of rhombic patterns : R_c, R_p, R_x, R_r, R_o.

Theorem 15T1

Every rhombic pattern has a triad axis ; and those which are not *regular* can be divided into four classes, three of which have respectively three planes, three dyad axes, and a centre of symmetry.   (Fig. 148.)

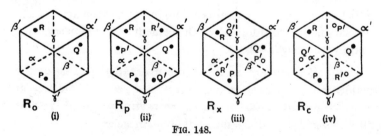

FIG. 148.

Let α, β, γ be faces at one end of a rhombic cell ; let α', β', γ' be the opposite faces, and let P be any point of the pattern.

> The point P can be anywhere in infinite space, so long as it is a point of the pattern ; but, to fix the ideas, we consider a particular point just inside the cell, near the face α, and represent it in our flat diagram by a black dot. The small rings in diagrams (iii) and (iv) stand in the same way for points just inside the cell, and near to the faces α', β', γ'.

Then, by definition, there must be points Q, R, ... , of the pattern such that, with direct and general congruence respectively, we get polar patterns with

$$\alpha\beta\gamma P \equiv \beta\gamma\alpha Q \equiv \gamma\alpha\beta R \; ; \tag{i}$$

and $\quad \alpha\beta\gamma P \equiv \beta\gamma\alpha Q \equiv \gamma\alpha\beta R \equiv \alpha\gamma\beta P' \equiv \beta\alpha\gamma Q' \equiv \gamma\beta\alpha R' \; ; \tag{ii}$

and non-polar patterns with

$$\alpha\beta\gamma P \equiv \beta\gamma\alpha Q \equiv \gamma\alpha\beta R \equiv \alpha'\gamma'\beta'P' \equiv \beta'\alpha'\gamma'Q' \equiv \gamma'\beta'\alpha'R'; \tag{iii}$$

and $\quad \alpha\beta\gamma P \equiv \beta\gamma\alpha Q \equiv \gamma\alpha\beta R \equiv \alpha'\beta'\gamma'P' \equiv \beta'\gamma'\alpha'Q' \equiv \gamma'\alpha'\beta'R'. \tag{iv}$

It is easy to see from the figures that all four patterns have a triad axis, and that patterns (ii), (iii), (iv) have respectively three planes, three dyad axes, and a centre of symmetry.

Thus there are five classes of rhombic patterns : *regular* (R_r), *irregular* (R_o), *planar* (R_p), *axial* (R_x), and *central* (R_c).

(Q.E.D.)

Theorem 15T2

There are four non-regular classes of tetragonal pattern with a tetrad axis, three of them having four planes, four dyad axes, and a centre of symmetry respectively ; while two classes of tetragonal patterns with a dyad instead of a tetrad axis are distinguished from one another by the presence or absence of two planes of symmetry. (Fig. 149.)

Let any tetragonal cell be represented by its projection on one end ϕ ; let ϕ' be the other end, α, β, γ, δ the sides, and P any point of the pattern.

To fix the ideas, suppose P to be just inside the cell, near to ϕ, and represent it by a black dot. In the same way, points inside the cell and near to ϕ' will be represented by small rings.

By definition, there must be points Q, R, ... , of the pattern, such that, with direct and general congruence respectively

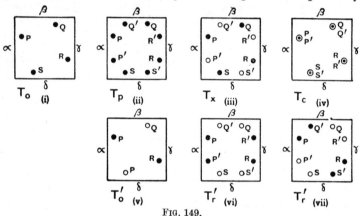

FIG. 149.

between consecutive corners of the base, we get polar patterns with

$$\phi\alpha\beta P \equiv \phi\beta\gamma Q \equiv \ldots \tag{i}$$

and
$$\phi\alpha\beta P \equiv \phi\beta\gamma Q \equiv \ldots \equiv \phi\alpha\delta P' \equiv \phi\beta\alpha Q' \equiv \ldots \tag{ii}$$

and non-polar patterns with

$$\phi\alpha\beta P \equiv \phi\beta\gamma Q \equiv \ldots \phi'\alpha\delta P' \equiv \phi'\beta\alpha Q' \equiv \ldots \tag{iii}$$

and
$$\phi\alpha\beta P \equiv \phi\beta\gamma Q \equiv \ldots \phi'\alpha\beta P' \equiv \phi'\beta\gamma Q' \equiv \ldots . \tag{iv}$$

It is clear from the diagrams that each of these patterns has a tetrad axis, and that (ii), (iii), (iv) have respectively four planes, four dyad axes, and a centre of symmetry.

(iv) has also a plane of symmetry parallel to the square faces ; but the *centre* of symmetry is sufficient to distinguish this class.

Thus, as in the case of rhombic patterns, we have *regular*, *irregular*, *planar*, *axial*, and *central* classes : T_r, T_o, T_p, T_x, T_c.

There are, however, polar tetragonal patterns in which the tetrad axis degenerates into dyad, the pattern being brought into self-congruence by a rotation through 90° followed by a " reflection " in a plane perpendicular to the axis of rotation. This process is known as **alternation**, and is indicated by means of a dashed letter for the index of the lattice-system.

Simple alternation, and alternation combined with reflection, give respectively

$$\phi\alpha\beta P \equiv \phi'\beta\gamma Q \equiv \phi\gamma\delta R \equiv \phi'\delta\alpha S \; ; \tag{v}$$

and $$\phi\alpha\beta P \equiv \phi'\beta\gamma Q \equiv \ldots \phi\alpha\delta P' \equiv \phi'\beta\alpha Q' \equiv \ldots , \tag{vi}$$

or $$\phi\alpha\beta P \equiv \phi'\beta\gamma Q \equiv \ldots \phi'\alpha\delta P' \equiv \phi\beta\alpha Q' \equiv \ldots . \tag{vii}$$

Clearly, patterns (vi) and (vii) share equally between them the planes and axes of symmetry proper to a regular pattern, and therefore belong to the same class of symmetry. They will be called **regular alternating** (T_r').

The only element of symmetry belonging to pattern (v) is its dyad axis ; it will therefore be called **irregular alternating** (T_o').

Thus there are seven distinct classes of tetragonal patterns : $T_r, T_o, T_p, T_x, T_c, T_r', T_o'$. (Q.E.D.)

Theorem 15T3

There are five classes of cubic patterns. (Fig. 150.)

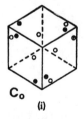 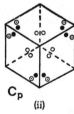 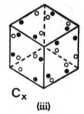 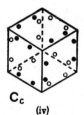

C_o (i) C_p (ii) C_x (iii) C_c (iv)

FIG. 150.

A cubic pattern has four rhombic and three tetragonal axes, parallel respectively to the diagonals and edges of a cell.

Hence the rhombic patterns R_r, R_o, R_p, R_x, R_c give the corresponding cubic patterns C_r, C_o, C_p, C_x, C_c ; and it is found that the eight tetragonal patterns lead to the same five cubic patterns, as follows :

$$T_r \rightarrow C_r \; ; \; T_o \rightarrow C_x \; ; \; T_p \rightarrow C_r \; ; \; T_x \rightarrow C_x \; ; \; T_c \rightarrow C_r \; ;$$
$$T_o{}' \rightarrow C_o \; ; \quad T_r{}' (\text{vi}) \rightarrow C_c \; ; \quad \text{and} \quad T_r{}' (\text{vii}) \rightarrow C_p.$$

Thus there are five, and only five, classes of cubic patterns.

(Q.E.D.)

Theorem 15T4

There are four non-regular classes of hexagonal patterns with a hexad axis, three of them having respectively six planes, six dyad axes, and a centre of symmetry; while two classes of hexagonal patterns with a triad instead of a hexad axis are distinguished from one another by the presence or absence of three planes of symmetry intersecting in the triad axis. (Fig. 151.)

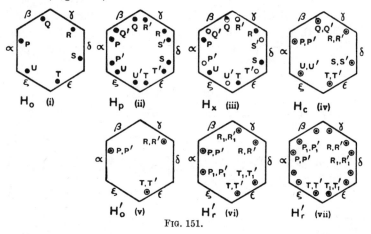

FIG. 151.

The first four classes correspond to the first four in the tetragonal system, and the proofs are exactly the same.

The hexagonal patterns, however, corresponding to $T_o{}'$ and $T_r{}'$ have merely rhombic symmetry, unless distinguished from the rhombic system by the possession of a plane of symmetry normal to the principal axis.

As the number of *pairs* of double-corners of a hexagonal cell is *odd*, a plane of symmetry parallel to the base does not prevent the pattern from being similarly related to them without being similarly related to all the *separate corners*.

Thus we have three patterns with

$$\phi\alpha\beta P \equiv \phi\gamma\delta R \equiv \phi\epsilon\zeta T \equiv \phi'\alpha\beta P' \equiv \phi'\gamma\delta R' \equiv \phi'\epsilon\zeta T' ; \qquad (v)$$

and $\quad \phi\alpha\beta P \equiv \phi\gamma\delta R \equiv \phi\epsilon\zeta T \equiv \phi'\alpha\beta P' \equiv \phi'\gamma\delta R' \equiv \phi'\epsilon\zeta T'$

$$\equiv \phi\alpha\zeta P_1 \equiv \phi\gamma\beta R_1 \equiv \phi\epsilon\delta T_1 \equiv \phi'\alpha\zeta P_1' \equiv \phi'\gamma\beta R_1' \equiv \phi'\epsilon\delta T_1'. \quad (vi)$$

and $\quad \phi\alpha\beta P \equiv \phi\gamma\delta R \equiv \phi\epsilon\zeta T \equiv \phi'\alpha\beta P' \equiv \phi'\gamma\delta R' \equiv \phi'\epsilon\zeta T'$

$$\equiv \phi\beta\alpha P_1 \equiv \phi\delta\gamma R_1 \equiv \phi\zeta\epsilon T_1 \equiv \phi'\beta\alpha P_1' \equiv \phi'\delta\gamma R_1' \equiv \phi'\zeta\epsilon T_1'. \quad (vii)$$

The diagrams show that each pattern has a plane of symmetry perpendicular to the triad axis, that each is similarly related to the three double-corners of a hexagonal cell, and that (vi) and (vii) share the remaining planes and dyad axes of the lattice. These therefore belong to the same regular alternating class (H_r'), while (v) is irregular alternating (H_o').

Thus there are seven distinct classes of hexagonal patterns : H_r, H_o, H_p, H_x, H_c, H_r', H_o'. $\qquad$ (Q.E.D.)

Theorem 15T5

The orthorhombic and monoclinic systems have each three classes of patterns, and the anorthic two. (Fig. 152.)

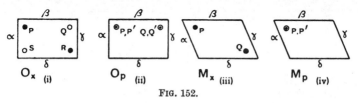

FIG. 152.

Let α, β, γ, δ be four consecutive rectangular faces of an orthorhombic or monoclinic cell; let ϕ, ϕ' be the two ends, and P any point of the pattern.

Represent the cell by its projection on ϕ, and suppose P to be just inside the cell, near to ϕ.

There must be points Q, R, ... , such that, with direct and reflex congruence respectively, we have orthorhombic patterns with

$$\phi\alpha\beta P \equiv \phi'\gamma\beta Q \equiv \phi\gamma\delta R \equiv \phi'\alpha\delta S, \qquad \text{(i)}$$

and $$\phi\alpha\beta P \equiv \phi\gamma\beta Q \equiv \phi'\alpha\beta P' \equiv \phi'\gamma\beta Q' ; \qquad \text{(ii)}$$

and monoclinic patterns with

$$\phi\alpha\beta P \equiv \phi\gamma\delta Q, \qquad \text{(iii)}$$

and $$\phi\alpha\beta P \equiv \phi'\alpha\beta P'. \qquad \text{(iv)}$$

We see from the figures that patterns (iii) and (i) have respectively one and three dyad axes, and no plane of symmetry ; and that (iv) has only a plane of symmetry, and (ii) has two planes and one dyad axis. Hence (iii) and (i) are called axial, and (iv) and (ii) planar.

Thus, including regular patterns, there are three distinct classes of patterns (O_r, O_p, O_x) in the orthorhombic, and three (M_r, M_p, M_x) in the monoclinic system.

Anorthic patterns fall naturally into two classes according to the presence or absence of a centre of symmetry. They are called regular and irregular respectively (A_r, A_o). (Q.E.D.)

NOTE : It follows from the above theorems that there are in all **thirty-two classes of patterns** differing from one another in the elements of symmetry already described.

The thirty-two symbols are shown in the following table :

System.	No. of Classes.							
Rhombic -	5	R_o	R_r	R_p	R_x	R_c		
Cubic - -	5	C_o	C_r	C_p	C_x	C_c		
Tetragonal -	7	T_o	T_r	T_p	T_x	T_c	T_o'	T_r'
Hexagonal -	7	H_o	H_r	H_p	H_x	H_c	H_o'	H_r'
Orthorhombic -	3		O_r	O_p	O_x			
Monoclinic -	3		M_r	M_p	M_x			
Anorthic -	2	A_o	A_r					
Total Number of Classes	32							

N.B.—Patterns belonging to the same class of symmetry may be based on either normal, cell-centred, base-centred, or face-centred lattices.

CRYSTALS

DEF. : A crystal is a portion of a space-pattern bounded by lattice-planes.

DEF. : If three concurrent lattice edges, OX, OY, OZ, are taken as axes, and if the plane of a given face intercepts on them intervals consisting of a, b, c cell-edges respectively, then the smallest integers h, k, l, proportional to $\frac{1}{a} : \frac{1}{b} : \frac{1}{c}$ are called the indices of the face.

If the face is parallel to OX, a is infinite, and therefore h is zero. Faces for which any of the indices are large must pass through relatively few lattice-points, and, in practical crystallography, indices greater than 6 or 7 are seldom met with.

In the case of a hexagonal pattern, the principal axis of a cell is taken as axis of l, and axes of h, i, k are taken normal to alternate rectangular faces.

NOTATION : The minus sign is usually placed *above*, not *before*, a negative index.

Theorem 15T6

If (h, i, k, l) are hexagonal indices of any plane, then

$h + i + k = 0$.

(Fig. 153.)

Employing a diagram in which cell-edges are all represented by equal lengths, let a, b, c be the intercepts of the plane

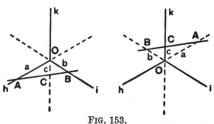

FIG. 153.

on the axes of h, i, k respectively ; let O be the origin, and A, B, C the points of intersection.

Then A, B, C are collinear, and two of the triangles OBC, OCA, OAB together make up the third, and their common side differs in sign from the other two intercepts.

In each case the sine of the angle at O is $\dfrac{\sqrt{3}}{2}$; $\therefore$ their areas are respectively

$$\frac{1}{2}\frac{\sqrt{3}}{2}\,bc,\ \frac{1}{2}\frac{\sqrt{3}}{2}\,ca,\ \frac{1}{2}\frac{\sqrt{3}}{2}\,ab.$$
$$\therefore\ bc+ca=-ab\ ;$$
$$\therefore\ bc+ca+ab=0\ ;$$
$$\therefore\ \frac{1}{a}+\frac{1}{b}+\frac{1}{c}=0\ ;$$
$$\therefore\ h+i+k=0. \hspace{2cm} \text{(Q.E.D.)}$$

DEF. : A set of faces parallel to the same straight line constitute a **zone**, and the indices of a plane normal to the zone are called the **indices** of the zone.

DEF. : If a given plane is repeated in accordance with specified conditions of symmetry with respect to given axes (e.g. if one of the 32 classes of patterns is quoted), the parts of the resulting planes between their lines of intersection constitute an open or closed polyhedron which is called a **form**.

Many **forms** are regular or vertically regular polyhedra, or rather less regular variations of these ; among others are the following :

> the **trapezohedron**, bounded by congruent **trapezoids**, or quadrilaterals with two pairs of equal adjacent sides ;
> the **scalenohedron**, bounded by congruent scalene (i.e. irregular) triangles ;
> and the **bisphenoid**, a tetrahedron with two opposite edges bisected by their common perpendicular.

THE DRAWING OF CRYSTALS

Instead of orthogonal projection (" plan-and-elevation " or " pictorial representation "), **clinographic projection** (i.e. oblique parallel projection) is generally employed in the drawing of crystals. This projection permits one axial plane to be represented without distortion, while lines normal to it appear as parallel oblique lines on a reduced scale. In our diagrams we shall make the latter scale one half of the former, and let the oblique lines be inclined at the angle $\tan^{-1} \frac{23}{60}$ to the horizontal. This direction is chosen so as to avoid confusion with the lines of intersection of lattice-planes with the plane of the paper. Fig. 157 shows a set of cubic or rhombic axes with index marks 1, 2, 3 at distances from the origin proportional to $1 : \frac{1}{2} : \frac{1}{3}$.

DEF. : The shape of a unit cell of a pattern or crystal is indicated by means of certain numbers called **characteristics**.

A rhombic crystal is determined by the *inclination* of an edge to the axis, or to another edge ; a hexagonal or tetragonal, by the *ratio* of the principal axis to one of the others.

In a monoclinic crystal, the axis of y is that which is perpendicular to two others, the *angle* between which must be specified in addition to the *ratios* of the axes. The characteristics of an orthorhombic crystal consist of the *axial ratios* of a cell ; an anorthic crystal requires also the statement of *three acute face-angles*.

WORKED EXAMPLES

15W1. One face of a form of class R_0 has indices $(a,\ b,\ c)$; find the indices of the remaining faces. (Fig. 154, a and b.)

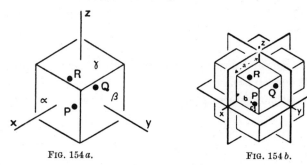

FIG. 154 a.   FIG. 154 b.

Represent a cell as in Fig. 148 (15T1), and take axes of x, y, z through the centres of faces α, β, γ.

Insert dots for P, Q, R, as in 14T1, but bring P (and, $\therefore$, the other points) into the positive octant.

Then the coordinates of P are all positive ; let them be (a, b, c).

Then Q, R have the coordinates (b, c, a), (c, a, b) respectively.

$\therefore$, if there is a plane P with *indices* (a, b, c), there must be planes Q, R with indices (b, c, a), (c, a, b) respectively.

Thus the required form is *open*, consisting of only three planes.

15W2. One face of a form of class C_0 has indices $(1, 2, 3)$; discuss the shape and arrangement of its faces.   (Figs. 155, 156.)

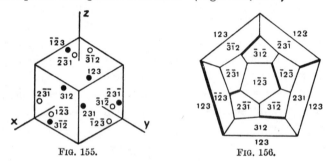

FIG. 155.   FIG. 156.

Represent a cell as in 15T3 and 15W1, and so obtain the indices of the twelve points, and insert them on the diagram (Fig. 155). It is clear that these points can only be grouped in threes, as no four neighbouring points are similarly related to one another.

$\therefore$ the required form consists of twelve faces grouped in threes at the vertices.

Suppose that there are n vertices to each face ; and v vertices in all.

Then $$3v = 12n ;$$

$$\therefore \ v = 4n.$$

Three edges meet at each vertex, and each edge joins two vertices ;

$$\therefore \ 3v = 2e \ ;$$
$$\therefore \quad e = \tfrac{3}{2}v = \tfrac{3}{2} \cdot 4n = 6n.$$

By Euler's Theorem, $f - e + v = 2$;   (11T1)

$$\therefore \ 12 - 6n + 4n = 2 \ ;$$
$$\therefore \qquad\qquad 2n = 10 \ ;$$
$$\therefore \qquad\qquad n = 5.$$

$\therefore$ the form resembles the regular dodecahedron in that it has 12 faces, 30 edges, and 20 vertices, and the faces are pentagons, and the vertices trihedral.

Hence (Fig. 156) we may employ the same distorted representation as in 11T3 (p. 137), and insert the indices of the faces by observing which points are adjacent to one another in the dot diagram (Fig. 155).

Any two points on the same cube face in the dot diagram will correspond with a pair of faces meeting in an edge parallel to that cube face and intersecting the axis through its centre. These edges have been thickened in the distorted representation.

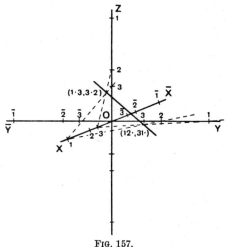

FIG. 157.

15W3. Draw the clinographic projection of the form discussed in 15W2. (Fig. 157.)

By definition, the intercepts of a face (123) on the axes are proportional to the reciprocals of the indices, i.e.

to $1 : \tfrac{1}{2} : \tfrac{1}{3}$, or $6 : 3 : 2.$

We accordingly mark off intercepts proportional to 6, 3, 2 on each axis, positive and negative, and label them with the appropriate indices.

Remembering that the distorted representation (Fig. 156) shows the faces from the *inside*, we now proceed to construct the edges where the face (123) meets the faces (312), (231), ($\bar{2}3\bar{1}$), ($\bar{3}\bar{1}2$), ($\bar{1}\bar{2}3$).

The edge (123,312) is drawn through the intersections of the pairs of lines (12·, 31·), (1·3, 3·2), joining the corresponding index marks on the axes.

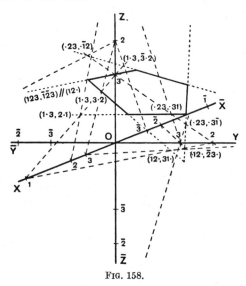

Fig. 158.

NOTE : The planes (123), (312) cut the axes in the index marks 1, 2, 3, and 3, 1, 2 respectively ; the line joining the index mark 1, on the axis of x, to the index mark 2, on the axis of y, can be called the line (12·), (read " one two dot "), the *dot* indicating which axis is not involved; similarly (1·3) is the line joining the index mark 1, on the axis of x, to the index mark 3, on the axis of z ; ∴ the point of intersection of the lines (12·), (31·) lies on both planes (123) and (312); hence the line of intersection of

these planes is the join of the points (12˙, 31˙) and 1˙3, 3˙2).
(Fig. 157.)

The remaining edges of the face (123) are drawn in the
same way, and their intersections determine its vertices. The
useless portions of these lines should now be rubbed out or

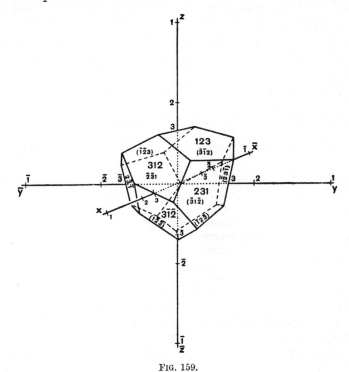

FIG. 159.

the face outlined with ink or blacker pencil (Fig. 158, on twice
the scale of Fig. 157).

The remaining edge at each vertex of the face (123) should
now be put in ; then each of the adjacent faces should be
completed in turn.

In the finished drawing (Fig. 159), edges at the back are
shown with dotted lines.

15W4. A crystal of class T_c consists of a combination of two forms determined by the faces (121), (100), the intercept of the former on the axis of x being four times that of the latter. Construct the clinographic projection of the crystal, its characteristics being 1 : 1 : 0·625.

(Fig. 160.)

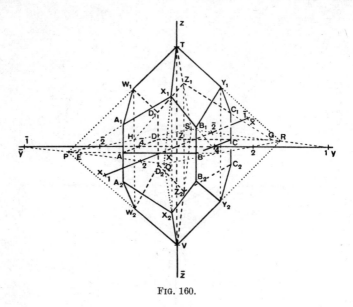

Fig. 160.

Draw a dot diagram for each form, and insert the indices.

Make the index marks 1, 2, 4 on the axes of x and y, and 1 on the axis of z.

The form (100) is an open square prism with faces parallel to the axial planes ZOX, ZOY, and cutting the axes of x and y in the index mark 4. Let ABCD be its section with the plane XOY.

The form (121) is a bipyramid with vertices T, V at the index marks 1 and $\bar{1}$ on the axis of z, and square base PQRS bounded by the lines (12·, 2$\bar{1}$·) (2$\bar{1}$·, $\bar{1}\bar{2}$·), etc.

Let AB cut PQ, QR in E, F ; let CD cut RS, SP in G, H ; and let the diagonals PR, QS cut AB, BC, CD, DA in X, Y, Z, W.

Vertical lines through these points cut the oblique edges of the bipyramid in eight corners of the crystal : X_1, X_2, Y_1, Y_2, Z_1, Z_2, W_1, W_2.

Verticals through A, B cut lines joining X_1, X_2 to E and F in the corners A_1, A_2, B_1, B_2 ; and verticals through C, D cut lines joining Z_1, Z_2 to G and H in the corners C_1, C_2, D_1, D_2.

It is now seen that the faces of the form (100) are hexagons, and those of (121) are quadrilaterals.

HEXAGONAL

H_r Regular.
Holosymmetric *
Holohedry †
1 (6) 3 (2) 3 (2) ‡
3 + 1 . . . 3 . . C §

H_p Planar.
Dihexagonal
  Pyramidal
Hemimorphic h.h.
1 (6) . . . .
3 . . . 3

H_x Axial.
Trapezohedral
Enantiomorph. h.h.
1 (6) 3 (2) 3 (2)
. . . .

H_c Central.
Bipyramidal
Paramorphic h.h.
1 (6) . . . . .
1 C

H_o Irregular.
Pyramidal
Tetartohedry
1 (6) . . . .
. . . . . .

H_r' RegularAlternating.
Ditrigonal
  Bipyramidal
Trigonal Holohedry
1 (3) . . . . .
3 + 1 . . . . .

H_o' Irreg. Alternating.
Trigonal
  Bipyramidal
*Trigonal
  Paramorphic h.h.*
1 (3) . . . . .
1 . . . . . .

RHOMBIC

R_r Regular.
Holosymmetric
Holohedry
1 (3) 3 (2) . .
. . . 3 . . C

R_p Planar.
Ditrigonal
  Pyramidal
Hemimorphic h.h.
1 (3) . .
. . 3 . . .

R_x Axial.
Trapezohedral
Enantiomorph. h.h.
1 (3) 3 (2)
. . . . . .

R_c Central.
Rhombohedral
Tetartohedry (ii)
1 (3) . . . .
. C

R_o Irregular.
Trigonal Pyramidal
Tetartohedry (i)
1 (3) . . . . .
. . . . . .

MONOCLINIC

M_r Regular.
Holosymmetric
Holohedry
1 (2) . . . .
1 C

M_p Planar.
Clinohedral
Hemihedry
. . . . . .
1 . . . . .

M_x Axial.
Hemimorphic
Hemimorphic h.h.
1 (2) . . . .
. . . . . .

---

* Encyclopaedia Britannica. † *Hilton's Mathematical Crystallography.*

‡ 1 hexad, 3 dyad, 3 dyad axes. § 3 + 1 axial, 3 diagonal planes; Centre.

OF SPACE-PATTERNS (OR CRYSTALS)

CUBIC

C_r Regular.
Holosymmetric
Holohedry
3(4) 4(3) 6(2)
3 . 6 . C

C_p Planar.
Tetrahedral
Hemimorphic h.h.
4(3) 3(2) . .
. . 6 . . . .

C_x Axial.
Plagihedral
Enantiomorph. h.h.
3(4) 4(3) 6(2)
. . . .

C_c Central.
Pyritohedral
Paramorphic h.h.
4(3) 3(2) . .
3 . . . C .

C_o Irregular.
Tetartohedral
Tetartohedry
4(3) 3(2) . .
. . . .

ORTHORHOMBIC

O_r Regular.
Holosymmetric
Holohedry
3(2) . . . .
3 . . . C .

O_p Planar.
Pyramidal
Hemimorphic h.h.
1(2) . . . .
2 . . . . . .

O_x Axial.
Bisphenoidal
Enantiomorph. h.h.
3(2) . . . .
. . . .

TETRAGONAL

T_r Regular.
Holosymmetric
Holohedry
1(4) 2(2) 2(2)
2+1 . 2 . . C

T_p Planar.
Ditetragonal
Pyramidal
Hemimorphic h.h.
1(4) . . . .
2 . . 2 . .

T_x Axial.
Trapezohedral
Enantiomorph. h.h.
1(4) 2(2) 2(2)
. . . . . .

T_c Central.
Bipyramidal
Paramorphic h.h.
1(4) . . . .
1 C

T_o Irregular.
Pyramidal
Tetartohedry (i)
1(4) . . . .
. . . . . .

T_r' Regular Alternating.
Scalenohedral
Hemihedry (ii)
1(2) 2(2) . . .
. . 2 . . .

T_o' Irreg. Alternating.
Bisphenoidal
Tetartohedry (ii)
1(2) . . . .
. . . . . .

ANORTHIC

A_r Regular.
Holosymmetric
Holohedry
. . . . .
. . . . C .

A_o Irregular.
Asymmetric
Hemihedry
. . . .
. . . .

SOLID GEOMETRY

TABLE OF CUBIC FORMS

determined by **typical indices** and deduced from the **dual solids** determined by the corresponding **coordinates**.

DUAL SOLID " F "		CUBIC FORM " V "

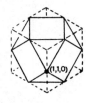

1. $(1, 0, 0)$
C_r, C_p, C_x, C_c, C_o
F3$_4$ *Octahedron.*
V3$_4$ Cube.

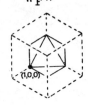

2. $(1, 1, 0)$
C_r, C_p, C_x, C_c, C_o
F3$_2$4$_2$ *Cuboctahedron.*
V3$_2$4$_2$ Rhombic
      dodecahedron.

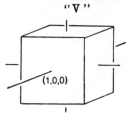

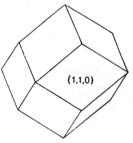

3. $(1, 1, 1)$
C_p, C_o
F3$_3$ *Tetrahedron.*
V3$_3$ Tetrahedron.

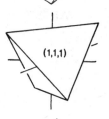

4. $(1, 1, 1)$
C_r, C_x, C_c
F4$_3$ *Cube.*
V4$_3$ Octahedron.

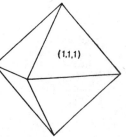

5. (2, 1, 0)

C_c, C_o

F3₂3₂ Icosahedron.

V3₂3₃ Pentagonal dodecahedron.

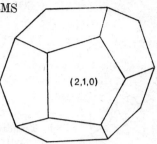

(2,1,0)

6. (2, 1, 0)

C_r, C_p, C_x

F4₁6₂ Truncated octahedron.

V4₁6₂ Tetrakis hexahedron.

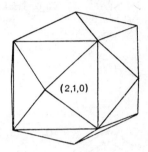

(2,1,0)

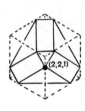

7. (2, 2, 1)

C_p, C_o

F3₁3₁4₂ Irregular cuboctahedron.

V3₁3₁4₂ Trapezoidal dodecahedron.

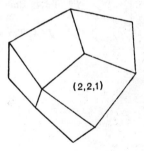

(2,2,1)

8. (2, 2, 1)

C_r, C_x, C_c

F3₁8₂ Truncated cube.

V3₁8₂ Triakis octahedron.

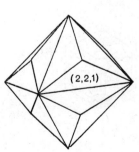

(2,2,1)

243

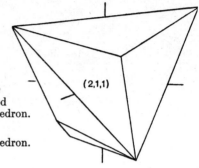

9.   (2, 1, 1)
C_p, C_o

F$3_1$6$_2$ Truncated
    tetrahedron.

V$3_1$6$_2$ Triakis
    tetrahedron.

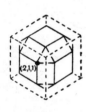

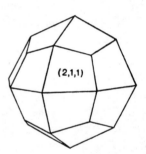

10.   (2, 1, 1)
C_r, C_x, C_c

F$3_1$4$_3$ Small rhombi-
    cuboctahedron.

V$3_1$4$_3$ Trapezoidal icosi-
    tetrahedron.

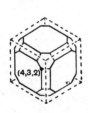

11.   (4, 3, 2)
C_r

F$4_1$6$_1$8$_1$ Great rhombi-
    cubocta-
    hedron.

V$4_1$6$_1$8$_1$ Hexakis
    octahedron.

244

12. (4, 3, 2)

C_p

F$4_1 6_1 6_1$ Irregularly truncated octahedron.

V$4_1 6_1 6_1$ Hexakis tetrahedron.

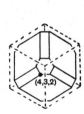

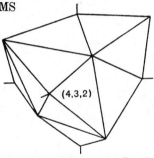

13. (4, 3, 2)

C_x

F$3_4 4_1$ Snub cube.

V$3_4 4_1$ Pentagonal icositetrahedron.

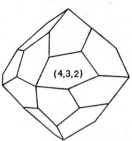

14. (4, 3, 2)

C_c

F$3_1 4_1 4_2$ Irregular small rhombicuboctahedron.

V$3_1 4_1 4_2$ Dyakis dodecahedron.

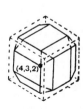

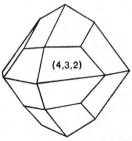

15. (4, 3, 2)

C_o

F$3_1 3_1 3_3$ Irregular icosahedron.

V$3_1 3_1 3_3$ Tetrahedral pentagonal dodecahedron.

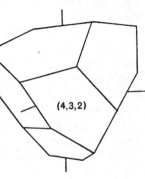

MISCELLANEOUS EXAMPLES

(Taken from recent examination papers set for the Higher School Certificate.)

M1. An equilateral triangle ABC of given size is projected orthogonally from the plane S into a triangle A'B'C' in the plane S'. Prove that the sum of the squares on the sides of the triangle A'B'C' is constant for all positions of the triangle ABC in the plane S.

(Camb. P. & A. 1929.)

M2. Prove that the lines joining the middle points of opposite edges of a tetrahedron are concurrent. (Camb. P. & A. 1929.)

M3. Show that the centre of gravity of the smaller portion of a uniform solid sphere of radius a, cut off by a plane distant b from the centre, is at a distance

$$\frac{3}{4} \frac{(a+b)^2}{(2a+b)}$$

from the centre.

Find also the position of the centre of gravity of the larger portion.

(Camb. P. & A. 1929.)

M4. Find the locus of points in a plane whose distances from two fixed points are in a constant ratio (i) when the plane passes through the two fixed points, (ii) when it does not. (Oxf. & Camb. 1929.)

M5. Show that a single straight line can be drawn to intersect at right angles each of two lines which are not in the same plane, and that the shortest distance between the two straight lines lies along this common perpendicular.

If the shortest distance between the edges DA and BC of a tetrahedron ABCD is the straight line joining the middle points of those edges, prove that DB = CA and DC = AB. (Oxf. & Camb. 1929.)

M6. Prove that the ratios of the lengths of parallel segments of lines in one plane are unaltered by orthogonal projection.

Prove that the rectangles under the segments of chords of an ellipse drawn through a fixed point are proportional to the squares of the parallel diameters of the ellipse. (Oxf. & Camb. 1929.)

246

M7. Show that the centre of gravity of a uniform wire forming a circular arc and subtending an angle 2θ at the centre O of the circle, the radius of which is a, is distant $a \sin \theta/\theta$ from O ; hence find the centre of gravity of a sector of a circle. (Camb. P. & A. 1929.)

M8. Prove that the area of the surface of a sphere of radius a is $4\pi a^2$.

A closed circular cylinder of height 6 cm. is inscribed in a sphere of radius 4 cm. Find the area of the whole surface of the cylinder, including its plane ends. (Joint Bd. Subs. Maths. 1929.)

M9. An ash-tray of sheet metal has a square base of edge 8 cm. The four sides have a slant height of 2 cm. and slope upwards and outwards, making angles of 150° with the base, so that the outer rim is also a square. Prove that the lengths of the top edges are 11·46 cm., and find the volume of water the tray could hold when standing on a horizontal table. (Joint Bd. Subs. Maths. 1929.)

M10. Find an expression for the area of the curved surface of a right circular cone, if its slant height is l and the radius of its base is r.

A plane through the vertex of a right circular cone divides the curved surface into two parts whose areas are in the ratio of 3 to 1. Taking π as $\frac{22}{7}$, prove that the volume of the cone is divided into parts in the ratio of 10 to 1. (Joint Bd. 1929.)

M11. A pyramid stands on a square base, and each slant face is an equilateral triangle.

Find the angle between each slant face and the base, and also the angle between two adjacent faces. (Joint Bd. 1929.)

M12. A plane meets the sides BC, CA, AB (produced if necessary) of a triangle ABC at P, Q, R, S. Prove that

$$\frac{BP}{PC} \cdot \frac{CQ}{QA} \cdot \frac{AR}{RB} = -1.$$

A transversal meets the sides AB, BC, CD, DA of a quadrilateral ABCD (plane or skew) at P, Q, R, S. Prove that

$$\frac{AP}{PB} \cdot \frac{BQ}{QC} \cdot \frac{CR}{RD} \cdot \frac{DS}{SA} = 1.$$

State the corresponding result for a five-sided figure.

(Joint Bd. 1929.)

M13. Find the centre of mass of a uniform solid hemisphere.

(C.W.B. Adv. Maths. 1929.)

M14. If a solid angle is bounded by three plane angles, prove (i) that any two of these angles are together greater than the third, and (ii) that the sum of the three angles is less than four right angles. (C.W.B. 1929.)

M15. In a tetrahedron two pairs of opposite edges are perpendicular ; prove that the third pair of opposite edges are also perpendicular.

Prove also that in this case the sum of the squares on each pair of opposite edges is the same. (C.W.B. 1929.)

M16. Obtain Simpson's rule for the volume of the frustum of a pyramid, namely
$$V = \tfrac{1}{6}h(X + 4Y + Z),$$
where h is the height of the frustum, X and Z are the areas of the parallel faces, and Y is the area of the parallel section midway between them.

An equilateral triangle ABC, each of whose sides is of length a, revolves round a straight line in its plane parallel to the side BC and at a distance b from it on the side remote from A. Find the volume of the solid swept out by the triangle. (C.W.B. 1929.)

M17. A pointer of uniform sheet metal consists of a rectangle 8 cm. long and 1 cm. wide, tipped with an equilateral triangle with each side 2 cm. long. Verify that the centre of gravity is distant 4·92 cm. from the point. (Camb. P. & A. 1929.)

M18. Find the centre of gravity of a solid right circular cone. A hollow right circular cone, without base, of mass M, and made of a thin metallic sheet, is placed with its axis vertical and vertex downwards. Water is poured in to a depth of one-half of the vertical height. Prove that, if the centre of gravity of the cone and its contents is at the surface of the water, the mass of the water is $\tfrac{4}{3}$M.
(Camb. P. & A. 1930.)

M19. OA, OB, OC are three edges of a parallelepiped, and P is the corner opposite to O. OP cuts the plane ABC at Q. Prove that Q is (i) a point of trisection of OP, (ii) the centroid of the triangle ABC.
(Camb. P. & A. 1930.)

M20. O is the vertex and A is the centre of the base of a segment, height h, of a sphere of radius R. Q and P are taken between O and A such that $OQ = \dfrac{3h}{4}$ and $OP = \dfrac{2h}{3}$. G is the centre of gravity of the segment. Prove that

$$\frac{GP}{GQ} = \frac{h}{3R}.$$ (Oxf. Adv. Maths. 1930.)

M21. OA, OB, OC are three straight lines not in one plane. Prove that the three planes, each of which passes through one of the lines and bisects the angle between the other two, have a common straight line. (Oxf. Adv. Maths. 1930.)

M22. Show how to draw a perpendicular to a given plane from a given point outside.

OA and OB are two intersecting straight lines and P is a point not in their plane. L is the foot of the perpendicular from P to OA, M is the foot of the perpendicular from P to OB, and N is the foot of the perpendicular from P to the plane OAB. Prove that ON is a diameter of the circle which can be circumscribed about the triangle LOM.

(Oxf. Subs. Maths. 1930.)

M23. The projections on a horizontal plane of two intersecting straight lines cut at right angles. If α, β, and θ are the respective inclinations of the two lines and of their plane to the horizontal plane, prove that $\tan^2\theta = \tan^2\alpha + \tan^2\beta$.

A, B, C are points on level ground such that $AB = 450$ yds., $AC = 300$ yds., and $B\hat{A}C = 90°$. Boreholes sunk vertically at A, B, C reach a seam of coal at points L, M, N whose depths are 1120 ft., 1045 ft., 1000 ft. respectively. Find the inclination of the seam (i.e. of the plane LMN) to the horizontal. (Oxf. 1930.)

M24. The radii of the top and the base of a frustum of a cone, whose generators are inclined at 45° to the base, are r and R respectively. If the volume of the frustum is constant, find the ratio of R to r for which its total surface area is a minimum. (Calculus required.) (Oxf. 1930.)

M25. A sphere touches a given plane and passes through two given points A, B on the same side of the plane. Find the locus of the point of contact of the sphere with the given plane (i) when AB is parallel to the given plane, (ii) when AB is not parallel to it.

Show also that, if AB is not parallel to the plane, the locus of the centre of the sphere is the curve in which a certain right circular cylinder is cut by a certain plane. (Joint Bd. 1930.)

M26. A sphere rests in a horizontal circular hole of radius 8 cm., with the lowest point of the sphere 4 cm. below the plane of the hole. Prove that the radius of the sphere is 10 cm.

Calculate (i) the area of the surface of that part of the sphere which is below the hole, (ii) the volume of that part of the sphere. Take $\pi = 3 \cdot 1416$. (Joint Bd. 1930.)

M27. Find the centre of gravity of a triangular lamina ; and show that it is the same as that of three equal particles at the mid-points of its sides.

A lamina in the shape of a trapezium has parallel sides AB, DC ; and EF is the straight line parallel to them which bisects AD and BC. Show that the centre of gravity of the trapezium coincides with that of masses proportional to AB, DC, 4EF at the mid-points of AB, DC, EF respectively. (Joint Bd. App. Maths. 1930.)

M28. Find the centre of gravity of (i) a uniform semicircular arc, (ii) a uniform semicircular plate.

A kite is made of a heavy uniform framework consisting of a back-bone, an isosceles triangle with height equal to its base, and a semi-circle. Find the position of the centre of gravity of the kite (i) when the weight of the paper is neglected, (ii) when the total weight of the paper is one-tenth that of the whole frame.

(C.W.B. App. Maths. 1931.)

M29. Prove that the volume of any tetrahedron is equal to one-third of the product of the base by the height, and deduce a formula for the volume of a right circular cone of height h standing on a base of radius r.

The gas-container of an airship consists of a cylinder of radius 50 feet and height 400 feet, closed in the back by a hemisphere and in front by a circular cone of height 100 feet. It is divided for safety into three equal portions by plane partitions perpendicular to the axis. Prove that each of these partitions is at a distance 77·8 feet from the central plan of the cylindrical part of the body.

(C.W.B. 1930.)

M30. Define the angle between (i) two skew lines, and (ii) a line and a plane.

AB and CD are two lines in space and S is any point. If AB is parallel to the plane SCD and CD is parallel to the plane SAB, prove that AB and CD are parallel. (C.W.B. 1930.)

M31. Prove that a line which is perpendicular to each of two intersecting lines at their point of intersection is perpendicular to any line in the plane containing them.

OA, OB, OC are three concurrent lines each of which is perpendicular to the other two, and OP is perpendicular to the plane ABC. Prove that P is the orthocentre of the triangle ABC.

(C.W.B. 1930.)

M32. Find the area of the portion of the surface of a sphere of radius a between two parallel planes at a distance h apart.

Two points B, C on the same diameter of a sphere of radius a and outside it are at distances $r(>a)$ and $2r$ from the centre on the same side. Prove that the difference between the areas of the sphere visible at the two points is $\pi a^3/r$.   (C.W.B. 1930.)

M33. Find the position of the centre of gravity of a hollow right circular cone, of slant height l and semi-vertical angle θ, made of uniform thin metal and closed at the base.

Such a cone is cut by a plane parallel to the base at half the perpendicular height and the upper portion is removed. Prove that the distance, from the base, of the centre of gravity is

$$\frac{2}{3} \cdot \frac{l\cos\theta}{3+4\sin\theta}.$$ (Lond. P. & A. 1930.)

M34. Show that a straight line can be drawn to intersect at right angles two given skew lines.

AB and CD are two given skew lines and a third line cuts them at X and Y. Find, for different positions of X and Y, the locus of a point Z dividing XY internally in a given ratio.   (Lond. P. & A. 1930.)

M35. Find the centre of gravity of a segment of a uniform circular lamina of radius a, cut off by a chord subtending an angle 2θ at the centre.

A uniform circular lamina is folded so that the arc of the folded portion passes through the centre. Find the distance of the centre of gravity of the lamina, when so folded, from the centre.

(Lond. P. & A. 1930.)

M36. ABCD is a lamina in the form of a trapezium with AB and CD as the parallel sides. AB is produced to X so that BX=CD, and CD is produced to Y so that DY=AB. XY meets EF, the join of the mid-points of AB and CD, in G. Prove that G is the centre of gravity of the lamina.

The lamina ABCD rests with its plane vertical and CD horizontal on a horizontal plane, and is just about to topple over with CB falling towards the horizontal plane. If p is the perpendicular distance between the parallel sides AB and CD, prove that

$$\cot ADC - \cot BCD = \frac{3b(a+b)}{p(b+2a)},$$

where $AB = a$, $CD = b$, and $a < b$. (Lond. P. & A. 1930.)

M37. An area S on a plane inclined at θ to the horizontal is projected on to the horizontal plane and the area of the projection is S_0. Show that $S_0 = S \cos \theta$.

Deduce that the ratios of coplanar areas are not altered by orthogonal projection.

A parallelogram of constant area is inscribed in an ellipse and is such that all its sides touch a concentric, similar and similarly situated ellipse. Determine its area in terms of the axes of the first ellipse. (Lond. P. & A. 1930.)

M38. The base of a rectangular box is ABCD, and the top is A′B′C′D′, the edges AA′, BB′, CC′, DD′ being parallel. If P, Q, R are the mid-points of AB, B′C′, DD′ respectively, show that the plane PQR is parallel to two planes, each passing through three corners of the box, and that its inclination to the base of the box is

$$\tan^{-1}\left(\frac{c\sqrt{a^2+b^2}}{ab}\right),$$

where $AB = a$, $BC = b$, and $AA′ = c$. (Lond. P. & A. 1930.)

M.39. Two chords PQ, P′Q′ of a sphere intersect at A. Prove that $AP \cdot AQ = AP′ \cdot AQ′$.

A system of spheres touch a plane at the same point O. Prove that any plane, not passing through O, cuts them in a series of coaxal circles. (Oxf. & Camb. 1931.)

M40. Prove that, if a plane area lies entirely on one side of an axis in its plane and revolves round this axis, the volume generated is equal to the area multiplied by the length of the path of its centroid. (Oxf. & Camb. 1931.)

M41. Prove that the section of a tetrahedron by a plane parallel to a pair of opposite edges is a parallelogram.

If the middle points of two pairs of opposite edges of a tetrahedron are concyclic, show that the remaining edges are at right angles. (Oxf. & Camb. 1931.)

M42. A tetrahedron ABCD has its opposite edges CA, BD, perpendicular, and also has its opposite edges AB, CD perpendicular; prove that the opposite edges BC, AD are also perpendicular.

If the three vertices A, B, C of such a tetrahedron are fixed, prove that the locus of the fourth vertex D is the straight line through the orthocentre of the triangle ABC and perpendicular to the plane ABC.   (Camb. P. & A. 1931.)

M43. Find the position of the centre of gravity of a uniform solid hemisphere.

A uniform hollow hemisphere has an external radius a and an internal radius b. Find an equation giving the ratio of a to b so that the centre of gravity of the body should lie on the inner surface, and verify that the outer radius is slightly more than $2\frac{1}{2}$ times the inner radius.   (Camb. P. & A. 1931.)

M44. AB is a quadrant of a circle whose centre is O, and P is any point on the arc AB. Show that, if the quadrilateral OAPB is revolved about OA, the volume generated is a maximum when the tangent of the angle AOP is the positive root of the equation

$$4x^3 - x^2 - 4x - 1 = 0. \quad \text{(Camb. P. & A. 1931.)}$$

M45. Prove that the centre of gravity of a uniform solid tetrahedron is the point which divides in the ratio 3 : 1 the connector of any vertex to the centroid of the opposite face.

AB, AC, AD are three edges of a uniform solid cube of which AA′ is a diagonal. Prove that the centre of gravity of the solid, which remains after the tetrahedron ABCD has been removed from the cube, divides AA′ in the ratio 11 : 9.   (Lond. App. Maths. 1931.)

M46. Prove that the volume of a segment of a sphere is

$$\pi x^2 \left(a - \frac{x}{3} \right),$$

where a is the radius of the sphere and x is the height of the segment.

A sphere is dropped carefully into a conical glass of depth h and semi-vertical angle α, which is full of water, the size of the sphere being such as will cause the greatest overflow. Show that the radius of the sphere is $h \sin \alpha (\sin \alpha + \cos 2\alpha)^{-1}$.   (Oxf. 1931.)

M47. From a point A on a straight road, inclined at an angle α to the horizontal, the angle of elevation of a stationary balloon, B, which is *not* vertically above any point on the road, is β. From each of two points on the road, P and Q, d feet, uphill and downhill respectively, from A, the angle of elevation of B is θ. If h feet is the height of B above the level of A, express BA, BP, BQ in terms of the above data and hence prove that

$$h = d \cdot \sqrt{\frac{1 - \sin^2 \alpha \, \operatorname{cosec}^2 \theta}{\operatorname{cosec}^2 \theta - \operatorname{cosec}^2 \beta}}.$$
(Oxf. 1931.)

M48. The shadows cast on level ground by two vertical walls, each $6\frac{1}{4}$ ft. high, one of which runs in a direction 34° North of West, and the other due East, lie within the obtuse angle formed by the walls and are 4 ft. and 6 ft. wide respectively. The sun is to the East of South : find its bearing and elevation. (Oxf. 1931.)

M49. Prove that the centre of gravity of a uniform triangular lamina coincides with that of three equal masses situated one at each vertex of the lamina.

D, E, F are points on the sides BC, CA, AB of a uniform triangular lamina ABC, such that

$$\frac{BD}{DC} = \frac{CE}{EA} = \frac{AF}{FB}.$$

Prove that the centre of gravity of the triangular portion DEF coincides with that of the whole lamina. (Oxf. 1931.)

M50. The length of each edge of a regular tetrahedron is a. Find the lengths of

(i) the perpendicular drawn from a vertex to the opposite face ;
(ii) the distance between the middle points of a pair of opposite edges. (Oxf. Subs. Maths. 1931.)

M51. Find an expression for the area of the curved surface of a right circular cone, the radius of the base being r and the slant side l.

Two diametrically opposite points P and Q are taken on the base of a right circular cone of height 1 ft. and semi-vertical angle 20°. Find by calculation the length of the shortest path from P to Q taken along the curved surface of the cone.

(Joint Bd. Subs. Maths. 1931.)

M52. A right pyramid of height 10 in. stands on a square base of side 6 in. Find

(i) the angle that a slant face makes with the base ;
(ii) the angle between two consecutive slant faces.

(Joint Bd. Subs. Maths. 1931.)

M53. A uniform circular disc ABC of radius r has its centre at O. With centre A and radius r an arc BOC is drawn, and the portion BOCA removed from the original disc. Find the centre of gravity of the remaining part of the disc. (Joint Bd. Subs. Maths. 1931.)

M54. Find the position of the centre of mass of a uniform plane triangular lamina.

A triangle ABC is made of three uniform, heavy rods. Show that its centre of mass is at the centre of the inscribed circle of the triangle formed by joining the mid-points of the sides of the triangle ABC.

(Joint Bd. App. Maths. 1931.)

M55. Find the area of the curved surface of the frustum of a circular cone of vertical angle 2α bounded by parallel circular sections of radii a_1 and a_2.

Two spheres, of radii a and b respectively, touch externally, and a circular cone with its axis along the line of centres includes and touches them both. Prove that the area of the part of the surface of this cone between the circles of contact on the two spheres is $4\pi ab$.

(Joint Bd. 1931.)

M56. The perpendicular height of a frustum of a right circular cone is 8 in., and the radii of the ends are 6 in. and 2 in. Calculate the volume of the frustum.

Assuming the moon to be a sphere of radius R, and the distance between an observer on the earth's surface and the centre of the moon to be 221R, prove that the observer would be able to see $\frac{110}{221}$ of the moon's surface. (Joint Bd. 1931.)

M57. A rectangular trap-door ABCD, which can turn about AB, occupies the horizontal position ABCD when closed and the position ABC′D′ when open. If AB = 4 ft., BC = 8 ft., C′D = 5 ft., find (i) the inclination of the open door to the horizontal, (ii) the inclination of C′D to the horizontal. (Joint Bd. 1931.)

M58. A plane is inclined at an angle α to the horizontal, and contains a straight line AB inclined at an angle θ to the line of greatest slope of the plane. Show that AB is inclined to the horizontal at an angle γ, given by $\qquad \sin \gamma = \sin \alpha \cos \theta$,

and that, if θ' is the projection of θ on the horizontal plane, then

$$\cos \gamma \cos \theta' = \cos \alpha \cos \theta.$$

If a second line, AC, makes an angle φ with the line of greatest slope, and AB and AC are two sides of a parallelogram ABDC, show,

H 2

without assuming any theorem on the ratio of an area and its projection, that ABDC projects orthogonally into a figure of area ABDC $\cos \alpha$. (Lond. P. & A. 1931.)

M59. Prove that the length of the common perpendicular to two skew lines is the shortest distance between them.

A square lamina ABCD, of side a, is rotated about AB through a right angle to take up the position ABC_1D_1. Find the length of the shortest distance between AC_1 and BD. (Lond. P. & A. 1931.)

M60. The middle points of the edges BC, CA, AB, DA, DB, and DC of a tetrahedron ABCD are respectively P, Q, R, P', Q', R'. Prove that PP', QQ', RR' meet in a point and bisect one another.

If the areas of the triangles ABC and ABD are equal, prove that the triangle PQR' is also equal in area to the triangle P'Q'R' and find the corresponding condition for the equality of the areas of the triangles PQ'R' and P'QR'. (Lond. P. & A. 1931.)

M61. A solid sphere of radius r is divided by a plane at a distance x from the centre into two parts, of which the volumes are V, V' and the *total* surface areas are S, S'.

Prove that

$$V : V' = (2r^3 + 3r^2x - x^3) : (2r^3 - 3r^2x + x^3),$$
$$S : S' = (3r^2 + 2rx - x^2) : (3r^2 - 2rx - x^2),$$

V being greater than V'. (Lond. 1931.)

M62. A uniform solid is in the form of a sphere of radius R, through which has been drilled a hole in the form of a cylinder, whose axis coincides with a diameter of the sphere. If the length of the hole is $2l$, show that the volume of the solid is $\dfrac{4\pi}{3} l^3$.

  (Oxf. Adv. Maths. 1931.)

M63. Prove that if a tetrahedron has two pairs of opposite edges perpendicular, the third pair will also be perpendicular.

Show that for such a tetrahedron the four lines drawn from the vertices perpendicular to the opposite faces are concurrent.

  (C.W.B. 1927.)

M64. AB and CD are two non-intersecting lines; if a point X be found in AB such that the plane XCD is perpendicular to AB, show that the perpendicular XY from X to CD is the common perpendicular to the two given lines, and that the plane ABY is perpendicular to CD.

Show that the perpendicular from A upon the plane BCD, the perpendicular from B upon the plane ACD, and the line XY are three concurrent lines. (C.W.B. 1927.)

M65. Find the area of the surface of a sphere.

Assuming the earth to be a sphere of radius 4000 miles, calculate approximately the area of the portion of it visible to an observer in an aeroplane at an altitude of 10,000 feet. (C.W.B. 1927.)

M66. Three equal spheres each 1 inch in diameter rest in contact with each other in a spherical bowl whose diameter is 6 inches ; find the distance of the plane passing through the centres of the spheres from the centre of the bowl. (C.W.B. 1933.)

M67. Show that, in any trihedral angle, the sum of any two face angles is greater than the third face angle.

OA, OB, OC are the three edges of a trihedral angle at O, and OX is another straight line within the solid angle determined by the planes OAB, OBC, OCA. Show that

(i) the sum of the angles AOX, BOX, COX is greater than half the sum of the angles AOB, BOC, COA ;

(ii) the sum of the angles AOX, COX is less than the sum of the angles AOB, COB. (C.W.B. 1933.)

M68. Prove that a plane cuts a sphere in a circular section.

A series of planes is drawn through a fixed point outside a sphere of radius a. Prove that the centres of all the circular sections made by the sphere on such planes lie on a spherical cap of area πa^2.

(C.W.B. 1933.)

M69. When is

(i) a line in space parallel to a plane, and

(ii) a line in space parallel to a second line ?

Prove that a plane parallel to two opposite edges of a tetrahedron cuts the tetrahedron in a parallelogram. Is it possible to choose the position of the plane so that the parallelogram is a rhombus ?

(C.W.B. 1932.)

M70. Find the area of a cap of a sphere of radius a cut off by a plane at a distance $(a-h)$ from the centre.

Two spheres of radii, a, b, cut orthogonally (at right angles). Prove that the area of the surface of the first sphere external to the second is

$$2\pi a^2 \left(1 + \frac{a}{\sqrt{(a^2+b^2)}} \right).$$ (C.W.B. 1932.)

M71. Prove that the sum of the plane angles that bound a solid angle is less than four right angles. A solid angle is formed by two planes intersecting at an angle of 60° and a third plane which is inclined at an angle of 60° to their line of intersection and also equally inclined to the other two planes.

Find the magnitudes of the three plane angles bounding the solid angle, and also the inclination of the latter plane to either of the first two planes. (C.W.B. 1930.)

M72. Find the centre of gravity of a wire in the form of an arc of a circle.

If a closed figure is made by a wire, and is in the form of an arc of a circle, with the two radii joining its ends to the centre, prove that the distance of its centre of gravity from the centre is

$$\frac{a}{2} \cdot \frac{2\sin\alpha + \cos\alpha}{\alpha + 1},$$

2α being the angle subtended by the arc at the centre, and a the radius of the circle. (C.W.B. 1930.)

M73. Prove that if a straight line is perpendicular to each of two intersecting straight lines it is perpendicular to every straight line in their plane.

Find the locus of a point which is equidistant from (i) two fixed points, (ii) three fixed points (not collinear).

How many points are equidistant from four fixed points (not coplanar) ? (C.W.B. 1932.)

M74. Prove that the volume of a spherical cap of thickness h is $\pi h^2 \left(r - \dfrac{h}{3} \right)$, where r is the radius of the sphere.

A sphere of radius r is inscribed in a cone so that the centre of the sphere is distant k from the vertex of the cone. Find the volume of the space which is entirely enclosed between the sphere and the curved surface of the cone. (C.W.B. 1933.)

M75. How do you measure the angle between (i) two non-intersecting lines, (ii) a line and a plane, (iii) two planes ?

ABCD and A'B'C'D' are two parallel faces of a rectangular parallelepiped, AA', BB', CC', DD' being parallel edges. If AB, BC, AA' are of lengths 4, 3, 6 in. respectively, find the angles between (i) the lines AC and BC', (ii) the line A'D' and the plane AB'C, (iii) the planes AB'C and ABCD. (C.W.B. 1933.)

ANSWERS AND HINTS

CHAPTER I

1A1. Octahedron. **1A2.** Rule 1. **1A3.** Area of triangle $=\frac{1}{2}$ parm. with same base and height. **1A4.** Str. line, circle, sphere. **1A5.** Pard. 8 v., 12 e., 6 f. ; tet. 4 v., 6 e., 4 f. ; oct. 6 v., 12 e., 8 f.

1B1. Rule 1. **1B2.** Rule 1. **1B3.** P. 79. **1B4.** Six vert. equidistant from origin. If all faces are opaque, the figure is an equilateral triangle inscribed in a regular hexagon, with the axes projecting from the vertices. **1B5.** A regular hexagon divided into three equal rhombuses from the centres of which emerge the nearer halves of the axes. **1B6.** Same ; or replace " str. lines " by " planes ". **1B7.** Replace " rect. " by " rectangular parallelepiped ", and " two adj. sides " by " three adj. edges ". **1B8.** " ... is the plane which bisects it at right angles ", or " ... from vertices of a triangle are equal, is the str. line through its circumcentre and at right angles to its plane ". **1B9.** " If two spheres intersect, their line of centres passes through the centre of their circle of intersection at right angles to its plane."

1C1. 1W2. **1C2.** Str. line, triangle, tetrahedron ; 1W4. **1C3.** Str. line, parallelogram, octahedron ; 1W4. **1C4.** " Any two sides of a triangle are together ... " **1C5.** Replace " circle ... three ... str. line " by " sphere ... four ... plane ". **1C6.** Circumf. folded $=\frac{1}{2}$ circumf. open ; $\therefore$ radius of rim $=\frac{1}{2}$ slant ht.

CHAPTER II

2A1. All possible except (3). **2A2.** (1) $a \parallel c$; (2) $\alpha \parallel c$; (3) $a \parallel \gamma$; (4) $b \parallel \alpha\gamma$; (5) $\beta \parallel$ plane ac, if a and c are coplanar. **2A3.** 8·28 cm.

2B1. Plane On. **2B2.** (1) plane mn ; (2) whole of space ; 2W6. **2B3.** A, B, C, D are not in a plane. **2B4.** Line of intersection of two planes ; 2B1. **2B5.** If two of the points bc, ca, ab, coincide, all three must do so ; if not, they determine a plane. **2B6.** Let line of heads cut table in X. **2B7.** $\frac{2}{3}$ in. from corner ; creases and free edge are concurrent. **2B8.** α, β, γ, ... contain x ; $\therefore$ $\alpha\theta$, $\beta\theta$, $\gamma\beta$ ... contain the point $x\theta$. **2B9.** P, Q, R, S are coplanar. **2B10.** $2\frac{6}{7}$ in. Plane cuts planes ABC, ADC in str. lines concurrent with AC.

2C1. Diagonals of base bisect one another; ∴ vertical isosceles triangles have a common altitude, and are, ∴, congruent. **2C2.** Cut off equal lengths DP, DQ, DR from DA, DB, DC, and let DX, DY, DZ cut QR, RP, PQ in X′, Y′, Z′. **2C3.** Use 2W5, or the particular case in which corresponding sides of the triangles are parallel. **2C4.** 2W5; draw any parallelogram in the given corner, with one diagonal along the given median : the third side of the triangle is parallel to the other diagonal. **2C5.** 2W5; if corresponding sides meet in P, Q, R, these lie in φφ′; ∴ 2W5 applied to triangles BRB′, CQC′ proves its converse with respect to triangles ABC, A′B′C′; exceptional case : the three joins parallel to one another.

CHAPTER III

3A3. Str. lines that divide two skew str. lines proportionally lie in parallel planes. **3A4.** Exclude. **3A5.** 3T1. **3A6.** 3T3. **3A7.** $\dfrac{4}{1+xyz}$; 3W5. **3A8.** 3T5. **3A9.** 3T4, 3T2 ; diagonals of parm.

3B1. ‖ lines determine a plane ; 3T1, 2, 1. **3B2.** 3W1, 3T1. **3B3.** Take any plane containing the line ; 3T4, 1. **3B4.** 3T1, 2. **3B5.** 3T3, 4. **3B6.** Line αβ ; 3T1, 2. **3B7.** 3W2. **3B8.** 3W2. **3B9.** 3W2. **3B10.** 3W2. **3B11.** Live cable is in line common to planes of shadows. **3B12.** Draw PQ ‖ AX; 3T2. **3B13.** 14 ft. 3T3, 5. **3B14.** 3W2. **3B15.** Omit ....

....

3B16. 3W6. **3B17.** 3W2. **3B18.** 2W6. **3B19.** 3T1. **3B20.** 3W5.

3C1. Three str. lines, traced by centres of parallelograms ABCD, ACBD, ABDC with vertices on a, b, c, d ; each line is the line of intersection of two planes ; 3T5. **3C2.** 3T1, 5. **3C3.** Draw lines of intersection of pairs of planes of opposite oblique faces. **3C4.** Thro' centre of ABCD draw line ‖ AP. **3C5.** 2W2 ; G is on pl. AXD, ∴ on join of mid. pts. of every pair of opp. edges. **3C6.** 3T3. **3C7.** 3B19, 3T5. **3C8.** 3W6. **3C9.** DX ; 3W6. **3C10.** Faces cannot be concurrent ; two diagonals determine planes of two parallel faces (3T3) whose remaining diagonals meet the third given diagonal. **3C11.** 3W4. **3C12.** Parallel chords. **3C13.** 3T5, 3W5.

CHAPTER IV

4A1. 3T6. **4A2.** 4T1, 3. **4A3.** $x \parallel y$; 4T1, 3. **4A4.** 4T4, 1, 3. **4A5.** If $\alpha \perp b \perp c$, let any plane thro' c cut α in x ; ∴ the coplanar lines c, x, are both $\perp b$; ∴ $c \parallel x$; ∴ $c \parallel \alpha$. **4A6.** 3T6. **4A7.** $\alpha\beta \perp \gamma$. **4A8.** 3T6, 4T1. **4A9.** 3T6, 4T1. **4A10.** Tangent plane. **4A11.** Congr. triangles. **4A12.** If X is mid. pt. of BD, BD $\perp$ AX, XC.

4B1. 4T1. **4B2.** $\alpha\beta \perp$ AC and AB. **4B3.** Congr. triangles. **4B4.** 4W2, 1. **4B5.** 4T1. **4B6.** Congr. triangles. **4B7.** Congr. triangles; 4T1. **4B8.** 4T2. **4B9.** Diags. of rect. are equal and bisect one another. **4B10.** If VN $\perp abc$, $a \perp$ AVN ; $\therefore$ $a \perp$ AN. **4B11.** 3T4, 6. **4B12.** Let Q' be image of Q in α; i.e. let α bisect QQ' at right angles; then PQ' cuts α in required pt. **4B13.** 4B12. **4B14.** BP, PQ, QR $\perp$ CY, 4T3. **4B15.** 4T2 ; thro' P, Q, R take planes $\alpha, \beta, \gamma, \perp$ BC, CA, AB ; $\triangle$ XYZ is in plane PQR. **4B16.** Draw AB' $\parallel$ DC ; 4T1, 3. **4B17.** Complete a rect. ; 4T1. **4B18.** 4W1 ; pl. thro' any three common pts. **4B19.** Spheres α, β, γ ; circles $\beta\gamma, \gamma\alpha, \alpha\beta$; pair of common points $\alpha\beta\gamma$. **4B20.** 4B19 ; planes of section of α, β, γ, have common line $\alpha\beta\gamma$, which meets each of the planes $\delta\alpha, \delta\beta, \delta\gamma$, in point $\alpha\beta\gamma\delta$. **4B21.** $\sqrt{2}$; diagonal of square. **4B22.** $2\sqrt{\frac{2}{3}}$; tetrahedron. **4B23.** 4W1. **4B24.** Congr. triangles. **4B25.** $2\sqrt{\frac{2}{3}}a$. **4B26.** $1 : \sqrt{2}$. **4B27.** 3T4. **4B28.** 3T4, 6. **4B29.** 4T2. **4B30.** 3W2. **4B31.** 3W2. **4B32.** QRS. **4B33.** Each edge *meets* 6 others; for Part (ii) consider the different cases. **4B34.** $1 : \sqrt{2}$; draw RP' $=$ and $\parallel$ QP. **4B35.** 4B1.

4C1. Right angles PQR, PRS, PSQ ; obtuse angle QRS ; Pythagoras. **4C2.** 3C13. **4C3.** Pyth. **4C4.** Pyth. **4C5.** Radical axis. **4C6.** Sphere ; internal and external bisectors of angle of triangle. **4C7.** Sphere ; Apollonius' Th. **4C8.** Tangents to sph. from same pt. are equal ; consider a plane through the line of centres. **4C9.** Part of radical plane, limiting positions of the line are the direct and transverse common tangents of sections through the line of centres. **4C10.** Annular space between circles of radii $(a \pm b)$ times the cosine of the inclination of a common tangent to the line of centres. **4C11.** Method of 4B20. **4C12.** Sphere ; plane ; take section through O and centre. **4C13.** Sphere ; plane at infinity. **4C14.** Circle; str. line ; 4B18, 4C12. **4C15.** Take P'Q'R' $\parallel$ PQR ; simplify the ratio PQ . QR : P'Q' . Q'R' by similar triangles. **4C16.** 3B19 ; section $\parallel$ two faces of cube, and containing one edge of tet., and bisecting the opp. edge. **4C17.** Draw equal lines OP, OA, OB, OC $\parallel$ given line and sides of triangle resp., and PN $\perp$ its plane. By congr. triangles O and N both coincide with the centre of the circle ABC. **4C18.** Equal angles in equal circular segments in planes equidistant from centre of sphere. **4C19.** Let angle $ab = cd = \varphi$; $bc = da = \theta$; diags. x, y ; $x^2 = a^2 + b^2 - 2ab \cos \varphi = \ldots$; $\therefore$ $x^2(ab - cd) = (ac - bd)(bc - ad)$, and so on. **4C20.** If a quadrilateral has two pairs of equal opposite angles, it is a parallelogram, and, $\therefore$, has two pairs of equal opposite sides. If a " crossed " quadrilateral has two pairs of equal opposite angles, it is cyclic, and the rectangle contained by the " crossed " sides is equal to the sum of those contained by the " diagonals " and the other sides.

(The "diagonals" are *sides*, and the "crossed" sides are *diagonals*, of an ordinary cyclic quadrilateral.)

CHAPTER V

5A1. 5T4, 4T3. **5A2.** 5T4. **5A3.** Three mutually perpendicular str. lines determine three mutually perpendicular planes. **5A4.** PM $\perp \alpha$, PN $\perp \beta$; $\therefore$ PMN $\perp \alpha\beta$ at O, say ; $\therefore$ MON is dihedral angle, and OP bisects it ; congr. triangles. **5A5.** PA, PB equally inclined to axis AB. **5A6.** 5T6. **5A7.** Let a, b, be semi-major and minor axes of ellipse, r any semi-diam., x, y its projections on a, b, and let dashed letters stand for corresponding lines in the auxiliary circle ; Pyth. ; 5T5. **5A8.** 5T7. **5A9.** Normal at in-centre ; 5T7 ; equal dihedral angles. **5A10.** Normal at centroid. **5A11.** Draw cuboid with given line as diagonal and edges $\parallel$ to axes. **5A12.** 5T6. **5A13.** 5A11. **5A14.** 5A11. **5A15.** 5T6, 3T3 ; or congr. triangles ; 5T7. **5A16.** A = B', B = A', C = C' = 90°. **5A17.** Make given line hypotenuse of a right-angled triangle with sides $\parallel$ and $\perp$ to axis of projection.

5B1. $\cos^{-1} \frac{1}{3} = 70° 30'$ approx. **5B2.** $\tan \frac{1}{2}\theta = \sqrt{2}$; $\cos \theta = -\frac{1}{3}$; $\therefore$ $\theta = 180° - 70° 30'$ approx. **5B3.** Let PM, PN $\perp \alpha$, β ; produce MP to Q, making PQ = PN ; then QM is constant ; $\therefore$ locus of Q is a plane $\varphi \parallel \alpha$; locus of P bisects dihedral angle $\beta\varphi$. **5B4.** If AA', BB', CC' are diagonals of the octahedron, B'A $\parallel$ A'B, and so on ; $\therefore$ we can complete the parallelograms AB'CV, BC'AV, CA'BV, ... ; dihedral angles are supplementary. **5B5.** AB = AC, whence BB' = CC' ; $\therefore$ BC $\parallel$ B'C', and, $\therefore$, $\parallel$ to axis.

5B6. Each edge is an orthogonal projection of the diagonal ; $\cos^{-1} \frac{1}{\sqrt{3}}$ = 54° 44'. **5B7.** Perp. to a diag. **5B8.** Project on a plane normal to the axis ; 5T7. **5B9.** A'B' + B'C' + C'A' = 0. **5B10.** Construct right-angled triangle with hyp. = AB, and one side = AA' - BB' ; third side = A'B'. **5B11.** If α, β, γ, ... $\perp \varphi$, then $\alpha\beta$, $\beta\gamma$, ... $\perp \varphi$; $\therefore$ $\alpha\beta \parallel \beta\gamma \parallel$ ... . **5B12.** Reduce all distances $\perp$ to axis in ratio $\cos \theta$. **5B13.** Line $\parallel$ to diag. ; 5B6. **5B14.** Perp. to one of the 4 diags. **5B15.** $a \perp \alpha$, $b \perp \beta$, ... ; $\therefore$ $ab \perp \alpha\beta$, ... ; $\therefore$ $\alpha\beta \parallel \beta\gamma \parallel$ ... ; but they have a common point ; $\therefore$ they coincide. **5B16.** $a \perp \alpha$; $\therefore$ $a \perp x$; 4T2. **5B17.** PM + MN + NO = const. ; $\therefore$ sum of projections on a line equally inclined to the axes is const. ; $\therefore$ locus is plane normal to that line. **5B18.** Fig. 47 ; draw BM, CN $\perp$ XYZ ; with centre N and radius = true length of BC, describe arc cutting BM produced in P ; draw XC'B' $\parallel$ NP.

5C1. AO $\perp$ OBC ; $\therefore$ plane thro' A $\perp$ BC cuts semicircle on BC in O, giving OB, OC. **5C2.** If ON $\perp$ ABC, $\sum\left(\dfrac{\text{triangle OAB}}{\text{triangle ABC}}\right)^2 = \Sigma \cos^2\text{NOC} = 1$.

5C3. PK, PM, PN are edges of a parallelepiped of which OP is a diagonal ; their inclinations to φ are α, β, γ ; $\therefore$, if OR $\perp \varphi$, OR $= \Sigma$PK sin α. **5C4.** Project on plane mid-way between the lines and $\parallel$ to them ; O'A' $\perp$ O'B', and P is the mid-point of A'B' ; $\therefore$ O'P $=$ PA' $=$ constant. **5C5.** 5T6, 4C17. **5C6.** 5W2. **5C7.** 5W2. **5C8.** 5W2. **5C9.** 5W2. **5C10.** Two sides of a triangle are together greater than the third ; in the six equations the distance of each vertex appears three times. **5C11.** 5T7.

CHAPTER VI

6A1. 4T1, 5T4. **6A2.** 6T1, 2. **6A3.** 6T1. **6A4.** Let AQ in plane $=$ given line AP, and let PN $\perp$ plane ; QN is greatest when it passes thro' A ; Pyth. ; Lemma. **6A5.** 6T2, applied four times. **6A6.** $d^2 + r^2 = R^2$. **6A7.** Omit V ; if $A\widehat{W}P = B\widehat{W}P$, W is circumcentre of triangle APB ; if not, take P' in PB such that $B\widehat{W}P' = A\widehat{W}P$; congr. and isosc. triangles ; $\therefore$ APP'B is a str. line ; $\therefore$ (ii) has no analogue unless W is at infinity. **6A8.** If BC $=$ B'C', CA $=$ C'A', and $B\widehat{A}C + B'\widehat{A}'C' = 180°$, then $A\widehat{B}C$ $= A'\widehat{B}'C'$; produce B'A' to B'', making A'B'' $=$ BA.

6B1. Let $A\widehat{V}B = A\widehat{V}C$, and AV $\perp$ plane ABC ; then BAC, BVC are isosceles triangles with the same base and equal vertical angles. **6B2.** Medians of reg. tet. **6B3.** Locus of points equidistant from three planes. **6B4.** Take equal arms VA, VB, VC ; planes bisect AB, BC, CA at right angles. **6B5.** 6W4. **6B6.** Reg. tet. **6B7.** Take VA $=$ VB $=$ VC ; circumcentre of triangle ABC. **6B8.** $\sin^{-1}\dfrac{1}{\sqrt{3}}$; reg. tet. **6B9.** VA $=$ VB $= \ldots$; VN $\perp$ ABC $\ldots$; $\therefore$ NA $=$ NB $= \ldots$. **6B10.** If $B\widehat{A}C =$ dih. B(VA)C, prove that BA, AC, BC $=$ corresponding lines in the other trihedral angle. **6B11.** 6T1, 6B10. **6B12.** Bisect the third dihedral angle. **6B13.** If two dihedral angles of a trihedral angle are equal, the face angles opposite to them are equal ; 6T1, 6B12. **6B14.** Diagonal plane ; 6B10. **6B15.** If a tetrahedral angle has two pairs of equal opposite dihedral angles, it has two pairs of equal opposite face angles ; 6T1, 6B14. **6B16.** Method of 6B10. **6B17.** $A\widehat{V}B$, $B\widehat{V}C$, and dih. angle B(AV)C are equal to the corresponding angles of the other trih. angle ; if A(BV)C $=$ A'(B'V')C', trih. angles are congruent, 6B10 ; if not, let V,ABD with dih. angle B(AV)C be congr. to V',A'B'C' ; then $B\widehat{V}D$

$= B\hat{V}C$; $\therefore$ $B(CV)D = B(DV)C$. **6B18.** 6T1, 6B16. **6B19.** 6T1, 6B17.
6B20. Symmetrical diag. plane gives 6B10; this, with the other diag.
plane, gives 6B16. **6B21.** Use diag. planes *separately* with 6B10, and
together with 6B18. **6B22.** 6T1, 6T3. **6B23.** Equal; produce $A'V'$ to A''
so that $A''\hat{V'}B' = 180° - A'\hat{V'}B' = A\hat{V}B$; 6B16. **6B24.** Supplementary;
let ξ, $\xi\eta$, η be supplements of $\beta\gamma$, γ, $\gamma\alpha$; let $\alpha'\beta'\gamma'$ be conjugate to $\alpha\beta\gamma$.
6B25. Supplementary; let V,ABC, V',A'B'C' be $\alpha\beta\gamma$, $\alpha'\beta'\gamma'$; produce
$A'V'$ to A''; 6B18.

6C1. Cf. 6B9; $A\hat{B}C = B\hat{C}D$; $\therefore$ arc ABC = arc BCD; $\therefore$ arc AB = arc
CD. **6C2.** Project whole figure on one of the parallel planes; obtain two
sets of congruent isosceles triangles; each angle of one polygon consists
of two base angles of one set and one vertical angle of the other. **6C3.**
Take $NBV \perp VAC$ and $NCV \perp VAB$, and $ABC \perp VN$; then $AC \perp NBV$,
and $AB \perp NCV$; $\therefore$ N is orthocentre of triangle ABC; $\therefore$ $AB \perp NVC$.
6C4. 6W3, four times. **6C5.** Take $VA = VB = VC = VD$, and X, Y mid-
points of BD, AC; then $BD \perp AX$, VX, CX; $\therefore$ A, V, C, X are coplanar,
$AX = VX = CX$, and VX bisects $A\hat{V}C$; $\therefore$ VXY is a str. line; and X, Y
are circumcentres of triangles VAC, VBD; $\therefore$ if one is inside its triangle,
the other is outside; $\therefore$ one triangle is acute- and the other obtuse-
angled. **6C6.** Rhombic dodecahedron (Fig. 106); side of large sq. = diag.
of small. **6C7.** Diagonals of rhombus are sides of squares in 6C6. **6C8.**
If C is mid-point of edge AB, $VC = \sqrt{2}AC$ (Pyth.). **6C9.** Section mid-
way between two opposite trihedral vertices is a reg. hexagon; aliter,
if VA, VB, VC, VD are edges, and $AE \perp VB$, AEC is dih. angle. **6C10.**
Each angle $= 180° - \dfrac{360°}{n}$, and is less than $\dfrac{360°}{m}$. **6C11.** 6T3, 1, 3. **6C12.**
P lies on a chord of a smaller segment. **6C13.** 6T2, 6W1. **6C14.** Vertex
at centre of cube, and arms bisect its edges. **6C15.** P may lie on a chord
of the " bulge " of the *greater* segment; $\therefore$ it may lie on either a greater
or on a smaller segment. **6C16.** If $P(WV)A$ and $P(WV)B$ are not equal,
take P' in PB such that $P'(WV)B = P(WV)A$; then 6B18 and 6B12
show that A, P, B, P, P' are coplanar; whence $WV \perp AVB$; $\therefore$ (ii)
if $P(WV)A$ and $P(WV)B$ are equal, apply 6B16, 13,7. **6C17.** $\alpha\gamma = \alpha'\gamma'$;
c.f. 6B24. **6C18.** $\beta = \beta'$, 6T1, 6C17.

CHAPTER VII

7A1. Octahedron; each corner $=\frac{1}{8}$ of whole. **7A2.** 1·540; diag. of
cube = diam. of sphere. **7A3.** 7T6. **7A4.** 7T1,4. **7A5.** Diagonals. **7A6.**
Pyramids of 7A5 quadrisected. **7A7.** 7T8. **7A8.** 7T1,4. **7A9.** Each

equivalent to a third parallelepiped with its upper face between same two pairs of parallel lines. **7A10.** One vertex of parallelepiped is common to the pyramids, whose bases are the three faces of the pyramid that meet the opposite vertex. **7A11.** 27·1 p.c. ; 7T8. **7A12.** 46·41 p.c. ; 7T8.

7B1. $8\sqrt{2}$ cu. in. ; two sq. pyr. with ht. $=\frac{1}{2}$ diag. **7B2.** $\dfrac{2\sqrt{2}}{3}$ cu. in.
7B3. $\dfrac{8\sqrt{3}}{27} r^3$; $r=\frac{3}{4}$ ht. **7B4.** Actually $\frac{1}{6}$. **7B5.** Actually $\frac{2}{9}$; edge of cube $=\frac{1}{3}$ of diag. of oct. **7B6.** $3(10\sqrt{2}-14) \times 100$ per cent. ; edge of oct. divided in ratio $m:n$; edge of cube : edge of oct. $=\dfrac{m}{m+n}$; edge of cube : diag. of oct. $=\dfrac{n}{m+n}$. **7B7.** Pyramid and prism. **7B8.** 7T4,5.
7B9. Sum of four tetrahedra $=$ given tet. **7B10.** $\dfrac{5\sqrt{2}}{3} a^3$; 7B1 ; two corners are equivalent to a regular octahedron $\frac{1}{8}$ of the whole ; 7T8.
7B11. $\frac{1}{2}h(A+B)$; 7T5 or 7T7. **7B12.** $\frac{1}{3}(2+\sqrt{2})$; 7T7. **7B13.** $\dfrac{h}{12}$; 7B9.
7B14. $\dfrac{h}{6}(2ab+2cd+ad+bc)$; 7T7. **7B15.** $\frac{1}{8}A\sqrt{3A}$; faces have equal altitudes ; $\therefore$, by congr. triangles, projection of vertex is centre of base ; hence ht. of pyr. $=\dfrac{\sqrt{3}}{2}$ times length of edge of base ; 5T6. **7B16.** Divide the cube of 1W3 by six triangles with a common vertex at the centre, and bases on the edges of the inscribed tetrahedron. **7B17.** Surf. of cube : surf. of tet. $=1:\sqrt[6]{3}$; take edges $2x$, $2y$; equate volumes ; 7B2. **7B18.** 7B17, 7T8 ; or method of 7B17 ; vol. of cube : vol. of tet. $=\sqrt{3}:1$.

7C1. Prove faces, and then tetrahedra, equal in height. **7C2.** If O is centre of section ABC... , OB, AC bisect one another ; $\therefore$, if length x is cut from axis, $x+b=a+c$. **7C3.** 4656 cu. ft. ; frustum of a tetrahedron 64 ft. high on base 96 ft. by 3 ft. **7C4.** Cut corners from a tetrahedron. **7C5.** Cut corners from a cube, and fit them together on two opposite faces. **7C6.** Ratio of sides of square and its inscribed octagon $=1:\sqrt{2}-1$; 7B16. **7C7.** 7T7. **7C8.** Consider vertical diagonal section. **7C9.** 7T7 ; each end divides into n, and the mid-section into $2n$ isosceles triangles. **7C10.** 6C2. **7C11.** 7T6 ; edge is a *two-sided* polygon, as a point travelling round a polygon must return to its point of departure. **7C12.** Section bisecting two opposite edges at right angles consists of two isosceles triangles ; $\therefore$ area $=\frac{1}{2}a^2\sqrt{2}$; $\therefore$ height $=\sqrt{\frac{2}{3}}a$. **7C13.** When $q=r=0$, $p=\dfrac{v}{a}$; given planes intersect in OA, OB, OC, which cut the locus in
A, B, C ; $\therefore \displaystyle\sum \frac{\text{POBC}}{\text{AOBC}} = \sum \frac{pa}{v} = \frac{1}{v}\Sigma pa = 1.$

CHAPTER VIII

8A1. 40 per cent. ; 8T3. **8A2.** 8T3 ; $\mp$ according as the parallels are in the same or different hemispheres. **8A3.** 7T4. **8A4.** $\pi h(a^2 - b^2)$.

8A5. $\frac{4}{3}\pi(a^3 - b^3)$. **8A6.** $\pi t\left(4r^2 + \frac{t^2}{3}\right)$. **8A7.** $\pi t(d + t)$. **8A8.** $A = B = C = \frac{1}{2}\pi$.

8A9. $r^2(5\pi - A - B - C)$. **8A10.** Volumes $\frac{1}{3}r . \pi r^2 : \frac{2}{3}\pi r^3 : r . \pi r^2$; total surfaces $\frac{1}{2}\sqrt{2}r . 2\pi r + \pi r^2 : 2\pi r^2 + \pi r^2 : r . 2\pi r + 2 . \pi r^2$.

8B1. Let S be vol. of inner cylinder, and find P + Q + S, Q + S, S ; 8T2. **8B2.** Tetrahedron consists of four tetrahedra in each of which is inscribed a cone ; ratio of volume of tet. to that of inscribed cone = ratio of their bases $= \sqrt{3} : \pi(\frac{1}{3}\sqrt{3})^2 = \frac{3\sqrt{3}}{\pi} = \frac{1}{\cdot605}$; $\therefore$ percentage of whole figure in *all* the unoccupied corners = 39·5 ; divide by the number of corners. **8B3.** See 8B2. **8B4.** 8A1. **8B5.** 1 : 2 ; 8T1, 3. **8B6.** 8T2. **8B7.** 4 : 3 ; 7T4, 8T6. **8B8.** 5 : 2 ; 7T4, 8T5. **8B9.** $\frac{1}{4}\pi d^3 + \pi a^2 d$, 8T6. **8B10.** 9 : 32 ; 7T4, 8T5. **8B11.** 7T8 ; ratio = cube of ratio of edge of cube to its diagonal. **8B12.** 8T1. **8B13.** 7T4. **8B14.** Section thro' axis is trapezium bounded by four pairs of equal tangents ; 8T1, 2, 3, 5. **8B15.** $2\sqrt{2}\pi h(r^2 + rh + \frac{1}{3}h^2)$; difference between the remainders from two spheres, when two cones are removed from each ; 8T3, 8T5. **8B16.** $\frac{5}{32}$; let θ be the semi-vertical angle, and h, H the heights of the small cone and cylinder.

8C1. $\frac{\pi}{3}(H - h)(3rH + 3rh - H^2 - Hh - h^2)$; 8T6. **8C2.** $\pi t^2\left(r - h - \frac{t}{3}\right)$; 8T6.

8C3. $\pi t(H^2 - 3Ht + 3t^2)$. **8C4.** Let θ be semi-vertical angle of frustum. **8C5.** Let ht. $= kr$; then $\frac{k^2}{k-2} = 4n$. **8C6.** Let a, b, r be radii of circles and sphere, and θ the semi-vertical angle of the conical zone ; then $\tan\theta = \frac{b-a}{b+a} . \frac{1}{k}$, and $r = \frac{1}{2}(a + b)\sqrt{(k^2 + 1)} \sec\theta$. **8C7.** Diameter of sphere = diagonal of face of cube ; 8T5,6. **8C8.** 8T3. **8C9.** 8T2,5,6. **8C10.** Radii of spindle and cylinder = R, r ; ht. of cyl. $= r\sqrt{2}$; $\frac{h}{r\sqrt{2}} = \frac{R}{R-r}$. **8C11.** $9\pi a^2$, $3\pi a^3$, 8T1, 3,2,6.

CHAPTER IX

9A1. 9T4. **9A2.** $x = \frac{r}{3}$. **9A3.** The median thro' a given vertex is the locus of centroids of sections parallel to it. **9A4.** 2W2, 9T4 ; elements of the cone are tetrahedra with the same vertex and height. **9A5.** Elements are triangles. **9A6.** 9A5, 8T1, 9T4. **9A7.** $\frac{1}{4}(a - b)$; 9A4, 9T4. **9A8.**

$\dfrac{3}{4}\dfrac{a^2+4ab+2b^2}{a+3b}$; 9T4. **9A9.** $2\pi^2ab^2$; 9T5. **9A10.** $4\pi^2ab$. **9A11.** $\dfrac{2a}{\pi}$

from centre ; 9W1. **9A12.** $\dfrac{4a}{3\pi}$ from centre ; 9W2. **9A13.** $2\pi(Ax+By)$;

9T5. **9A14.** On axis mid-way between the planes of its circular edges ;
9T4, 8T3. **9A15.** On axis at distance $r-\frac{1}{2}h$ from centre ; 9A14. **9A16.**

$\dfrac{4\sqrt{2}a}{3\pi}$ from centre. **9A17.** At distances $\dfrac{4a}{3\pi}$, $\dfrac{4b}{3\pi}$ from axes, and $\dfrac{4}{3\pi}\sqrt{(a^2+b^2)}$

from centre ; 9A12, 9T4. **9A18.** $\dfrac{5h}{8}$ from base ; 9T4, 9A4. **9A19.**

$\dfrac{b^3c}{a^3-b^3}$; 9T4.

9B1. If M′ is *any* area, or a one-dimensional figure such that C′ is the
middle point of every chord which passes thro' it, then C′ is centroid of
M′ ; but not *generally* in the case of a one-dimensional figure ; because
its elements are not all reduced in the same ratio ; compare 5T4 with
5T5. **9B2.** Corresponding elements of volume are proportional, but not
corresponding elements of areas ; cf. 9B1. **9B3.** $\frac{3}{8}$ of radius ; 9A14.

9B4. $\dfrac{3\sqrt{3}}{8}$ of radius ; 9B3, 9T4. **9B5.** 9B4, 9T4. **9B6.** 9A16, 9T4. **9B7.**

9T4. **9B8.** Centroid lies on str. line bisecting parallel sides. **9B9.** 9T5 ;

$\dfrac{\pi h}{3}(a^2+ab+b^2)$. **9B10.** 9T4, 9B2,3, 9A4. **9B11.** $\pi ht(2w+h-t)$; 9T4,5.

9B12. $\dfrac{b^2-3a^2}{4(2a+b)}$; 9T4, 9A4, 9B2,3. **9B13.** $\frac{3}{4}(a-\frac{1}{2}h)$; 9A4. **9B14.** 9T5,

9W2. **9B15.** 9A12, 9T5. **9B16.** 9T5. **9B17.** 9A16, 9T5. **9B18.** 9T6,
9A16 ; eight truncated half-cylinders at the crossing. **9B19.** 9A12. **9B20.**
Let θ be the semi-vertical angle ; 9A4, 9T4. **9B21.** 9T5. **9B22.** $\frac{3}{8}(a+b)$

from centre ; 9W2, 9A4,14. **9B23.** $\dfrac{3}{4}\dfrac{(a+b)^2}{2a+b}$; 9T4, 9B22.

9C1. 8W3 ; angle of segment 120° ; 9T4,5. **9C2.** 9A12, 9T5. **9C3.**
9W1, 9T6. **9C4.** 9W2. 9T4,6. **9C5.** 9W2, 9T4. **9C6.** 8T6, 9T5. **9C7.**
8W3, or 9C5, 9T5. **9C8.** 9W2, 9T4. **9C9.** 9C8, 9T5. **9C10.** 9A12, 9T5.
9C11. 9A16, 9T5. **9C12.** 9W1, 9T6. **9C13.** 9C5, 9T6. **9C14.** 9W2,3.
9C15. If x, y are distances of centre from centroids of complementary
segments A, B, then $xA=yB$; 9T4, 9C1.

CHAPTER X

10A1. $3\sqrt{3}=5\cdot20$ in. ; $\cos^{-1}\sqrt{\frac{2}{3}}=54°\ 44'$. **10A2.** $3\cdot5\sqrt{2}=4\cdot95$ in. ;

$2\cos^{-1}\dfrac{1}{\sqrt{3}}=109°\ 28'$. **10A3.** $\sqrt{6}=2\cdot45$ in. **10A4.** $\dfrac{2\cdot5}{\sqrt{2}}=1\cdot768$ in.

10A5. Radius $4\cdot01$ in. ; centre $2\frac{3}{8}$ in. above centre of circle. **10A6.**

65° 54′. **10A7.** 1·55 in., 2·69 in., 2·26 in. ; 4W4. **10A8.** 3·85 cm. ; this is found as the hypotenuse of a right-angled triangle with one side = dist. between mid-points of 8 in. edge and projection of 6 in. edge on the 8 in., 7 in., 5 in., face, and the other side = half of corresponding altitude of tet. **10A9.** Given P and Q in face α, and R in β ; PQ meets $\alpha\beta$ in S ; SR cuts every edge of β. **10A10.** Plane cuts opposite faces in parallel lines. **10A11.** 2 : 3 ; 10W1. **10A12.** 53° 8′, 41° 25′. **10A13.** Construct vertical section bisecting two base edges ; 1·25 in. **10A14.** 2·45 in. ; diag. section. **10A15.** 3·46 in. $= \dfrac{6}{\sqrt{3}}$. **6A16.** Must be tetrahedron (six edges) ; 6T4.

10B1. 6C12. **10B2.** 6C15. **10B3.** 6B10,18 ; common altitude of two isosceles triangles ⊥ to plane of their bases. **10B4.** Project A, B to A′, B′ on face γ, so that AB meets A′B′ at D in γ. **10B5.** Project A, B, C to A′, B′, C′ in δ, a face adjacent to α, β, γ, so that AB, A′B′ intersect in D, and BC, B′C′ in E. **10B6.** Divides OD in ratio 3 : 2 ; AP and RQ produced meet on OX ∥ AB. **10B7.** 1·59 in. ; construct section of any cube containing two opposite edges, circumscribe section of cone with required angle, and reduce (or increase) the scale. **10B8.** 5·464 in. $= 2(\sqrt{3} + 1)$; horizontal section thro' four centres, then vertical section thro' two opposite centres. **10B9.** Draw consecutive adjacent angles α, β, ... $\varkappa$, α, β, ... $\varkappa$, α, β, ... to represent the face angles α, β, ... $\varkappa$ unrolled into a flat surface ; however small the vertical angles may be, we can, if necessary ; repeat the faces until the sum is greater than 180° ; the bandage is represented by two str. lines ; in the case of a cone, the bandage, supposed infinitely narrow, becomes a spiral curve, and there is one generator, VT, say, which is its asymptote ; i.e., after being wrapped a certain number of times round the cone, the bandage crosses every generator on one side of VT, without crossing VT itself ; true in *all* cases. **10B10.** $\cos^{-1}(2 \sin 15°) = 58°\ 50′$; $\cos^{-1}(\sqrt{3} \tan 15°) = 62°\ 15′$. **10B11.** 25° 20′ ; ·66 units ; project D to D′ in ABC ; rabat D to D_1, D_2, D_3 about BC, CA, AB ; let $D′D_3$ cut AB, BC in P, Q ; rabat DPQ to D_4PQ ; let PE_4 bisect $D_4\hat{P}Q$, and let BE_1 cut CD_1 in F_1. **10B12.** 2·31 ; 10W4. **10B13.** Four times that of tet. GABC, each of whose oblique edges is $\frac{3}{4}$ of corresponding median ; 2W2 ; DD′ = 1·27, AD = 1·82, BD = 2·40, CD = 2·70. **10B14.** S. 60° 57′ W., downward ; if A′B′C′D′ is the field, find E′ in A′D′ on same level as B′. **10B15.** Length = ·89 of edge of cube ; parallel to faces ABCD and XYZW, and its distance from them are in the ratio 3 : 2. **10B16.** $\sqrt{(c^2 + d^2 - a^2)}$; CA ⊥ BD$_1$ when ACD is rabatted to ACD$_1$. **10B17.** $\sqrt{(y^2 + z^2)}$, $\sqrt{(z^2 + x^2)}$, $\sqrt{(x^2 + y^2)}$; 3W2, opp. edges equal. **10B18.** 3·35,

7·34 ; 5·83, 8·20 ; 4·58, 8·03 ; 3W2. **10B19.** Side $1\frac{11}{12}$ in., at $1\frac{1}{4}$ in. from
the 2·5 in. edge ; draw trapezium with parallel sides 2·5 in., and 3·5 in.,
and diagonal 3 in. long at right angles to them ; the join of mid-points of
parallel sides cuts diagonal at point on the square section. **10B20.** 33° 12′,
50° 44′, 108° 32′ ; 10W3. **10B21.** 100° 49′, 110° 54′, 121° 43′ ; 10W3.
10B22. 129° 16′, 71° 28′, 146° 48′ ; see Note following 10W5. **10B23.**
69° 11′, 79° 6′, 58° 17′ ; see Note following 10W5. **10B24.** 10W3 ; take
OA_1 as unit of length. **10B25.** Length 5·00 units, at 10·54 units from
C ; 10W5.

10C1. 4·71 in. ; 10W4. **10C2.** 25° 16′ ; find distances of initial and
final positions of upper end of jib from vertical line through its lower end ;
and difference between their altitudes ; hence distance between them.
10C3. 126°, $36\frac{1}{2}$° ; draw sections of both roofs both having same height
and so obtain their widths ; hence construct plan, and rabat on it the
two oblique triangular surfaces cut off between the gutter and the right
sections at the innermost angle ; on these, draw perpendiculars to the
gutter, and, by comparison with the plan, find the angle between them
no difference, as one case is the image of the other reflected in a horizontal plane. **10C4.** ·6 ; 10W4 twice, 10W1 ; bisect dihedral angle.
10C5. AR = ·7, CS = 1·9, AT = ·91 ; rabat BCD to BCD_1 in plane ABC ;
let X, Y be mid-points of AD, BC, so that G is mid-point of XY ; rabat
AYD to AYD_2 ; P_2G_2 cuts D_2Y in Z_2 ; QZ_1 cuts CD_1 in S_1 ; rabat ACD
to ACD_3 ; then S_3P_3 cuts CA in T, and QT cuts AB in R. **10C6.** Required
line is = and ‖ to join of centroids of opposite faces. **10C7.** 2 : 1 ; take
section thro' centre of sphere and thro' two opposite edges of the
cube. **10C8.** $\sqrt{14}$AB ; draw PQ ⊥ YZ ; produce CQ to cut BY in R ;
draw RS ‖ PQ, cutting AY in S ; then SP cuts DC. **10C9.** $\frac{1}{3}\sqrt{21}$AB ;
plane APZ cuts plane BCZY in ZR ‖ PA. **10C10.** 3T1, 3W1, 4W4.
10C11. PQRS,XYZW is cube inscribed in tet. ABCD ; (i) PQ, RS,
XW, YZ in ABC, ABD, DCA, DCB ; (ii) PQ, QR, PS,WZ in ABD,BDC,
ADC, ABC ; (iii) PQ, PS, ZW, YZ in ABD, ADC, ABC, BDC.
[N.B.—*The cube need not, in any of these cases, lie completely* inside *the
tetrahedron.*] **10C12.** If MN cuts planes PQRS, XYZW in T, V respectively in Case (i),

$$\frac{XY}{AB} + \frac{QR}{CD} + \frac{PQ}{MN} = \frac{VN}{MN} + \frac{MT}{MN} + \frac{TV}{MN} = 1.$$

10C13. $1\frac{1}{8}$; draw square MNHK, and produce KM, HN, to E, F, making
ME = AB, NF = CD ; let MF cut NE in G, and let KG, HG cut
MN in K′H′ ; then K′H′ is the length of PQ. **10C14.** 2 units ; draw
MN ⊥ NDC, and ME = AB, and ‖ NC and in the same sense ; on opposite

side of ME to N draw square MEFG; let DF cut MC in H, and draw HJ ∥ FM, cutting MD in J; construct square HIJK; then JI : ME = JH : MF = JD : MD ; ∴ JI is the required length. **10C15.** 1·8; rabat MNDC into the plane of ABMN so that angles AMN, MNC are alternate ; draw BE cutting AN in E, and making angle ABE = 45° ; draw MF = and ∥ BE, and CG ∥ BE cutting MD produced in G ; let join of mid-points of MF and CG cut MD in H ; draw HI ∥ EB, cutting MC in I ; IJ ∥ BA cutting BN in J ; and JK ∥ BE, cutting AN in K ; then HI and JK are diagonals of the square sections of the inscribed cube with planes through MN ⊥ AB and CD respectively. **10C16.** 17° ; let OA, OB, OC be ropes ; make OC' = OA = OB = 55 ft. ; let D be mid-point of AB ; draw triangles OAB, C'AB, ODC', ODC ; circumcentre of triangle ABC' is vertically beneath O. **10C17.** 8·3 in., 2·6 in. ; draw axial sections of pyramid bisecting two parallel edges ; inscribe semicircle, and draw tangent ∥ to base. **10C18.** 48° 13′, 4° 13′ ; let V be vertex, A, B, C centres of bases, and D centre of triangle ABC ; construct sections VAB, ABC, VBD. **10C19.** $\Delta = rs$; if VN ⊥ ABC, NO ⊥ VAB, and VO meets AB in M, OM . MV = MN². **10C20.** $\tan^{-1} \tfrac{1}{2}\sqrt{3} = 40° 54′$; planes of bases are slant faces of the tet. of 10C14. **10C21.** 50° 28′ ; rabat B$\hat{V}$C to B$_1$$\hat{V}$C in plane AVC, and make str. line ACB ⊥ VC ; rabat B$\hat{C}$A to B$_2$$\hat{C}$A, and V$\hat{A}$B to V$_3$$\hat{A}B_2$. **10C22.** 77° ; construct a supplement of the conjugate angle ; 10C16. **10C23.** $\varphi = \sin^{-1}\left(\dfrac{2}{\sqrt{3}} \sin \theta\right) \pm \theta$. **10C24.** 4·88; 76° ; let V, ABCD be the given pyramid, and AB″C″D″ the section ⊥ to axis ; construct VB″C″, AB″C″D″, VAC, and then VBD ; draw line of intersection of planes ABCD, AB″C″D″, and a pair of lines of slope. **10C25.** Dihedral angles ; BC 49° 20′, CA 52° 30′, AB 25° 40′ ; edges : AD 2·04, BD 2·14, CD 2·78 ; altitude DD′ 1·04 ; draw triangle ABC and its altitudes AX, BY, CZ ; then rabat AXP to AXP₁ on same side as C, and so on ; from XC, etc., cut off equal lengths Xx, etc., and draw xp, etc., ∥ XA, etc., cutting XP, etc., in p, etc. ; then parallels to BC, etc., thro' p, etc., intersect in pairs on D′A, D′B, D′C ; this gives D′ ; draw D′d ⊥ BC, dD₄ ∥ XP₁, D′D₄ ∥ BC, giving height of tet.

CHAPTER XI

11A1. (i) 8 equilateral triangles (reg. oct.) ; (ii) 4 hexagons and 4 equilat. triangles. **11A2.** (i) 6 sq. and 8 equilat. triangles ; (ii) 6 octagons and 8 equilat. triangles. **11A3.** (i) Same as 11A2 (i) ; (ii) 8 hexagons and 6 sq. **11A4.** (i) 12 reg. pentagons and 20 equilat. triangles ; (ii) 12 decagons and 20 triangles. **11A5.** (i) Same as 11A4 (i) ; (ii) 12 pentagons and 20 hexagons. **11A6.** Vert. : $4, 5, 6, \ldots n$; faces : $4, 5, 6, \ldots n$; edges : $6, 8, 10, \ldots 2(n-1)$. **11A7.** Vert. : $6, 8, 10, \ldots 2n$; faces : $5, 6, 7, \ldots (n+2)$; edges : $9, 12, 15, \ldots 3n$. **11A8.** Three ; 6T4. **11A9.** Vert. : $6, 8, 10, \ldots 2(n-1)$; faces : $8, 10, 12, \ldots 2n$; edges : $12, 16, 20, \ldots 4(n-1)$. **11A10.** Vert. $9, 12, 15, \ldots 3n$; faces : $11, 14, 17, \ldots (3n+2)$; edges : $18, 24, 30, \ldots 6n$. **11A11.** Each regular solid angle gives a regular face, and vice versa. **11A12.** 11A1-5, case (i) of each. **11A13.** 7T6. **11A14.** 11A11, 13. **11A15.** Take section thro' vert. of octahedron and nearest edge of tet. **11A16.** Tet. 8 v. 12 f. 18 e. ; oct. : 14 v. 24 f. 36 e. ; cube : 14 v. 24 f. 36 e. ; dodecahedron and icosahedron : 32 v. 60 f. 90 e. **11A19.** 11W5. **11A20.** Fig. 102, p. 144. **11A22.** Orthocentre of triangle XYZ is the projection of the actual origin ; Fig. 102, p. 144. **11A23.** 11A6 ; vert. : $12, 16, 20, \ldots 4(n-1)$; faces : $8, 10, 12, \ldots 2n$; edges : $18, 24, 30, \ldots 3(n-1)+(n-1)+2(n-1)=6(n-1)$. **11A24.** 3T6, 4T1.

11B1. $\frac{1}{2}\sqrt{2}a$; take section containing an edge and the mid-point of the opposite edge. **11B2.** $\sqrt{\frac{2}{3}}a$; take section bisecting two opposite edges at right angles. **11B3.** The twelve edges are the diagonals of the faces of a cube. **11B4.** Cube. **11B5.** Reg. octahedron ; 11B4, 11A12, or 11A1. **11B6.** Reg. octahedron ; the 24 edges are diagonals of the faces of a rhombic dodecahedron. **11B7.** 11A2. **11B8.** Rhombic dodecahedron ; Fig. 106. **11B9.** Reg. icosahedron. **11B10.** 11A4. **11B11.** 30 rhombic faces, 12 pentahedral, and 20 trihedral vertices, 60 edges, rhombic triacontahedron. **11B12.** Vertices of cube may be at centres of faces 2, 4, 6, 10, 12, 13, 16, 19 in Figs. 96 and 104. **11B13.** North and south on horizontal faces, east and west on two vertical faces, and vertical on the other two ; remaining 8 vertices on diagonals of cube. **11B14.** BED_1C_1, $D_2C_2B_3E_3$ in Figs. 95 and 103. **11B15.** Cf. 11B13, all 12 vertices being on faces of cube. **11B16.** $1 : \sqrt{3}$. **11B17.** Ratios of sides $3 : 3 : 5$. **11B18.** 6C16 ; let W be the centre of the tetrahedron, and AVB a face. **11B19.** $3 : 3 : 5$; 11B16. **11B20.** $5 : 6$; 6 longer, 12 shorter edges. **11B21.** $135°$, $115°, 110°$; draw O'O (Fig. 102) any convenient length ; as OO'X, etc., are complements of the given angles, O'X, etc., can be found ; hence construct right-angled triangles YO'Z, etc., and then triangle XYZ, and its altitudes.

11B22. $O'X = \text{cosec } \alpha$; $\therefore YZ = \sqrt{(\text{cosec}^2 \beta + \text{cosec}^2 \gamma)}$; $X\hat{O}Y$ is supplement of $X\hat{Z}Y$. **11B23.** Fig. 113 ; find O, the orthocentre of given triangle XYZ, and draw $OW \perp ZO$, cutting semicircle on ZV in W ; then $W\hat{Z}O =$ inclination of O'Z to plane of paper.

11B24. $\cos W\widehat{Z}O$

$$= \frac{OZ}{ZW} = \frac{ZX}{ZV} = \sqrt{\frac{OZ}{ZV}} = \sqrt{\frac{XZ \cdot \cos Z}{\sin Y} \cdot \frac{1}{XZ \sin X}} = \sqrt{\frac{-\cos XOY}{\sin XOZ \cdot \sin YOZ}}.$$

11B25. Draw A'B', cutting C'D', D'E' in F', G' ; then FG, in plane CDE, cuts AB in the required point H. **11B26.** Draw OD, OE $\perp$ BC, CA ; AD, BE intersect in foot of normal ; 1W2, 4T1. **11B27.** Find Q in P_3P_4 such that $P_3Q : P_3P_4 =$ the ratio of the diagonals of cuboids whose edges are the axial lengths of P_1P_2 and P_3P_4 respectively. **11B28.** Construct rhombus and diagonal; 11B27. **11B29.** Use 11B27, and plane geometry. **11B30.** $F = f + e$, $E = 4e$, $V = v + 2e$. **11B31.** $F = f + v$, $E = 3e$, $V = 2e$.

11C1. Fig. 106. **11C2.** $1 : \sqrt{2}$; short diagonal of rhombus $= \frac{1}{2}$ long diag. of solid. **11C3.** $\frac{16a^3}{3\sqrt{3}}$; volume of rhombic dodecahedron is twice that of the cube whose edges are the short diagonals of its faces. **11C4.** Distorted representation reveals the solid of 11A2 (i). **11C5.** $\frac{5\sqrt{2}}{3} a^3$; 11A2 (i) ; edge of cube $= \sqrt{2}a$. **11C6.** Distorted repn. gives 11A2 (ii). **11C7.** $\frac{7}{3}(3 + 2\sqrt{2})a^3$; edge of cube $= a(1 + \sqrt{2})$. **11C8.** Distorted repn. gives 11A3 (ii). **11C9.** $8\sqrt{2}a^3$; edge of octahedron $= 3a$. **11C10.** Construct congruent regular pyramids on the faces of a regular dodecahedron so that the faces unite in pairs to form rhombuses. **11C11.** 11B13 ; dodecahedron has 30 edges, and cube has only 6 faces ; $\therefore$ 5 different cubes can be circumscribed about the same dodecahedron. **11C12.** If edges of cube and icosahedron are $2a$ and $2x$ respectively, the square on an edge *inside* the cube $= (a - x)^2 + a^2 + x^2$. **11C13.** If edges of cube and dodecahedron are $2a$ and $2x$ respectively, the square on a face-diagonal $= (a - x)^2 + a^2 + x^2$. **11C14.** Take plane section, bisecting BC at right angles, and notice that DEF $\parallel$ ABC. **11C15.** Let BCEF be plane of paper ; rabat AXA' to A_1XA'. **11C16.** 11W1 ; (tet.). **11C17.** 11B16. **11C18.** 11W1 ; (cube). **11C19.** 11B16, but with right angles at G. **11C20.** Distorted representation ; the two sets of irregular solid angles are vertices of a rectangle and a square. **11C21.** Let long and short sides of rectangle be 2 and $2x$ units respectively ; then $4x^2 =$ sq. on short diag. of one of the 8 remaining faces $= (1 - x)^2 + x^2 + 1$. **11C22.** Lines joining mid-point of a diag. to the other four vertices are perp. to the diag., and, $\therefore$, coplanar. **11C23.** 11W4. **11C24.** Remaining vertices are coplanar ; 11W4. **11C25.** Let F be mid-point of AB ; then DF is equal to the sum of the projections of AE and DE upon it ; if AB $= 2x$, and edge of cube $= 2a$, we get

$$x^4 - 4a^2x^2 - a^3x + 2a^4 = 0 ;$$

factorise by remainder theorem. **11C26**. Reg. icosahedron ; each of the points A, B, C, D, E is at same distance from nearest edge of cube ; hence, if DD′, CC′, EE′ are lines corresponding to AB, we have AD′ = AE = ED = ED′, and so on. **11C27**. Reg. hexagon ; if AB, BC are sides of the section, and M, N their mid-points, calculate MB, BN, MN, and show that MBN = 120°. **11C28**. Let VA, VB, VC be consecutive edges of the given solid, and let them be cut by a plane section in X, Y, Z, so that VX = VY = VZ = x ; let PQ be one edge of the new solid, with its ends on XY, and YZ ; let M be mid-point of VB ; then PQ = XY − 2PY ; whence the required equation. **11C29**. Cube, 3 : 4 ; tet., 3 : 5 ; oct., $2 - \sqrt{2} : 1$.

CHAPTER XII

12A1. Table 12T5 and distorted representation ; cf. 11A1-5 ; let the change be represented symbolically by A→B or C→D according as the original edges are, or are not, completely cut away at the same time as each corner. Then :

$$
\begin{array}{l}
\qquad\qquad\nearrow \text{F}3_1 6_2 \\
\text{F}3_3 \rightarrow \text{F}3_4 \searrow \\
\qquad\qquad\quad \searrow \text{F}3_2 4_2 \quad \nearrow \text{F}3_1 4_3 \\
\qquad \text{F}4_3 \Big\langle \qquad\qquad\quad \searrow \text{F}4_1 6_1 8_1 \\
\qquad\qquad\quad \searrow \text{F}3_1 8_2 \\[4pt]
\qquad\qquad\nearrow \text{F}5_1 6_2 \\
\qquad \text{F}3_5 \searrow \\
\qquad\qquad\quad \searrow \text{F}3_2 5_2 \quad \nearrow \text{F}3_1 4_2 5_1 \\
\qquad \text{F}5_3 \Big\langle \qquad\qquad\quad \searrow \text{F}4_1 6_1 10_1 \\
\qquad\qquad\quad \searrow \text{F}3_1 10_1
\end{array}
$$

12A2. $V4_2 n_1$, semi-regular bipyramids ; each face is an isosceles triangle. **12A3**. $V3_3 n_1$, regular trapezohedra ; each face is a " kite " with three equal angles. **12A4**. $\text{F}3_3 \rightarrow V3_1 6_2$; $\text{F}3_4 \rightarrow V3_1 8_2$; $\text{F}3_5 \rightarrow V3_1 10_2$; $\text{F}4_3 \rightarrow V4_1 6_2$; $\text{F}5_3 \rightarrow \text{F}5_1 6_2$. **12A5**. Table of 12T5 ; sum of suffixes = 5 in case of $V3_4 4_1$ and $V3_4 5_1$. **12A6**. $V3_3 n_1$, trapezohedra ; 12A3. **12A7**. $V4_1 6_1 8_1$, $V4_1 6_1 10_1$, and $V3_1 4_2 5_1$. **12A8**. (a) Regular polyhedral angles with the same number of face angles *need not be* congruent ; (b) The vertically regular solid $Va_p b_q$ has p congruent regular a-hedral angles, and q congruent regular b-hedral angles at each face ; (b) is true in spite of (a), because the *faces* of a vertically regular solid are all congruent to one another. **12A9**. No ; the tetrahedral angles of such a bipyramid need not be *regular*, as the dihedral angles at the equator need not be equal to those at the oblique edges. **12A10**. Regular prisms ; $\text{F}4_2 n_1$. **12A14**. There are eight triangular faces of a snub cube which are not adjacent to

squares ; show that these are normal to the diagonals of the circumscribing cube. **12A15.** Two ; (enantiomorphous). **12A16.** Only one ;
of the twenty-four triangular faces adjacent to squares, no three are
similarly related to a fourth ; ∴ no eight of them can lie in the faces of
a regular octahedron.

12A17.

Fig.	Inscribed in Dodecahedron.	Icosahedron.	Circumscribed about Dodecahedron.	Icosahedron.
117		$SF5_5$	$SF5_5$	
118	$SF5_3$			$SF5_3$
119		$SP5_5$	$SP5_5$	
120		$SP5_3$		$SP5_3$

Notice, however, that the edges of $SP5_3$ intersect in threes at the vertices
of a regular dodecahedron, and the planes of its faces intersect
in threes in the vertices of a *nearly* semi-regular $F5_16_2$. **12A18.** 12T8,
3T5. **12A19.** Each gives its dual, (another regular solid). **12A20.**
Dual of 12T1 : " If, adjacent to each face of a vertically regular
solid, there are m_3 3-hedral angles, m_4 4-hedral, m_5 5-hedral, and so on,
the number of faces $= f = \dfrac{4}{2 - \frac{1}{3}m_3 - \frac{2}{4}m_4 - \frac{3}{5}m_5 - \ldots}$." In the same way
every step of the proof can be translated ; and, as f and v enter symmetri-
cally into Euler's identity, the dual theorem is established. COR. 2. :
" A vertically regular solid cannot have more than five vertices to each
face." COR. 3 : " A vertically regular solid cannot have solid angles of
more than 3 different shapes." *Dual of* 12T2 : " If a certain polyhedral
angle occurs only once or twice at each face of a vertically regular solid,
the vertices sharing edges with it must either be all of the same kind, or
of two kinds alternating with one another." *Dual of* 12T3 : " With the
exception of bipyramids, there are not more than four vertically regular
solids with one odd and two even polyhedral angles at each face." *Dual
of* 12T4 : " With the exception of bipyramids, there are not more than
three vertically regular solids with three even polyhedral angles at each
face." *Dual of* 12T5 : " With the exception of trapezoids, there are not
more than seven vertically regular solids with more than three vertices
to each face." COR. : Excluding bipyramids, trapezoids, and regular
solids, there are not more than thirteen vertically regular solids." **12A21.**
The solid angles are all regular ; ∴ the dihedral angles at the same vertex

are equal; but every dihedral angle belongs to two vertices. **12A22.**
The faces of a vertically regular solid are congruent and equidistant from
the centre (12T7); ∴ the solid can be divided into congruent pyramids
having a common vertex at the centre. A facially regular solid can be
inscribed in a sphere (12T6), and its faces are regular; ∴ each is the base
of a regular pyramid with its vertex at the centre of the solid, and those
pyramids that are on congruent bases are congruent, as their oblique
edges are equal to the radius of the sphere. **12A23. 12A21.**

12B1. $SF5_5$ and $SP5_5$; a star polyhedron is *not* divided into two parts
by the perimeter of a face; (notice, however, that, if we count all
"spurious" vertices, Euler's Theorem is satisfied by the outer surfaces
of *solid models* of the star polyhedra: thus a model of $SF5_5$, Fig. 117,
would have 32 vertices: 12 convex and 20 concave; 60 isosceles triangular faces, and 90 edges, arranged three-at-a-time in straight lines).
12B2. By definition, a polyhedral solid is "a single portion of space *not
pierced by holes* ... "; suppose that the ring surrounding the hole be
broken by removing a very thin slice; we have left a polyhedral solid
satisfying Euler's Theorem; if the thin slice has n corners, the n faces
and n edges of the *hole* are both doubled, without altering $f - e$; and each
of the 2 new faces contributes n edges and n vertices, without altering
$v - e$; ∴, if f be the number of faces in the pierced solid, we have

$$(f+2) - e + v = 2;$$
$$\therefore f - e + v - 2 = -2.$$

12B3. As in 12B2, break the rings, and then repair them one by
one; each repair reduces the value of f by 2; ∴, to obtain a solid
satisfying Euler's Theorem, we must replace f by $f + 2n$. **12B4.** A circular
cylindrical surface; *not* a double cone, as corresponding oblique edges
contain an angle equal to that between consecutive edges on the equator;
and this, in the limit, is 180°. **12B5.** "To what does a facially regular
prismoid approximate as the number of its faces is continually increased?" A circular disc; the thickness vanishes at the same time
as the length of each individual chord of the rims. **12B6.** 12T8, 6T1.
12B7. 12T8, 12T6, Cor. 2. **12B8.** Let AB be the edge, C its point of
contact with the sphere, and O the centre of the latter; then OA, OB
pass through the centres of the given faces, and C is the mid-point of the

edge in which they meet; hence $O\hat{A}C = \alpha$, $O\hat{B}C = \beta$, and $OC \perp AB$.
12B9. 12T8, 6T1.

12B	Face-gon	(i)	(ii)	(iii) tan φ	φ	(iv) cot ½θ	θ
10.	3	$\frac{1}{4}\sqrt{\frac{2}{3}}$	$\frac{1}{3}\frac{\sqrt{3}}{2}$	$\frac{1}{\sqrt{2}}$	35° 16′	$\frac{1}{\sqrt{2}}$	109° 28′
11.	3	$\frac{1}{\sqrt{6}}$	$\frac{1}{3}\frac{\sqrt{3}}{2}$	$\sqrt{2}$	54° 44′	1	90°
12.	3	$3(\frac{3}{4}-\frac{1}{3})\sqrt{\frac{2}{3}}$	$\frac{1}{3}\frac{\sqrt{3}}{2}$	$\frac{5}{2}\sqrt{2}$	74° 12′	$\frac{3}{2}\sqrt{2}$	50° 28′
	6	$\frac{3}{4}\sqrt{\frac{2}{3}}$	$\frac{1}{2}\sqrt{3}$	$\frac{1}{2}\sqrt{2}$	35° 16′		
13.	3	$\frac{\sqrt{3}}{6}(3+2\sqrt{2})$	$\frac{1}{6}\sqrt{3}$	$3+2\sqrt{2}$	80° 16′	$2+\sqrt{2}$	32° 40′
	8	$\frac{1}{2}(1+\sqrt{2})$	$\frac{1}{2}(1+\sqrt{2})$	1	45°		
14.	4	$\sqrt{2}$	$\frac{1}{2}$	$2\sqrt{2}$	70° 32′	3	36° 52′
	6	$\sqrt{\frac{3}{2}}$	$\frac{1}{2}\sqrt{3}$	$\sqrt{2}$	54° 44′		
15.	4	$1\frac{1}{2}+\frac{1}{2}\sqrt{2}$	$\frac{1}{2}$	$3+\sqrt{2}$	77° 14′	$\sqrt{12+6\sqrt{2}}$	24° 56′
	6	$\frac{\sqrt{3}}{2}(1+\sqrt{2})$	$\frac{1}{2}\sqrt{3}$	$1+\sqrt{2}$	67° 30′		
	8	$\frac{1}{2}+\sqrt{2}$	$\frac{1+\sqrt{2}}{2}$	$3-\sqrt{2}$	57° 46′		
16.	3	$\sqrt{\frac{2}{3}}$	$\frac{1}{6}\sqrt{3}$	$2\sqrt{2}$	70° 32′	$\sqrt{3}$	60°
	4	$\frac{1}{2}\sqrt{2}$	$\frac{1}{2}$	$\sqrt{2}$	54° 44′		
17.	3	$\frac{x+y}{4\sqrt{3}}\sqrt{3-(x-y)^2}$	$\frac{1}{6}\sqrt{3}$	$\frac{x+y}{2}\sqrt{3-(x-y)^2}$		$\frac{1}{2}\sqrt{1+(x+y)^2}$ $[=\frac{1}{2}\sqrt{3-(x-y)^2+4y^2}]$	
	n	$\frac{1}{4}\sqrt{3-(x-y)^2}$	$\frac{1}{2}y$	$\frac{1}{2y}\sqrt{3-(x-y)^2}$			
18.	4	$\frac{1}{2}y$	$\frac{1}{2}$	y		y	
	n	$\frac{1}{2}$	$\frac{1}{2}y$	$\frac{1}{y}$			

where $x=\operatorname{cosec}\dfrac{180°}{n}$, and $y=\cot\dfrac{180°}{n}$. **12B19.** As the snub cube can be inscribed in a sphere, similar chains of faces form congruent figures in space; **12A14.**

13A1. Base-centred orthorhombic. **13A2.** 4 : 1 ; each set of face-centres consists of as many points as the original lattice. **13A3.** One system of centres gives a lattice, B, congruent to the given lattice, A ; a second system forms the base-centres of B, giving a lattice, C, 13T2 ; the third system forms the cell-centres of C, giving a lattice, D, 13T3. **13A4.** The cell-centres of A form a lattice, B, congruent to A ; the mid-points of the edges of A are the face-centres of B ; ∴, with its vertices, they form a lattice, C, 13T3. **13A5.** Let cells of the original lattice be grouped together in eights to form similar cells with twice their linear dimensions ; the process of obliterating points removes the centres of these new cells, together with the middle points of their edges, and leaving their vertices and face-centres.

Table required in Answers, **13A6-14.**

	Centre.	Planes bisecting Edges.	Diagonal Planes.	Axes of Symmetry.				
				6-*ad*	4-*ad*	3-*ad*	2-*ad* bisectg. Edges.	2-*ad* ⊥ Faces.
(6)	1	3	6		3	4	6	
(7)	1	3	2		1		2	2
(8)	1	3						3
(9)	1		3			1	3	
(10)	1	1						1
(11)	1							
(12)	1	3 + 1	3	1			3	3
(13)	and (14) same as cubic, (6)							

13A15. Triangles, squares, and hexagons ; $(m-2)(n-2)=4$; 11T2. **13A16.** (i) Produce the sides of a hexagon, forming adjacent triangles ; complete the hexagons adjacent to the triangles, and repeat the process indefinitely ; (ii) form a chain of hexagons with common sides all parallel to one another ; similar chains can be joined together at their free vertices, leaving rhombic spaces to be filled each with two triangles. **13A17.** Each square is adjacent to four octagons, and each octagon to squares and octagons on alternate sides. **13A18.** Each hexagon is adjacent to six squares, each triangle to three squares, and each square to hexagons and triangles on alternate sides.

No.	Pattern.	Position of Centre of Pattern.	Elements of Symmetry.			
			Centre.	Lines bisecting Edges.	Diagonal Lines.	Pole at Centre.
13A19.	15 (i)	Vertex	1	3	3	$6 - ad$
		Centre		3		$3 - ad$
		Mid-point of side	1	1	1	$2 - ad$
13A19.	15 (ii)	Vertex or centre	1	2	2	$4 - ad$
		Mid-point of side	1	1	1	$2 - ad$
13A19.	15 (iii)	Vertex			3	$3 - ad$
		Centre	1	3	3	$6 - ad$
		Mid-point	1	1	1	$2 - ad$
13A20.	16 (i)	Vertex	1	1	1	$2 - ad$
		Centre of hexagon	1	3	3	$6 - ad$
		Centre of triangle		3		$3 - ad$
13A20.	16 (ii)	"Free" vert.	1		2	$2 - ad$
		Centre of hexagon	1	1	1	$2 - ad$
13A20.	(17)	Centre of square	1	2	2	$4 - ad$
		Centre of octahedron	1	4		$4 - ad$
13A20.	(18)	Centre of hexagon	1	3	3	$6 - ad$
		Centre of triangle		3		$3 - ad$

13A21. (*a*) We lose the centre, the 4 dyad axes, and the plane parallel to the base ; (*b*) we lose the centre and the three planes and three dyad axes which do not pass through the centre of the sphere, while the tetrad axis degenerates to dyad. **13A22.** We lose the centre, the planes bisecting the cube-edges, and the dyad axes through their mid-points ; but retain the 4 triad axes in the diagonals of the cube, and the 6 planes in its diagonal planes ; while the 3 tetrad axes degenerate to dyad. **12A23.** The vertices of the octahedron are face-centres of a cubic lattice. **13A24.** Same symmetry as a cubic lattice ; 13A6. **13A25.** $1 : 1 + \sqrt{2} : 1 + \sqrt{2}$.

13B1. Base-centred cubic. **13B2.** Face-centred cubic. **13B3.** The black (or the white) cubes of a 3-dimensional chessboard. **13B4.** Place cubes alternately above and below the black squares of an infinite plane chessboard, and build up a stack of similar double layers of cubes, so that corresponding cubes are vertically over one another. **13B5.** Take a horizontal square lattice with lines running N.E. and N.W., and divide each square into four others labelled N,. E., S., and W. respectively ; then build up a structure of cubes over the N.'s, E.'s S.'s and W.'s in consecutive layers. **13B6.** Label the black squares of an infinite plane chessboard alternately 1 and 3 in the odd rows, and 2 and 4 in the even ; then build up a structure of cubes over the 1's, 2's, 3's and 4's in consecutive layers. **13B7.** Inscribed in the cubes of 13B3. **13B8.** Inscribed in the cubes of 13B6 ; the same structure is described from a different point of view in 14W3. **13B9.** The octahedra have their centres at the vertices and cell-centres of a cubic lattice, and their vertices at the mid-points of its edges. **13B10.** The spaces between the octahedra of 13B9. **13B11.** 14W3, Note 1. **13B12.** Projection, 13A18 ; build up the structure with cubes over the three systems of squares in successive layers. **13B13.** Inscribed in the cubes of 13B12. **13B14.** (3) and (7) face-centred cubic, (8 cubes ; 4 occupied) ; (4) cell-centred cubic, (8 cubes ; 2 occupied) ; (6) and (8) cell-centred cubic, (64 cubes) ; (5) tetragonal, (16 cubes forming a square prism) ; (9) and (10) face-centred cubic, (cube having vertices of an octahedron at centres of its faces) ; or 60° rhombic, (octahedron with regular tetrahedra on two opposite faces). **13B15.** *Hexagonal*, (hexagonal prism, with height equal to twice that of a tetrahedron, and edge of base equal to four-thirds of the altitude of a face of a tetrahedron, the vertices of the prism being the centroids of the equilateral triangles) ; or *monoclinic*, (rhombic prism with base consisting of a hexagon with equilateral triangles on two opposite sides, and height equal to twice that of a tetrahedron) ; or *base-centred orthorhombic*, (each cell consisting of the halves of four of the rhombic prisms). **13B16.** *Hexagonal*, (hexagonal prism with height equal to three times that of a cube, and vertices of base at centres of six hexagons surrounding, though not adjacent to, a seventh hexagon ; the side of the base being equal to $1+\sqrt{3}$ times that of the square) ; or *monoclinic*, (with height equal to three times that of a cube, and vertices of base at centres of four hexagons ; the side of the base being equal to $1+\sqrt{3}$ times the edge of a cube); or *base-centred orthorhombic*, (each cell being composed of the halves of four of the rhombic prisms).

CHAPTER XIV

14A1. Centres of large and small spheres at alternate points of a straight line. **14A2.** At alternate vertices of a pattern of regular hexagons. **14A3.** If a plane pattern is formed by circles of two different sizes so that equal circles are similarly related to the rest, and only equal circles are in contact, the pattern is called *a compound circle-pack*. If every circle is at the centre of a straight line, equilateral triangle, or regular polygon, the vertices of which are the centres of the circles in contact with it, the pack is said to be *regular*. **14A4.** Centres of large and small circles at alternate points of a straight line. **14A5.** At centres and vertices of a pattern of equilateral triangles separated by regular hexagons. **14A6. 14A2. 14A7.** At centres and vertices of a square lattice. **14A8.** At vertices of a square lattice and at the mid-points of its sides. **14A9.** At centres and vertices of a pattern of regular hexagons. **14A10. 13A5.**

14B1. $\dfrac{\pi}{6}$.   **14B2.** $\dfrac{2\sqrt{3}}{27}\pi$.   **14B3.** $\dfrac{\sqrt{3}\pi}{9}$.   **14B4.** $\dfrac{\sqrt{3}}{8}\pi$.

14B5. Close hexagonal or cubic (14T3) $\dfrac{\sqrt{2}\pi}{9}$ $= \cdot 741.$

    Centred cubic   (14B4) $\dfrac{\sqrt{3}\pi}{8}$ $= \cdot 680.$

    Hexagonal   (14B3) $\dfrac{\sqrt{3}\pi}{9}$ $= \cdot 605.$

    Open hexagonal   (14B2) $\dfrac{2\sqrt{3}\pi}{27}$ $= \cdot 595.$

    Cubic   (14B1) $\dfrac{\pi}{6}$ $= \cdot 524.$

    Tetrahedral   (14W1) $\dfrac{\sqrt{3}\pi}{16}$ $= \cdot 340.$

    Open tetrahedral   (14W2) $\sqrt{\tfrac{3}{2}}\pi(\sqrt{3}-\sqrt{2})^3 = \cdot 123.$

14B6. Centres and vertices of a cubic lattice. **14B7.** $\dfrac{\sqrt{3}\pi}{2}\dfrac{(r^3+1)}{(r+1)^3}$.   **14B8.**

Centred cubic. **14B9.** At alternate vertices of a cubic lattice. **14B10.**
$\dfrac{2\pi}{3}\dfrac{(r^3+1)}{(r+1)^3}$. **14B11.** Cubic. **14B12.** Centres and vertices of the structure
in 13B3. **14B13.** $\dfrac{\sqrt{3}\pi}{4}\dfrac{r^3+2}{(r+1)^3}$. **14B14.** Cubic and face-centred cubic.
14B15. Centres and vertices of structure of 13B4. **14B16.** $\dfrac{\sqrt{3}\pi}{8}\dfrac{r^3+4}{(r+1)^3}$.
14B17. Centres form a cell-centred cubic lattice. **14B18.** Vertices and
mid-points of edges of a cubic lattice. **14B19.** $\dfrac{\pi}{6}\dfrac{r^3+3}{(r+1)^3}$.

14C1. 13W1. **14C2.** $\frac{1}{3}(3\sqrt{2}-4)\pi\dfrac{r^3+2}{(r+1)^3}$; 14T5; $\frac{1}{4}$ of the unit of
pattern contains four quarter-octahedra. **14C3.** Tetragonal, 13W2.
14C4. Centre; planes ∥ to each ribbon and ⊥ to both; tetrad axis
(the pattern is brought into self-coincidence by rotation through
90° *accompanied by translation along the axis of rotation*); dyad axis
⊥ to each ribbon. **14C5.** Centres and vertices of the structure in
13B7; replace the spheres of a tetrahedral pack (Fig. 142) by spheres
of two different sizes alternating with one another. **14C6.** $\dfrac{\sqrt{3}\pi}{4}\dfrac{r^3+1}{(r+1)^3}$;
14T5, 6. **14C7.** 4 triad, coinciding with altitudes of tetrahedron; 3 dyad
axes, bisecting pairs of opposite edges; 6 planes bisecting edges at right
angles. **14C8.** 3 planes bisecting edges of hexagon, and normal to 3 dyad
axes, and intersecting in a triad axis; the pack referred to in Note 1 has
also a plane of symmetry ⊥ to the triad axis. **14C9.** Centres of tetrahedra are centres of a tetrahedral pack; and their vertices are centres of
a semi-regular pack with coordination-symbol 6 : 6. **14C10.** A face-
centred cubic lattice consists of 4 simple cubic lattices; the centres of a
tetrahedral pack are the points of two face-centred cubic lattices; each
sphere of a tetrahedral pack is replaced by four spheres of an open tetrahedral pack; ∴ the centres of each of the four systems form 8 simple
cubic lattices. **14C11.** The vertices of the triangles are the centres of the
octahedra, and *vice versa*. **14C12.** The diagonals of adjacent squares
must be collinear, but their planes may be at right angles; hence the
section containing any square consists of squares separated by octagons;
and the projection of the whole structure upon one of these planes consists of two such patterns, with the squares of one at the centres of the
octagons of the other. **14C13.** Symmetry of a cubic lattice; 13A6.
14C14. $\dfrac{\pi}{8}\dfrac{r^3+2}{(r+1)^3}$; distance between neighbouring planes of squares
$=2(r+1)$; consider volume of spheres inside a square prism which has

its ends in these planes, and vertices of one end at centres of the squares adjacent to a given octagon ;

$$\text{volume of spheres} = \tfrac{4}{3}\pi[r^3(8 \cdot \tfrac{1}{4} + 8 \cdot \tfrac{1}{8}) + 4 \cdot \tfrac{1}{2} + 16 \cdot \tfrac{1}{4}] ;$$
$$\text{volume of prism} = [4(r+1)]^2 \cdot 2(r+1).$$

14C15. The spheres of one system occupy the vertices and centres of the vertical faces of a cubic lattice, while those of the other system are placed at the mid-points of the horizontal edges, and at the cell-centres.

14C16. $\dfrac{\pi}{2} \dfrac{r^3+1}{(r+1)^3}$;   volume of cube $= [2(r+1)]^3$;

$$\text{volume of spheres} = \tfrac{4}{3}\pi[r^3(8 \cdot \tfrac{1}{4} + 1) + 4 \cdot \tfrac{1}{2} + 8 \cdot \tfrac{1}{8}].$$

14C17. Same as tetragonal lattice with axis vertical; 13A7.   **14C18.** Two tetrahedra meet at every vertex, and corresponding edges are collinear ; 13B8 ; coordination-symbol 2 : 4 ; 14W3.   **14C19.** The altitudes lie in consecutive diagonals of the cubes in which the tetrahedra are inscribed ; let ABCD, A'B'C'D' be the cube above the plane ABCD, and DEFG,D"E"F"G" the adjacent cube below it, DCE being an equilateral triangle ; then $\overset{\wedge}{\text{BDF}} = 150°$;

$$\overset{\wedge}{\text{B'DF''}} = 2\sin^{-1}\frac{\text{B'F''}}{2\text{B'D}} = 2\sin^{-1}\sqrt{\left(\frac{4+\sqrt{3}}{6}\right)} = 155°\,36'.$$

MISCELLANEOUS EXAMPLES

M1. $\frac{3}{2}a^2(1+\cos^2\alpha)$. Let α be the angle between the planes S and S$'$, a the length of a side of the equilateral triangle, and θ its inclination to the axis of projection, so that $\theta=\varphi$, or $\varphi\pm\dfrac{2\pi}{3}$. The sum of the squares on the sides of A$'$B$'$C$'=a^2\Sigma\{\cos^2\theta+\sin^2\theta\cos^2\alpha\}$

$$=\frac{a^2}{2}\Sigma(1+\cos2\theta)+\frac{a^2}{2}\Sigma\cos^2\alpha(1-\cos2\theta).$$

M2. 3W2. **M3.** 9B23, 25. **M4.** Let internal and external bisectors of angle APB meet AB in X and Y. Locus is plane section of sphere on diameter XY. **M5.** 4T4 ; project on plane $\perp$ PQ. **M6.** 5T6 ; regard ellipse as orthogonal projection of auxiliary circle. **M7.** 9W1,2. **M8.** (a) 8T3 ; (b) $2\pi(7+6\sqrt7)=144$ sq. cm. **M9.** Length of rim $=8+2(2\cos30°)$; volume $=96$ cu. cm. ; height $=1$ in. ; 7T7 or 8T2. **M10.** 8T1 ; arc of segment of base is a quadrant ; ratio of bases $=\frac{1}{4}\pi r^2-\frac{1}{2}r^2:\frac{3}{4}\pi r^2+\frac{1}{2}r^2=\pi-2:3\pi+2$.

M11. $\cos^{-1}\dfrac{1}{\sqrt3}=54°\,44'$; $2\cos^{-1}\dfrac{1}{\sqrt3}=109°\,28'$; 6W4. **M12.** (i) Draw CR$'\parallel$PQR cutting AB in R$'$; $\dfrac{\text{BP}}{\text{PC}}\dfrac{\text{CQ}}{\text{QA}}\dfrac{\text{AR}}{\text{RB}}=\dfrac{\text{BR}}{\text{RR}'}\dfrac{\text{RR}'}{\text{RA}}\dfrac{\text{AR}}{\text{RB}}=-1$; (ii) 3W5 ; or let plane cut AC in R$'$, and apply (i) twice ; (iii) $\dfrac{\text{AP}}{\text{PB}}\dfrac{\text{BQ}}{\text{QC}}\dfrac{\text{CR}}{\text{RD}}\dfrac{\text{DS}}{\text{SE}}\dfrac{\text{ET}}{\text{TA}}=-1$; let plane cut AD in S$'$, and apply (i) and (ii). [N.B.—These propositions are true even when the transversal is a *plane*; if it is a straight line, the figures cannot be skew.] **M13.** Distance from centre $=\dfrac{3a}{8}$; 9A14, 9B3. **M14.** 6T2, 3. **M15.** 4W4 ; AB$^2+$CD$^2=4$PX^2.

M16. $\frac{1}{4}\pi a^2(a+2\sqrt3b)$; difference between a cylinder and the sum of two equal frusta of cones ; 8T2 ; *or* two equal prismoids, one edge of each being the circumference of a circle, a mere edge with zero area ; 7T7. **M17.** $\dfrac{34+8\sqrt3}{8+\sqrt3}$; 9T4. **M18.** (i) 2W2, 9T4. (ii) 9A5, 9T4. **M19.** Let z be the corner opposite to C, and let OP, OZ cut plane ABC in G, D respectively ; then OG : GP $=$ DG : GC $=$

OD : CP $=1:2$. **M20.** If X is centre of sphere, $XG=\dfrac{3}{4}\dfrac{(2R-h)^2}{3R-h}$; M3.

M21. From OA, OB, OC cut off equal lengths OA′, OB′, OC′. **M22.**
(i) 4B1. (ii) OL⊥plane LPN ; 4T1. **M23.** (i) Let NA, NB be projections
of PA, PB, and let PM⊥AB, and let PN $=a$; then AN.NB $=$ AB.NM ;
Pythagoras. (ii) $\tan\alpha=\dfrac{1120-1045}{3\times450}$, $\tan\beta=\dfrac{1120-1000}{300}$, whence
$\tan\theta=\frac{13}{90}=\cdot14444$; $\therefore\;\theta=8°\,13′$.

M24. R : $r=\sqrt{2}+1:\sqrt{2}-1$; let R : $r=x$;

$$\text{then } V=\frac{\pi}{3}r^3(x^3-1),\qquad S=\pi r^2x^2(\sqrt{2}+1)-\pi r^2(\sqrt{2}-1) ;$$

V is constant ; $\therefore\;\dfrac{dV}{dx}=0$; when S is a minimum, $\dfrac{dS}{dx}=0$; eliminating
$\dfrac{dr}{dx}$ between the equations $\dfrac{dV}{dx}=0,\;\dfrac{dS}{dx}=0$, we get the required value of x.

M25. Let AB cut plane α in C, and let P be the point of contact of the
sphere ; then $CP^2=CA.CB=$const. ; $\therefore$ locus of P is a circle ; if
AB $\parallel\alpha$, the circle becomes a straight line ⊥AB ; locus of centre of sphere
is the ellipse in which the plane bisecting AB at right angles cuts the
right cylinder standing on the locus of P. **M26.** Take vertical section ;
then $4(2r-4)=8^2$; $S=251\cdot3$ sq. cm. ; 8T3 ; $V=435\cdot6$ cu. cm. ; 8T6.

M27. (i) A median bisects elements between pairs of straight lines parallel
to the side bisected by it ; hence the point of intersection of the medians is
the centroid of the triangle ; 9T3, using two sides as axes ; (ii) distance
of each centroid from DC $=\dfrac{h}{3}\dfrac{2AB+DC}{AB+DC}$, where h is the distance between

AB and DC. **M28.** 9W1, 2, where $\alpha=\dfrac{\pi}{2}$; distance of centroid from point :

(i) $2a\cdot\dfrac{\pi+5\frac14+\sqrt5}{\pi+5+2\sqrt5}=1\cdot68a$; (ii) $\dfrac{2a}{11}\left(10\cdot\dfrac{\pi+5\frac14+\sqrt5}{\pi+5+2\sqrt5}+\dfrac13\dfrac{3\pi+10}{\pi+4}\right)=1\cdot69a$;
where a is the radius of the semicircle. **M29.** 7T4, assuming 7T3

volumes : hemisphere, $\dfrac{2\pi}{3}\cdot50^3$; cylinder, $\pi\cdot50^2\cdot400$; cone, $\frac13\pi\cdot50^2\cdot100$;

total, $\frac23\pi\cdot50^2(50+600+50)$ cu. ft. ; $\therefore$ centroid of whole is centroid of
cylinder, and whole is equivalent to a cylinder of length $\frac23(700)$ ft. ;
$\therefore$ distance of each partition from centre $=\frac16\frac23(700)$ ft. $=77\frac79$ ft. **M30.**
Def. 3T6, 5T1 ; Ax. 3, 3T1, 2. **M31.** 4T1 ; BC⊥OA and OP. **M32.** 8T3,
8W2. **M33.** Distance of centroid from base $=\dfrac13\dfrac{l\cos\theta}{1+\sin\theta}$; centroid of
hollow baseless cone divides altitude in ratio 2 : 1 ; 9T4. **M34.** 4T4 ;
Plane $\parallel$ AB and CD ; 3T3, 2W6, 3T5. **M35.** $\dfrac{2a}{3}\cdot\dfrac{\sin^3\theta}{\theta-\sin\theta\cos\theta}$; 9W4 ;

$\dfrac{a}{12\pi}(9\sqrt{3}+2\pi)$ away from the fold. **M36.** 9T4 ; divide ABCD into two triangles, and take AB as axis. **M37.** 5T7 ; $2ab$; projection of two circles and a square inscribed in one and circumscribed about the other. **M38.** Planes AB'D', BC'D ; 3T5 ; draw CN$\perp$BD ; then required inclination $=\mathrm{C}\widehat{\mathrm{N}}\mathrm{C}$. **M39.** 4W1 ; notice that A need not be inside the sphere ; let A be any point on the intersection of the two planes, and find rectangles equivalent to AO². **M40.** 9T5. **M41.** 3T3, 3T4, 3T2 ; cyclic parallelogram is rectangle ; 3T6. **M42.** 4W4, 4W5. **M43.** $\frac{2}{3}a$ from centre ; 9A14, 9B3 ; $b=\dfrac{3}{8}\dfrac{a^4-b^4}{a^3-b^3}$; 9T4 ; hence the cubic equation $3a^3-5a^2b-5ab^2-5b^3=0$; show that $f(2\cdot5)$ and $f(2\cdot6)$ have opposite signs, so that root must lie between 2·5 and 2·6. **M44.** Volumes generated by triangles OAP, OBP are $2\pi\cdot\dfrac{a\sin\theta}{3}\cdot\dfrac{a^2}{2}\sin\theta$ and $2\pi\cdot\dfrac{2}{3}\dfrac{a}{2}(1+\sin\theta)\cdot\dfrac{a^2}{2}\cos\theta$, where $\tan\theta=x$; volume is maximum when $\dfrac{x^2+x+\sqrt{1+x^2}}{1+x^2}$ is maximum ; differentiate. **M45.** 2W2, 9T4 ; plane ABC trisects AA', and tetrahedron $=\frac{1}{6}$ of cube. **M46.** 9T6 : depth of segment $=h-r(\operatorname{cosec}\alpha-1)$; $\mathrm{V}=\dfrac{\pi}{3}\{r(\operatorname{cosec}\alpha-1)-h\}^2\{r(2+3)\operatorname{cosec}\alpha-h\}$; putting $x=\dfrac{r(\operatorname{cosec}\alpha-1)}{h}$, and differentiating, we find that V is maximum or minimum when $x=1$ or $\dfrac{\operatorname{cosec}}{\operatorname{cosec}\alpha+2}$; if $x=1$, the sphere is just out of the water, and touches, not the conical vessel itself, but the conical surface which may be supposed to be continued upwards. Clearly this gives a minimum (zero) overflow. **M47.** Let vertical lines through P, A, Q meet horizontal planes through B in P', A', Q' ; BA $=h\operatorname{cosec}\beta$; BP $=(h-d\sin\alpha)\operatorname{cosec}\theta$, BQ $=(h+d\sin\alpha)\operatorname{cosec}\theta$; then apply Apollonius' Theorem. **M48.** S. 9° 12' E. ; 45° 46' ; let ABC be corner of shadow, and let W' be orthogonal projection on BC of W, the corner of the wall ; then BW' $=6\cot34°-4\operatorname{cosec}34°$, and BWW' $=16°$ 12'. **M49.** M27 ; replace each triangle by particles of mass m at its vertices ; let BD : DC $=n:1-n$, and apply 9T3, using AB, BC as axes. **M50.** $\sqrt{\tfrac{2}{3}}a$, $\dfrac{a}{\sqrt{2}}$. **M51.** $\pi r l$; 8T1 ; 24 sec 20° sin (90° sin 20°) in. $=13\cdot1$ in. ; imagine the conical surface cut along the generators through P and Q ; the shortest path PQ becomes the chord of a sector with radius 12 sec 20° in. and arc $12\pi\tan20°$, whence its angle must be $360°\cdot\dfrac{12\pi\tan20°}{2\pi\cdot12\sec20°}$.

M52. (i) $\cot^{-1} \frac{3}{10}$; (ii) let V,ABCD be the pyramid, $AM \perp VB$, and $VN \perp ABCD$; $A\hat{M}C = 2 \tan^{-1} \frac{NB}{NM} = 2 \tan^{-1} \sec B\hat{V}N$

$$= 2 \tan^{-1} \frac{\sqrt{10^2 + 3^2 + 3^2}}{10} = 2 \tan^{-1}\sqrt{1 \cdot 18} = 2 \, (49^\circ \, 43') = 99^\circ \, 26'.$$

M53. Distance of centroid from centre of original disc $= \frac{r}{2} \cdot \frac{4\pi - 3\sqrt{3}}{2\pi + 3\sqrt{3}}$; centroid of BOCA is mid-point of OA, and its area is twice that of the segment BAC ; 9W4. **M54.** Let A′, B′, C′ be mid-points of BC, CA, AB, and G the centroid of the rods; let B′C′ cut A′G produced in X; take as axes GA′ and GH ∥ C′B′; then $AB \cdot C'X = AC \cdot B'X$; 9T4 ; $\therefore \ C'X : B'X = AC : AB = A'C' : A'B'$; $\therefore$ A′G is the bisector of B′A′C′. **M55.** $\frac{\pi (a_2^2 - a_1^2)}{\sin \alpha}$; 8T1 ; here $\sin \alpha = \frac{a - b}{a + b}$, $a_1 = b \cos \alpha$, $a_2 = a \cos \alpha$. **M56.** $4\frac{1}{3}^\circ\pi$; 8W2. **M57.** $2 \sin^{-1} \frac{3}{16} = 21^\circ \, 36'$, $\sin^{-1} \frac{3}{80} \sqrt{247} = 36^\circ \, 7'$; note that $C'CD = 90^\circ$, and draw $C'N \perp BC$. **M58.** Let horizontal plane through B cut AC in C, the vertical through A in N, and the line of slope through A in M; then $ABDC = 2ABC = 2 \,(AMC - AMB)$, and so on. **M59.** 4T4 ; $\frac{a}{\sqrt{3}}$; draw C_1E, $D_1F = $ and ∥ BC; then $ABCD, D_1C_1EF$ is a cube, and AC_1F and EDB are parallel planes trisecting CD_1 at right angles. **M60.** 3W2 ; $\triangle PQR' = \frac{1}{4}\triangle ABD = $, etc. ; condition : that $\triangle BCD = \triangle ACD$. **M61.** 8T3, 6 ; $S = \pi (r^2 - x^2) + 2\pi r \,(r + x)$: $V = \frac{\pi (r + x)^2}{3} \,(2r - x)$; for S′ and V′, change the sign of x. **M62.** 8W3.

M63. 4W5. **M64.** 4T1 ; $AB \perp CD$; if $BQ \perp ACD$, $BQ \perp AY$, and if $AP \perp BCD$, $AP \perp BY$; altitudes of $\triangle ABY$ are concurrent. **M65.** 8T3, 8W2 ; approximately 16000π, or 50000 sq. miles. **M66.** 2·43 in. ; let O, A, B, C be centres of bowl and spheres, and O′ the projection of O on ABC; then $OA = 2\frac{1}{2}$ in., and $AB = BC = CA = 1$ in., $\therefore O'A = \frac{2}{3} \frac{\sqrt{3}}{2}$; $\therefore OO'^2 = \frac{25}{4} - \frac{3}{9} = \frac{21}{36}\frac{1}{}$. **M67.** 6T2 ; (i) $\Sigma (A\hat{O}X + B\hat{O}X) > \Sigma A\hat{O}B$; $\therefore \ 2\Sigma A\hat{O}X > \Sigma A\hat{O}B$; (ii) let AX produced meet BOC in Y, and apply 6T2 successively to O,XYB and O,ACY. **M68.** 4W1 ; let C be the given point, B the centre of the sphere, P any point on the locus, T a point where the locus cuts the sphere, and N the foot of the perpendicular from T to BC ; then $CTB = CPB = $ right angle ; $\therefore$ locus is part of a sphere with diameter BC ; i.e., the cap with depth BN ; its area

$$= 2\pi \cdot \frac{BC}{2} \cdot BN = \pi BT^2 = \pi a^2.$$

M69. Def. : p. 3 ; 3T1 ; let the plane ∥ AB and CD divide AC in the ratio

CD : AB. **M70.** $2\pi ah$, 8T3 ; let **A**, **B** be centres, **C** a common point, and CN $\perp$ AB ; then required area $= 2\pi a\,(a + $ AN$)$, and AN $= \dfrac{AC^2}{AB} = \dfrac{a^2}{\surd\,(a^2 + b^2)}$.

M71. 6T3 ; $\tan^{-1}2$, $\tan^{-1}2$, $2\tan^{-1}\tfrac{1}{2}$; and $\tan^{-1}\!\surd\overline{15}$; ($= 63°\ 26'$, $63°\ 26'$, $53°\ 8'$; and $75°\ 31'$) ; let **V,ABC** be the angle, with VB $\perp$ ABC, and ABC $= 60°$; let **D** be mid-point of **AC**, and draw BE $\perp$ VD, and EF $\perp$ VA ; then, if VE $= 1$, VB $= 2$, BD $= 2\surd3$, VD $=$ BA $= 4$, DA $= 2$, VA $= 2\surd5$, FE $= \dfrac{1}{\surd5}$; check by 6T4, sines being

$$\frac{\surd3}{2},\ \frac{\surd{15}}{4},\ \frac{\surd{15}}{4},\ \text{and}\ \frac{4}{5},\ \frac{2}{\surd5},\ \frac{2}{\surd5}.$$

M72. 9W1 ; 9T4. **M73.** 4T1 ; plane bisecting at right angles the line joining the given points ; line through centre of circle through the given points and normal to its plane ; one, 4W2. **M74.** 8T6 ; $\dfrac{\pi}{3}\dfrac{r^2}{k}(k-r)^2$; cone $\dfrac{\pi}{3}\dfrac{r^2}{k^3}(k^2-r^2)^2$; segment $\dfrac{\pi}{3}\dfrac{r^3}{k^3}(k-r)^2(2k+r)$. **M75.** Defs. : 3T6, 5T2, 5T3 ; draw BK $\perp$ AC, BM $\perp$ AB′, BN $\perp$ A′C′ ; angle (AC, BC′) $= B\hat{C}'N = \cos^{-1}\dfrac{3}{5\surd5} = 74°\ 26'$; angle (A′D′,AB′C) $= B\hat{C}M = \tan^{-1}\dfrac{4}{\surd{13}} = 47°\ 58'$; angle (AB′C,ABCD) $= B\hat{K}B' = \tan^{-1}2{\cdot}5 = 68°\ 12'$.

INDEX

CATALOGUE OF DOVER BOOKS

MATHEMATICS, ELEMENTARY TO INTERMEDIATE

HOW TO CALCULATE QUICKLY, Henry Sticker. This handy volume offers a tried and true method for helping you in the basic mathematics of daily life—addition, subtraction, multiplication, division, fractions, etc. It is designed to awaken your "number sense" or the ability to see relationships between numbers as whole quantities. It is not a collection of tricks working only on special numbers, but a serious course of over 9,000 problems and their solutions, teaching special techniques not taught in schools: left-to-right multiplication, new fast ways of division, etc. 5 or 10 minutes daily use will double or triple your calculation speed. Excellent for the scientific worker who is at home in higher math, but is not satisfied with his speed and accuracy in lower mathematics. 256pp. 5 x 7¼.   T295 Paperbound **$1.00**

TEACH YOURSELF books. For adult self-study, for refresher and supplementary study. ·

The most effective series of home study mathematics books on the market! With absolutely no outside help, they will teach you as much as any similar college or high-school course, or will helpfully supplement any such course. Each step leads directly to the next, each question is anticipated. Numerous lucid examples and carefully-wrought practice problems illustrate meanings. Not skimpy outlines, not surveys, not usual classroom texts, these 204- to 380-page books are packed with the finest instruction you'll find anywhere for adult self-study.

TEACH YOURSELF ALGEBRA, P. Abbott. Formulas, coordinates, factors, graphs of quadratic functions, quadratic equations, logarithms, ratio, irrational numbers, arithmetical, geometrical series, much more. 1241 problems, solutions. Tables. 52 illus. 307pp. 6⅞ x 4¼.
Clothbound **$2.00**

TEACH YOURSELF GEOMETRY, P. Abbott. Solids, lines, points, surfaces, angle measurement, triangles, theorem of Pythagoras, polygons, loci, the circle, tangents, symmetry, solid geometry, prisms, pyramids, solids of revolution, etc. 343 problems, solutions. 268 illus. 334pp. 6⅞ x 4¼.
Clothbound **$2.00**

TEACH YOURSELF TRIGONOMETRY, P. Abbott. Geometrical foundations, indices, logarithms, trigonometrical ratios, relations between sides, angles of triangle, circular measure, trig. ratios of angles of any magnitude, much more. Requires elementary algebra, geometry. 465 problems, solutions. Tables. 102 illus. 204pp. 6⅞ x 4¼.   Clothbound **$2.00**

TEACH YOURSELF THE CALCULUS, P. Abbott. Variations in functions, differentiation, solids of revolution, series, elementary differential equations, areas by integral calculus, much more. Requires algebra, trigonometry. 970 problems, solutions. Tables. 89 illus. 380pp. 6⅞ x 4¼.
Clothbound **$2.00**

TEACH YOURSELF THE SLIDE RULE, B. Snodgrass. Fractions, decimals, A-D scales, log-log scales, trigonometrical scales, indices, logarithms. Commercial, precision, electrical, dualistic, Brighton rules. 80 problems, solutions. 10 illus. 207pp. 6⅞ x 4¼.   Clothbound **$2.00**

ARITHMETICAL EXCURSIONS: AN ENRICHMENT OF ELEMENTARY MATHEMATICS, H. Bowers and J. Bowers. For students who want unusual methods of arithmetic never taught in school; for adults who want to increase their number sense. Little known facts about the most simple numbers, arithmetical entertainments and puzzles, figurate numbers, number chains, mysteries and folklore of numbers, the "Hin-dog-abic" number system, etc. First publication. Index. 529 numbered problems and diversions, all with answers. Bibliography. 50 figures. xiv + 320pp. 5⅜ x 8.   T770 Paperbound **$1.65**

HOW DO YOU USE A SLIDE RULE? by A. A. Merrill. Not a manual for mathematicians and engineers, but a lucid step-by-step explanation that presents the fundamental rules clearly enough to be understood by anyone who could benefit by the use of a slide rule in his work or business. This work concentrates on the 2 most important operations: multiplication and division. 10 easy lessons, each with a clear drawing, will save you countless hours in your banking, business, statistical, and other work. First publication. Index. 2 Appendixes. 10 illustrations. 78 problems, all with answers. vi + 36pp. 6⅛ x 9¼.   T62 Paperbound **60¢**

THE THEORY AND OPERATION OF THE SLIDE RULE, J. P. Ellis. Not a skimpy "instruction manual", but an exhaustive treatment that will save you hours throughout your career. Supplies full understanding of every scale on the Log Log Duplex Decitrig type of slide rule. Shows the most time-saving methods, and provides practice useful in the widest variety of actual engineering situations. Each operation introduced in terms of underlying logarithmic theory. Summary of prerequisite math. First publication. Index. 198 figures. Over 450 problems with answers. Bibliography. 12 Appendices. ix + 289pp. 5⅜ x 8.
S727 Paperbound **$1.50**

COLLEGE ALGEBRA, H. B. Fine. Standard college text that gives a systematic and deductive structure to algebra; comprehensive, connected, with emphasis on theory. Discusses the commutative, associative, and distributive laws of number in unusual detail, and goes on with undetermined coefficients, quadratic equations, progressions, logarithms, permutations, probability, power series, and much more. Still most valuable elementary-intermediate text on the science and structure of algebra. Index. 1560 problems, all with answers. x + 631pp. 5⅜ x 8.   T211 Paperbound **$2.25**

COORDINATE GEOMETRY, L. P. Eisenhart. Thorough, unified introduction. Unusual for advancing in dimension within each topic (treats together circle, sphere; polar coordinates, 3-dimensional coordinate systems; conic sections, quadric surfaces), affording exceptional insight into subject. Extensive use made of determinants, though no previous knowledge of them is assumed. Algebraic equations of 1st degree, 2 and 3 unknowns, carried further than usual in algebra courses. Over 500 exercises. Introduction. Appendix. Index. Bibliography. 43 illustrations. 310pp. 5⅜ x 8.   S600 Paperbound **$1.65**

A TREATISE ON PLANE AND ADVANCED TRIGONOMETRY, E. W. Hobson. Extraordinarily wide coverage, going beyond usual college level trig, one of the few works covering advanced trig in full detail. By a great expositor with unerring anticipation and lucid clarification of potentially difficult points. Includes circular functions; expansion of functions of multiple angle; trig tables; relations between sides and angles of triangle; complex numbers; etc. Many problems solved completely. "The best work on the subject." Nature. Formerly entitled "A Treatise on Plane Trigonometry." 689 examples. 6 figures. xvi + 383pp. 5⅜ x 8.
S353 Paperbound **$1.95**

FAMOUS PROBLEMS OF ELEMENTARY GEOMETRY, Felix Klein. Expanded version of the 1894 Easter lectures at Göttingen. 3 problems of classical geometry, in an excellent mathematical treatment by a famous mathematician: squaring the circle, trisecting angle, doubling cube. Considered with full modern implications: transcendental numbers, pi, etc. Notes by R. Archibald. 16 figures. xi + 92pp. 5⅜ x 8.   T298 Paperbound **$1.00**

MONOGRAPHS ON TOPICS OF MODERN MATHEMATICS, edited by J. W. A. Young. Advanced mathematics for persons who haven't gone beyond or have forgotten high school algebra. 9 monographs on foundation of geometry, modern pure geometry, non-Euclidean geometry, fundamental propositions of algebra, algebraic equations, functions, calculus, theory of numbers, etc. Each monograph gives proofs of important results, and descriptions of leading methods, to provide wide coverage. New introduction by Prof. M. Kline, N. Y. University. 100 diagrams. xvi + 416pp. 6⅛ x 9¼.   S289 Paperbound **$2.00**

HIGHER MATHEMATICS FOR STUDENTS OF CHEMISTRY AND PHYSICS, J. W. Mellor. Not abstract, but practical, building its problems out of familiar laboratory material, this covers differential calculus, coordinate, analytical geometry, functions, integral calculus, infinite series, numerical equations, differential equations, Fourier's theorem, probability, theory of errors, calculus of variations, determinants. "If the reader is not familiar with this book, it will repay him to examine it," CHEM. & ENGINEERING NEWS. 800 problems. 189 figures. Bibliography. xxi + 641pp. 5⅜ x 8.   S193 Paperbound **$2.25**

TRIGONOMETRY REFRESHER FOR TECHNICAL MEN, A. Albert Klaf. 913 detailed questions and answers cover the most important aspects of plane and spherical trigonometry. They will help you to brush up or to clear up difficulties in special areas. The first portion of this book covers plane trigonometry, including angles, quadrants, trigonometrical functions, graphical representation, interpolation, equations, logarithms, solution of triangle, use of the slide rule and similar topics. 188 pages then discuss application of plane trigonometry to special problems in navigation, surveying, elasticity, architecture, and various fields of engineering. Small angles, periodic functions, vectors, polar coordinates, de Moivre's theorem are fully examined. The third section of the book then discusses spherical trigonometry and the solution of spherical triangles, with their applications to terrestrial and astronomical problems. Methods of saving time with numerical calculations, simplification of principal functions of angle, much practical information make this a most useful book. 913 questions answered. 1738 problems, answers to odd numbers. 494 figures. 24 pages of useful formulae, functions. Index. x + 629pp. 5⅜ x 8.   T371 Paperbound **$2.00**

TEXTBOOK OF ALGEBRA, G. Chrystal. One of the great mathematical textbooks, still about the best source for complete treatments of the topics of elementary algebra; a chief reference work for teachers and students of algebra in advanced high school and university courses, or for the mathematician working on problems of elementary algebra or looking for a background to more advanced topics. Ranges from basic laws and processes to extensive examination of such topics as limits, infinite series, general properties of integral numbers, and probability theory. Emphasis is on algebraic form, the foundation of analytical geometry and the key to modern developments in algebra. Prior course in algebra is desirable, but not absolutely necessary. Includes theory of quotients, distribution of products, arithmetical theory of surds, theory of interest, permutations and combinations, general expansion theorems, recurring fractions, and much, much more. Two volume set. Index in each volume. Over 1500 exercises, approximately half with answers. Total of xlviii + 1187pp. 5⅜ x 8.
S750 Vol I Paperbound **$2.35**
S751 Vol II Paperbound **$2.35**
The set **$4.70**

MATHEMATICS—INTERMEDIATE TO ADVANCED

General

INTRODUCTION TO APPLIED MATHEMATICS, Francis D. Murnaghan. A practical and thoroughly sound introduction to a number of advanced branches of higher mathematics. Among the selected topics covered in detail are: vector and matrix analysis, partial and differential equations, integral equations, calculus of variations, Laplace transform theory, the vector triple product, linear vector functions, quadratic and bilinear forms, Fourier series, spherical harmonics, Bessel functions, the Heaviside expansion formula, and many others. Extremely useful book for graduate students in physics, engineering, chemistry, and mathematics. Index. 111 study exercises with answers. 41 illustrations. ix + 389pp. 5⅜ x 8½.
S1042 Paperbound **$2.00**

OPERATIONAL METHODS IN APPLIED MATHEMATICS, H. S. Carslaw and J. C. Jaeger. Explanation of the application of the Laplace Transformation to differential equations, a simple and effective substitute for more difficult and obscure operational methods. Of great practical value to engineers and to all workers in applied mathematics. Chapters on: Ordinary Linear Differential Equations with Constant Coefficients;; Electric Circuit Theory; Dynamical Applications; The Inversion Theorem for the Laplace Transformation; Conduction of Heat; Vibrations of Continuous Mechanical Systems; Hydrodynamics; Impulsive Functions; Chains of Differential Equations; and other related matters. 3 appendices. 153 problems, many with answers. 22 figures. xvi + 359pp. 5⅜ x 8½.
S1011 Paperbound **$2.25**

APPLIED MATHEMATICS FOR RADIO AND COMMUNICATIONS ENGINEERS, C. E. Smith. No extraneous material here!—only the theories, equations, and operations essential and immediately useful for radio work. Can be used as refresher, as handbook of applications and tables, or as full home-study course. Ranges from simplest arithmetic through calculus, series, and wave forms, hyperbolic trigonometry, simultaneous equations in mesh circuits, etc. Supplies applications right along with each math topic discussed. 22 useful tables of functions, formulas, logs, etc. Index. 166 exercises, 140 examples, all with answers. 95 diagrams. Bibliography. x + 336pp. 5⅜ x 8.
S141 Paperbound **$1.75**

Algebra, group theory, determinants, sets, matrix theory

ALGEBRAS AND THEIR ARITHMETICS, L. E. Dickson. Provides the foundation and background necessary to any advanced undergraduate or graduate student studying abstract algebra. Begins with elementary introduction to linear transformations, matrices, field of complex numbers; proceeds to order, basal units, modulus, quaternions, etc.; develops calculus of linears sets, describes various examples of algebras including invariant, difference, nilpotent, semi-simple. "Makes the reader marvel at his genius for clear and profound analysis," Amer. Mathematical Monthly. Index. xii + 241pp. 5⅜ x 8.
S616 Paperbound **$1.50**

THE THEORY OF EQUATIONS WITH AN INTRODUCTION TO THE THEORY OF BINARY ALGEBRAIC FORMS, W. S. Burnside and A. W. Panton. Extremely thorough and concrete discussion of the theory of equations, with extensive detailed treatment of many topics curtailed in later texts. Covers theory of algebraic equations, properties of polynomials, symmetric functions, derived functions, Horner's process, complex numbers and the complex variable, determinants and methods of elimination, invariant theory (nearly 100 pages), transformations, introduction to Galois theory, Abelian equations, and much more. Invaluable supplementary work for modern students and teachers. 759 examples and exercises. Index in each volume. Two volume set. Total of xxiv + 604pp. 5⅜ x 8.
S714 Vol I Paperbound **$1.85**
S715 Vol II Paperbound **$1.85**
The set **$3.70**

COMPUTATIONAL METHODS OF LINEAR ALGEBRA, V. N. Faddeeva, translated by **C. D. Benster.** First English translation of a unique and valuable work, the only work in English presenting a systematic exposition of the most important methods of linear algebra—classical and contemporary. Shows in detail how to derive numerical solutions of problems in mathematical physics which are frequently connected with those of linear algebra. Theory as well as individual practice. Part I surveys the mathematical background that is indispensable to what follows. Parts II and III, the conclusion, set forth the most important methods of solution, for both exact and iterative groups. One of the most outstanding and valuable features of this work is the 23 tables, double and triple checked for accuracy. These tables will not be found elsewhere. Author's preface. Translator's note. New bibliography and index. x + 252pp. 5⅜ x 8.
S424 Paperbound **$1.95**

ALGEBRAIC EQUATIONS, E. Dehn. Careful and complete presentation of Galois' theory of algebraic equations; theories of Lagrange and Galois developed in logical rather than historical form, with a more thorough exposition than in most modern books. Many concrete applications and fully-worked-out examples. Discusses basic theory (very clear exposition of the symmetric group); isomorphic, transitive, and Abelian groups; applications of Lagrange's and Galois' theories; and much more. Newly revised by the author. Index. List of Theorems. xi + 208pp. 5⅜ x 8.
S697 Paperbound **$1.45**

ESSAYS ON THE THEORY OF NUMBERS: 1. CONTINUITY AND IRRATIONAL NUMBERS; 2. THE NATURE AND MEANING OF NUMBERS, Richard Dedekind. The two most important essays on the logical foundations of the number system by the famous German mathematician. The first provides a purely arithmetic and perfectly rigorous foundation for irrational numbers and thereby a rigorous meaning to continuity in analysis. The second essay is an attempt to give a logical basis for transfinite numbers and properties of the natural numbers. Discusses the logical validity of mathematical induction. Authorized English translations by W. W. Deman of "Stetigkeit und irrationale Zahlen" and "Was sind und was sollen die Zahlen?" vii + 115pp. 5⅜ x 8.   T1010 Paperbound **$1.00**

Geometry

THE FOUNDATIONS OF EUCLIDEAN GEOMETRY, H. G. Forder. The first rigorous account of Euclidean geometry, establishing propositions without recourse to empiricism, and without multiplying hypotheses. Corrects many traditional weaknesses of Euclidean proofs, and investigates the problems imposed on the axiom system by the discoveries of Bolyai and Lobachevsky. Some topics discussed are Classes and Relations; Axioms for Magnitudes; Congruence and Similarity; Algebra of Points; Hessenberg's Theorem; Continuity; Existence of Parallels; Reflections; Rotations; Isometries; etc. Invaluable for the light it throws on foundations of math. Lists: Axioms employed, Symbols, Constructions. 295pp. 5⅜ x 8.
S481 Paperbound **$2.00**

ADVANCED EUCLIDEAN GEOMETRY, R. A. Johnson. For years the standard textbook on advanced Euclidean geometry, requires only high school geometry and trigonometry. Explores in unusual detail and gives proofs of hundreds of relatively recent theorems and corollaries, many formerly available only in widely scattered journals. Covers tangent circles, the theorem of Miquel, symmedian point, pedal triangles and circles, the Brocard configuration, and much more. Formerly "Modern Geometry." Index. 107 diagrams. xiii + 319pp. 5⅜ x 8.
S669 Paperbound **$1.65**

HIGHER GEOMETRY: AN INTRODUCTION TO ADVANCED METHODS IN ANALYTIC GEOMETRY, F. S. Woods. Exceptionally thorough study of concepts and methods of advanced algebraic geometry (as distinguished from differential geometry). Exhaustive treatment of 1-, 2-, 3-, and 4-dimensional coordinate systems, leading to n-dimensional geometry in an abstract sense. Covers projectivity, tetracyclical coordinates, contact transformation, pentaspherical coordinates, much more. Based on M.I.T. lectures, requires sound preparation in analytic geometry and some knowledge of determinants. Index. Over 350 exercises. References. 60 figures. x + 423pp. 5⅜ x 8.   S737 Paperbound **$2.00**

CONTEMPORARY GEOMETRY, André Delachet. Translated by Howard G. Bergmann. The recent developments in geometry covered in uncomplicated fashion. Clear discussions of modern thinking about the theory of groups, the concept of abstract geometry, projective geometry, algebraic geometry, vector spaces, new kinds of metric spaces, developments in differential geometry, etc. A large part of the book is devoted to problems, developments, and applications of topology. For advanced undergraduates and graduate students as well as mathematicians in other fields who want a brief introduction to current work in geometry. 39 figures. Index. xix + 94pp. 5⅜ x 8½.   S988 Paperbound **$1.00**

ELEMENTS OF PROJECTIVE GEOMETRY, L. Cremona. Outstanding complete treatment of projective geometry by one of the foremost 19th century geometers. Detailed proofs of all fundamental principles, stress placed on the constructive aspects. Covers homology, law of duality, anharmonic ratios, theorems of Pascal and Brianchon, foci, polar reciprocal figures, etc. Only ordinary geometry necessary to understand this honored classic. Index. Over 150 fully worked out examples and problems. 252 diagrams. xx + 302pp. 5⅜ x 8.   S668 Paperbound **$1.75**

AN INTRODUCTION TO PROJECTIVE GEOMETRY, R. M. Winger. One of the best introductory texts to an important area in modern mathematics. Contains full development of elementary concepts often omitted in other books. Employing the analytic method to capitalize on the student's collegiate training in algebra, analytic geometry and calculus, the author deals with such topics as Essential Constants, Duality, The Line at Infinity, Projective Properties and Double Ratio, Projective Coordinates, The Conic, Collineations and Involutions in One Dimension, Binary Forms, Algebraic Invariants, Analytic Treatment of the Conic, Collineations in the Plane, Cubic Involutions and the Rational Cubic Curve, and a clear discussion of Non-Euclidean Geometry. For senior-college students and graduates. "An excellent textbook . . . very clearly written . . . propositions stated concisely," A. Emch, Am. Math. Monthly. Corrected reprinting. 928 problems. Index. 116 figures. xii + 443pp. 5⅜ x 8.
S949 Paperbound **$2.00**

ALGEBRAIC CURVES, Robert J. Walker, Professor of Mathematics, Cornell University. Fine introduction to algebraic geometry. Presents some of the recently developed algebraic methods of handling problems in algebraic geometry, shows how these methods are related to the older analytic and geometric problems, and applies them to those same geometric problems. Limited to the theory of curves, concentrating on birational transformations. Contents: Algebraic Preliminaries, Projective Spaces, Plane Algebraic Curves, Formal Power Series, Transformations of a Curve, Linear Series. 25 illustrations. Numerous exercises at ends of sections. Index. x + 201pp. 5⅜ x 8½.   S336 Paperbound **$1.60**

THE ADVANCED GEOMETRY OF PLANE CURVES AND THEIR APPLICATIONS, C. Zwikker. An unusual study of many important curves, their geometrical properties and their applications, including discussions of many less well-known curves not often treated in textbooks on synthetic and analytic Euclidean geometry. Includes both algebraic and transcendental curves such as the conic sections, kinked curves, spirals, lemniscates, cycloids, etc. and curves generated as involutes, evolutes, anticaustics, pedals, envelopes and orthogonal trajectories. Dr. Zwikker represents the points of the curves by complex numbers instead of two real Cartesian coordinates, allowing direct and even elegant proofs. Formerly: "Advanced Plane Geometry." 273 figures. xii + 299pp. 5⅜ x 8½.   S1078 Paperbound **$2.00**

A TREATISE ON THE DIFFERENTIAL GEOMETRY OF CURVES AND SURFACES, L. P. Eisenhart. Introductory treatise especially for the graduate student, for years a highly successful textbook. More detailed and concrete in approach than most more recent books. Covers space curves, osculating planes, moving axes, Gauss' method, the moving trihedral, geodesics, conformal representation, etc. Last section deals with deformation of surfaces, rectilinear congruences, cyclic systems, etc. Index. 683 problems. 30 diagrams. xii + 474pp. 5⅜ x 8.
S667 Paperbound **$2.75**

A TREATISE ON ALGEBRAIC PLANE CURVES, J. L. Coolidge. Unabridged reprinting of one of few full coverages in English, offering detailed introduction to theory of algebraic plane curves and their relations to geometry and analysis. Treats topological properties, Riemann-Roch theorem, all aspects of wide variety of curves including real, covariant, polar, containing series of a given sort, elliptic, polygonal, rational, the pencil, two parameter nets, etc. This volume will enable the reader to appreciate the symbolic notation of Aronhold and Clebsch. Bibliography. Index. 17 illustrations. xxiv + 513pp. 5⅜ x 8. S543 Paperbound **$2.75**

AN INTRODUCTION TO THE GEOMETRY OF N DIMENSIONS, D. M. Y. Sommerville. An introduction presupposing no prior knowledge of the field, the only book in English devoted exclusively to higher dimensional geometry. Discusses fundamental ideas of incidence, parallelism, perpendicularity, angles between linear space; enumerative geometry; analytical geometry from projective and metric points of view; polytopes; elementary ideas in analysis situs; content of 'hyper-spacial figures. Bibliography. Index. 60 diagrams. 196pp. 5⅜ x 8.
S494 Paperbound **$1.50**

GEOMETRY OF FOUR DIMENSIONS, H. P. Manning. Unique in English as a clear, concise introduction. Treatment is synthetic, and mostly Euclidean, although in hyperplanes and hyperspheres at infinity, non-Euclidean geometry is used. Historical introduction. Foundations of 4-dimensional geometry. Perpendicularity, simple angles. Angles of planes, higher order. Symmetry, order, motion; hyperpyramids, hypercones, hyperspheres; figures with parallel elements; volume, hypervolume in space; regular polyhedroids. Glossary. 78 figures. ix + 348pp. 5⅜ x 8.   S182 Paperbound **$2.00**

CONVEX FIGURES AND POLYHEDRA, L. A. Lyusternik. An excellent elementary discussion by a leading Russian mathematician. Beginning with the basic concepts of convex figures and bodies and their supporting lines and planes, the author covers such matters as centrally symmetric convex figures, theorems of Euler, Cauchy, Steinitz and Alexandrov on convex polyhedra, linear systems of convex bodies, planar sections of convex bodies, the Brunn-Minkowski inequality and its consequences, and many other related topics. No more than a high school background in mathematics needed for complete understanding. First English translation by T. J. Smith. 182 illustrations. Index. x + 176pp. 5⅜ x 8½.
S1021 Paperbound **$1.50**

NON-EUCLIDEAN GEOMETRY, Roberto Bonola. The standard coverage of non-Euclidean geometry. It examines from both a historical and mathematical point of view the geometries which have arisen from a study of Euclid's 5th postulate upon parallel lines. Also included are complete texts, translated, of Bolyai's SCIENCE OF ABSOLUTE SPACE. Lobachevsky's THEORY OF PARALLELS. 180 diagrams. 431pp. 5⅜ x 8.   S27 Paperbound **$2.00**

ELEMENTS OF NON-EUCLIDEAN GEOMETRY, D. M. Y. Sommerville. Unique in proceeding step-by-step, in the manner of traditional geometry. Enables the student with only a good knowledge of high school algebra and geometry to grasp elementary hyperbolic, elliptic, analytic non-Euclidean geometries; space curvature and its philosophical implications; theory of radical axes; homothetic centres and systems of circles; parataxy and parallelism; absolute measure; Gauss' proof of the defect area theorem; geodesic representation; much more, all with exceptional clarity. 126 problems at chapter endings provide progressive practice and familiarity. 133 figures. Index. xvi + 274pp. 5⅜ x 8. S460 Paperbound **$1.50**

INTRODUCTORY NON-EUCLIDEAN GEOMETRY, H. P. Manning. Sound elementary introduction to non-Euclidean geometry. The first two thirds (Pangeometry and the Hyperbolic Geometry) require a grasp of plane and solid geometry and trigonometry. The last sections (the Elliptic Geometry and Analytic Non-Euclidean Geometry) necessitate also basic college calculus for understanding the text. The book does not propose to investigate the foundations of geometry, but rather begins with the theorems common to Euclidean and non-Euclidean geometry and then takes up the specific differences between them. A simple and direct account of the bases of this important branch of mathematics for teachers and students. 94 figures. vii + 95pp. 5⅜ x 8.   S310 Paperbound **$1.00**

BOOKS EXPLAINING SCIENCE AND MATHEMATICS

Engineering, technology, applied science etc.

TEACH YOURSELF ELECTRICITY, C. W. Wilman. Electrical resistance, inductance, capacitance, magnets, chemical effects of current, alternating currents, generators and motors, transformers, rectifiers, much more. 230 questions, answers, worked examples. List of units. 115 illus. 194pp. 6⅞ x 4¼.　　　　　　　　　　　　　　　　　　　　　　　　Clothbound **$2.00**

ELEMENTARY METALLURGY AND METALLOGRAPHY, A. M. Shrager. Basic theory and descriptions of most of the fundamental manufacturing processes involved in metallurgy. Partial contents: the structure of metals; slip, plastic deformation, and recrystalization; iron ore and production of pig iron; chemistry involved in the metallurgy of iron and steel; basic processes such as the Bessemer treatment, open-hearth process, the electric arc furnace —with advantages and disadvantages of each; annealing, hardening, and tempering steel; copper, aluminum, magnesium, and their alloys. For freshman engineers, advanced students in technical high schools, etc. Index. Bibliography. 177 diagrams. 17 tables. 284 questions and problems. 27-page glossary. ix + 389pp. 5⅜ x 8.　　　　　　　　　S138 Paperbound **$2.25**

BASIC ELECTRICITY, Prepared by the Bureau of Naval Personnel. Originally a training course text for U.S. Navy personnel, this book provides thorough coverage of the basic theory of electricity and its applications. Best book of its kind for either broad or more limited studies of electrical fundamentals . . . for classroom use or home study. Part 1 provides a more limited coverage of theory: fundamental concepts, batteries, the simple circuit, D.C. series and parallel circuits, conductors and wiring techniques, A.C. electricity, inductance and capacitance, etc. Part 2 applies theory to the structure of electrical machines—generators, motors, transformers, magnetic amplifiers. Also deals with more complicated instruments, synchros, servo-mechanisms. The concluding chapters cover electrical drawings and blueprints, wiring diagrams, technical manuals, and safety education. The book contains numerous questions for the student, with answers. Index and six appendices. 345 illustrations. x + 448pp. 6½ x 9¼.　　　　　　　　　　　　　　　　S973 Paperbound **$2.95**

BASIC ELECTRONICS, prepared by the U.S. Navy Training Publications Center. A thorough and comprehensive manual on the fundamentals of electronics. Written clearly, it is equally useful for self-study or course work for those with a knowledge of the principles of basic electricity. Partial contents: Operating Principles of the Electron Tube; Introduction to Transistors; Power Supplies for Electronic Equipment; Tuned Circuits; Electron-Tube Amplifiers; Audio Power Amplifiers; Oscillators; Transmitters; Transmission Lines; Antennas and Propagation; Introduction to Computers; and related topics. Appendix. Index. Hundreds of illustrations and diagrams. vi + 471pp. 6½ x 9¼.　　　　　　　S1076 Paperbound **$2.75**

BASIC THEORY AND APPLICATION OF TRANSISTORS, Prepared by the U.S. Department of the Army. An introductory manual prepared for an army training program. One of the finest available surveys of theory and application of transistor design and operation. Minimal knowledge of physics and theory of electron tubes required. Suitable for textbook use, course supplement, or home study. Chapters: Introduction; fundamental theory of transistors; transistor amplifier fundamentals; parameters, equivalent circuits, and characteristic curves; bias stabilization; transistor analysis and comparison using characteristic curves and charts; audio amplifiers; tuned amplifiers; wide-band amplifiers; oscillators; pulse and switching circuits; modulation, mixing, and demodulation; and additional semiconductor devices. Unabridged, corrected edition. 240 schematic drawings, photographs, wiring diagrams, etc. 2 Appendices. Glossary. Index. 263pp. 6½ x 9¼.　　　　　　　S380 Paperbound **$1.25**

TEACH YOURSELF HEAT ENGINES, E. De Ville. Measurement of heat, development of steam and internal combustion engines, efficiency of an engine, compression-ignition engines, production of steam, the ideal engine, much more. 318 exercises, answers, worked examples. Tables. 76 illus. 220pp. 6⅞ x 4¼.　　　　　　　　　　　　　　　　　　　　Clothbound **$2.00**

Prices subject to change without notice.

Dover publishes books on art, music, philosophy, literature, languages, history, social sciences, psychology, handcrafts, orientalia, puzzles and entertainments, chess, pets and gardens, books explaining science, intermediate and higher mathematics, mathematical physics, engineering, biological sciences, earth sciences, classics of science, etc. Write to:

Dept. catrr.
Dover Publications, Inc.
180 Varick Street, N.Y. 14, N.Y.